Agriculture in the Congo Basin

AGRICULTURE

IN THE

CONGO BASIN

Tradition and Change in African
Rural Economies

Marvin P. Miracle

The University of Wisconsin Press
Madison, Milwaukee, and London

1967

S
471
C75
M4J5
cop. 2

Published by the University of Wisconsin Press
Madison, Milwaukee, and London
U.S.A.: Box 1379, Madison, Wisconsin 53701
U.K.: 26–28 Hallam Street, London, W.1

Printed in the United States of America by
North Central Publishing Co., St. Paul, Minnesota

Library of Congress Catalog Card Number 67-26628

To Diane

Preface

Agriculture has been the major problem of development planners in many of the less developed countries in recent years and continues to be especially troublesome. Success in planning and achieving increases in production and productivity requires better understanding of present production methods and of how past technological change was brought about. The objective of this study is to examine in some detail the character of agricultural methods in the tribal economies of the area drained by the Congo River and to analyze evidence of changes in them.

Traditional agricultural methods are here defined as those found in small-scale agriculture outside of development schemes attempting to make large changes in production techniques. Tribal economies are the economies of the respective tribal areas. Tribes of tropical Africa differ greatly in such things as resource endowments, property rights, dependence on other economic units, and economic history. In precolonial times each tribe had its own legal and tax or tribute structure and its own methods of regulating trade within the tribal area and with other economies. Thus colonial powers created the present national economies by grouping tribal economies; adding nontribal elements, such as mines and plantations; and taking over or controlling certain powers of tribal authorities. But while tribal economies may have been modified through colonial rule, they continue to be the basic unit for analysis of agriculture.

Despite several decades of experimental work and the considerable attention that has been given certain problems, particularly those connected with export crops, we are only beginning to understand the nature of the tribal economies of tropical Africa. General characteristics of tropical African agriculture — the use of "slash and burn" methods, the prevalence of hoe culture, and the slight importance of animal husbandry in many areas — have long been established; but except for some export crops, little effort has been made to describe techniques of agricultural production in detail, and detailed examinations of intertribal differences in agricultural methods are few. C. G. Trapnell's classical study of agricultural systems in Zambia and works by Pierre de Schlippe are important contributions, but De Schlippe covers only three tribes, while Trapnell omits all discussion of harvesting, storage, and processing. Most writers who discuss problems of improving African agricultural methods as part of efforts to accelerate economic development either imply that all African agricultural systems are roughly the same or specifically cite the methods of one or two tribes as though they were representative of most of Africa.

Tropical Africa has, by a big margin, the largest continuous belt of shifting cultivation in the world. When this study was begun little was known about similarities and differences in shifting cultivation from continent to continent, or even within countries; most observers interested in the agricultural sector of tropical economies had treated the practice as simple and everywhere much the same. Chapters 3 to 6 of this book present data which abundantly demonstrate that shifting cultivation is extremely complex and varied in the Congo Basin. Chapter 7 attempts to analyze the differences observed, and Chapter 8 compares shifting cultivation in the Congo Basin with what is now known about it elsewhere in Africa.

This book is based mainly on published materials in English and French. In addition to government studies, and major periodicals on the Congo Basin such as the *Bulletin Agricole du Congo Belge, Congo*, and the *Rhodes-Livingstone Journal*, all issues of which were searched, attempt was made to check all well-known anthropological studies of tribes of the Congo Basin which appeared likely to have anything on agriculture or economics. All of the extensive private library on the Belgian Congo collected by Jean Leyder, a sociologist and early administrator in the Belgian Congo, was scanned. In a few instances published material was supplemented by unpublished field notes that I learned of as the study progressed. I hope that much more material of this sort will be forth-coming.

For some tribes of the Congo Basin data are available on traditional agriculture from as early as the seventeenth century, and for a few tribes observations on agricultural methods were made as late as the 1950's; most data presented here come from material published in the last seventy-five years. Thus differences in agricultural practices that emerge in comparing one tribe with another result not only from geographical differences in agricultural systems but possibly also from secular changes.

The available observations on traditional African agriculture vary greatly in completeness and presumably also in reliability. In most instances there has been no basis for cross-checking observations, for at any point in time only one account is available for each tribe.

Except as noted in later sections, tribes are referred to by the appellations adopted by G. P. Murdock in his tribal map of Africa (Map 1-3), and it has been assumed that tribal boundaries are roughly as Murdock fixes them (*272*). Despite inadequacies, so far his is the most complete reference work on tribes of the Congo Basin.

A number of acknowledgments are due. The study grew out of a proposal made to the National Academy of Sciences–National Research Council by William O. Jones, and he read much of the manuscript. Jan Vansina generously made his field notes available and guided me to a number of relevant studies. Igor Kopytoff, C. M. N. White, Philip A. Noss, and Claude Bernard Ngondo also helped with field notes or unpublished data on particular points. A large part of the research was done under the auspices of the National Academy of Sciences–National Research Council. The author alone, however, is responsible for all conclusions.

Patricia Cedarleaf helpfully criticized maps and illustrations and put them in their final form.

Portions of Chapters 1, 9, and 10 appeared as part of a chapter in Martin S. Peterson and Donald K. Tressler, editors, *Food Technology the World Over*, Vol. 2 (Westport, Conn.; Avi Publishing Co., 1965), and much of Chapter 11 was first published as an article in *The Western Economic Journal*, Vol. 1, No. 2, Spring 1963.

M.P.M

Madison, Wisconsin
May 1967

Contents

Illustrations

Figures

Maps

xiii

Charts

Tables

PART I The Congo Basin

This map shows places or boundaries mentioned in the text for the time of reference. Some are as early as 1913, some as late as 1967.

1

The Area and
Its Tribal Economies

The Area

The area drained by the Congo River forms a gigantic saucer about 1,000 miles from edge to edge in its smallest diameter (Map 1-1). Its 1,425,000 square miles or more make it roughly the size of the eleven western states of the United States including Texas, or twenty-eight times the size of England. The center of this great basin, sunk in the middle of the African continent, has an almost level bottom that slopes gently toward the west. Toward the rim the sides rise, sometimes gradually, sometimes abruptly, to 2,000 or 3,000 feet in most of the west and north; to 8,000 feet in much of the east, where Lakes Tanganyika, Kivu, Edward, and Albert are found near the Basin's rim; and to 5,000 or 6,000 feet in most of the south. In the west a narrow gap gives the Congo River passage to the sea.

Although exceeded in length by several other rivers in the world, the Congo is second only to the Amazon in volume of water. Named after the ancient Kingdom of Congo once located around its mouth, the Congo River starts in Katanga as the Lualaba and flows slowly north some 800 miles to Kisangani, where it becomes the upper Congo; it then gradually reverses its direction, swinging in a broad arch to the west and south. On its southward course it is joined by two major tributaries, the Ubangi coming from the north and the Kasai coming from the south.

3

In the heart of the Congo Basin, where the gradient is extremely gentle, the rivers are wide, sluggish, and sprinkled with islands. The Congo River looks more like a lake than a river in many places. In this part of the Congo Basin the rivers are navigable. Steamers are obstructed at Stanleyville by cataracts formed as the Congo River enters the floor of the Basin and below Kinshasa by rapids formed as the waters rush from the Basin floor to sea level.

The middle of the Congo Basin — from two to three degrees south of the equator to four or five degrees north of it — has rain almost all year and is covered with a dense forest (Map 1-2). Humidity is high throughout the year, and the dry season is limited to a total of two months or less, usually divided into two periods. As one moves south, the dry season lengthens and total rainfall diminishes. Dense humid forest gives way first to open forest, then to vegetation that is dominated not by trees but by grasses. Across most of the northern edge of the Congo Basin, the dry season lasts three or four months; at the southern edge from six to eight months. In the central portion of the eastern edge forest gives way to grassland in some of the higher areas because of altitude; in other areas grassland has replaced forests eliminated by cultivation.

Most of the Congo Basin is sparsely populated, with less than 4 persons per square kilometer (10.4 persons per square mile); but along its eastern edge — in portions of Rwanda and Burundi, which collectively average over 100 persons per square kilometer (259 per square mile) — is found one of the highest population densities in tropical Africa.

The Tribal Economies

The ways Africans in the Congo Basin used scarce resources to satisfy their needs before European rule varied considerably. Temperatures are high enough in most of the Basin to make clothing and shelter unnecessary, and protection from the sun is provided by natural vegetation. In the limiting case, economic activity conceivably could consist only of obtaining food and drink and deciding how these would be distributed among the producer's family and associates.

All the tribal economies for which we have data are more complex than this limiting case. For as long as we have records, food production in the Congo Basin has exceeded needs enough in most, if not all, areas for a considerable amount of energy to be devoted to construction of dwellings, production of clothing and ornaments, art, and a variety of enter-

MAP 1-1

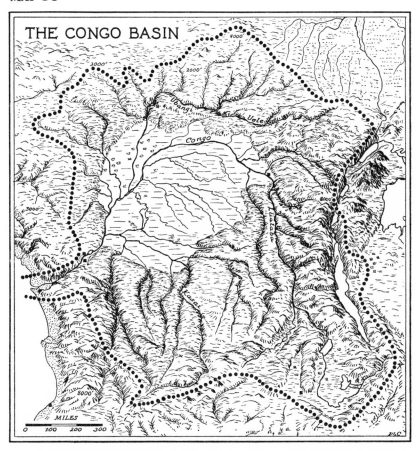

THE CONGO BASIN

Data from A. K. Lobeck, *Physiographic Diagram of Africa* (New York: Geographical Press, Columbia University, 1946). Map: Food Research Institute.

MAP 1-2

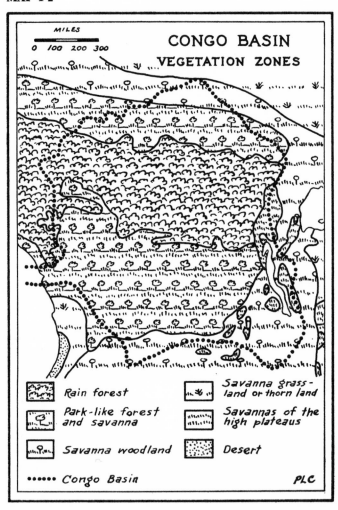

Data in part from Gaston Delevoy, "Le Congo Forestier," *Encyclopédie du Congo Belge*, Vol. 2 (Brussels: Editions Bieveld, n. d.). Map: Food Research Institute.

6

MAP 1-3

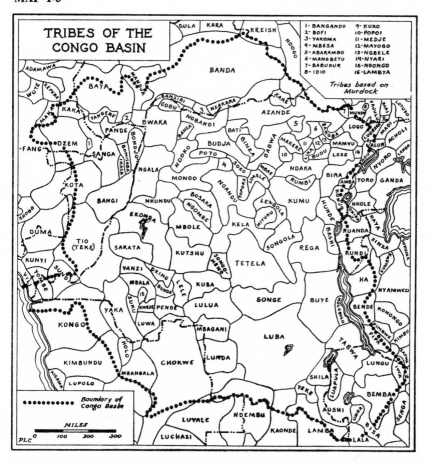

Adapted from G. P. Murdock, *Africa, Its Peoples and Their Culture History* (New York: McGraw Hill, 1959), Map 17. Map: Food Research Institute.

MAP 1-4

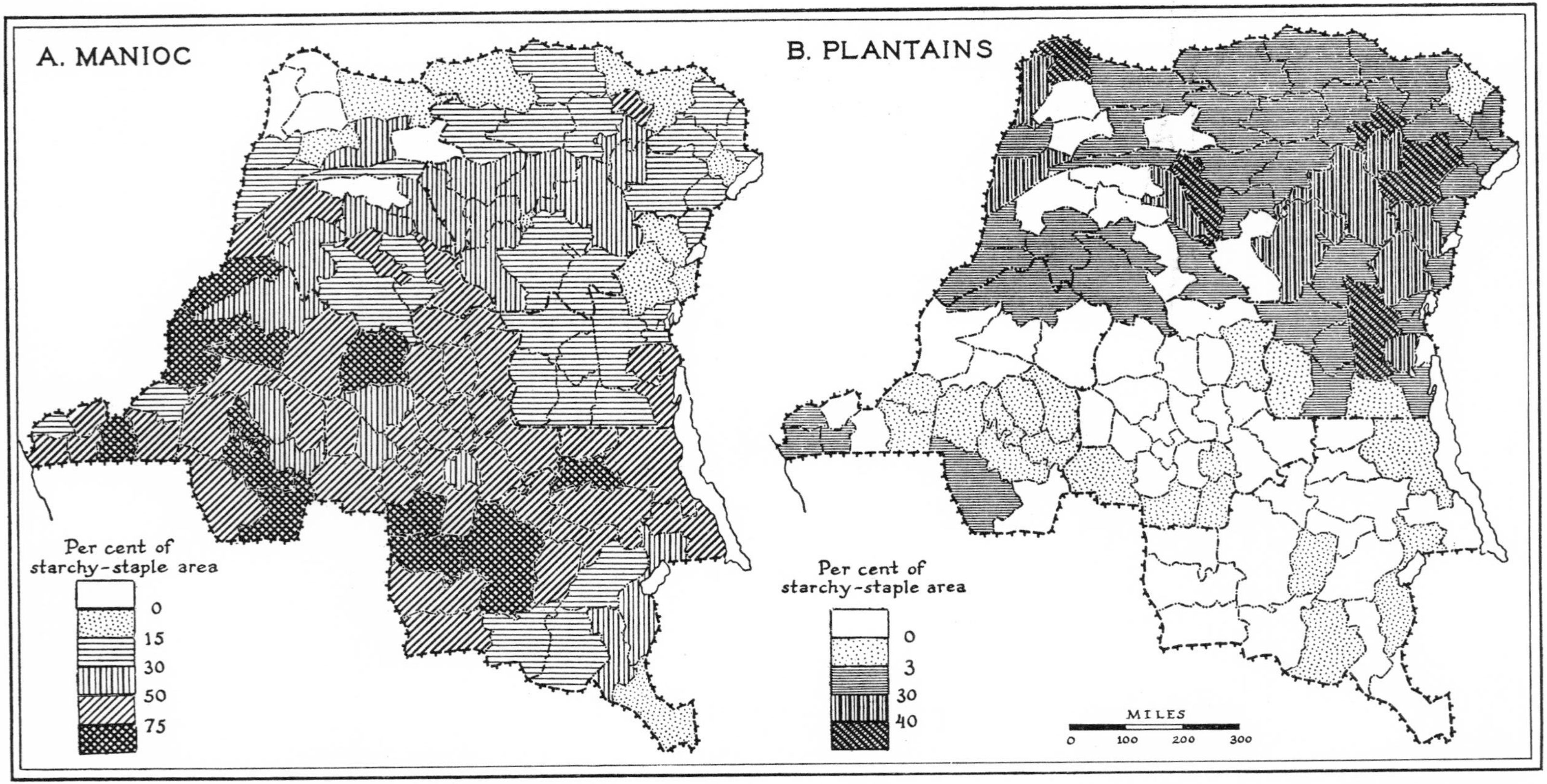

A. MANIOC

B. PLANTAINS

Per cent of
starchy-staple area

0
15
30
50
75

Per cent of
starchy-staple area

0
3
30
40

MILES

0   100   200   300

Adapted from P. Gourou, *La Densité de la population rurale au Congo Belge* (Brussels: 1955), pp. 142, 144. Map: Food Research Institute.

MAP 1-5

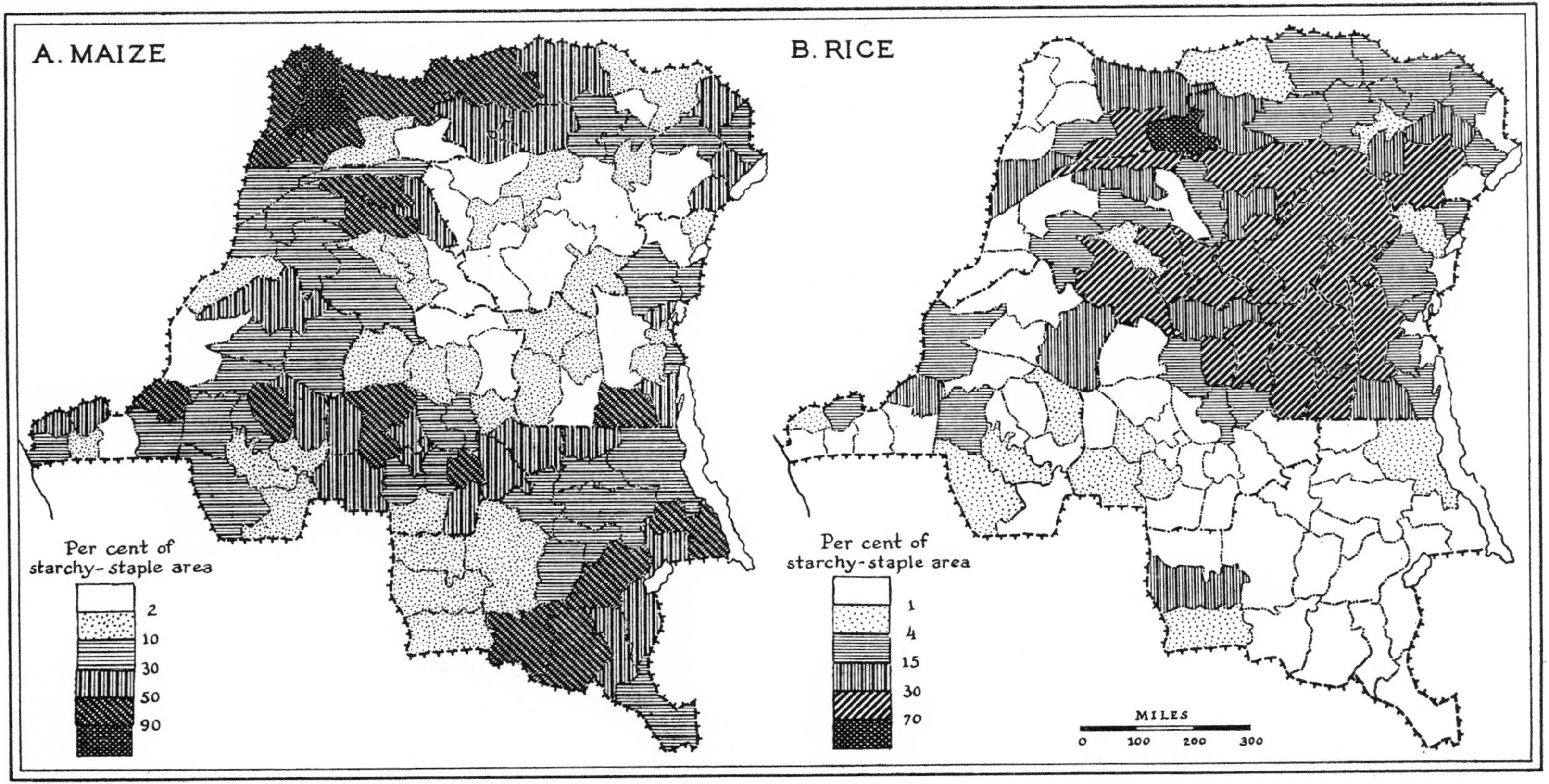

A. MAIZE

B. RICE

Per cent of
starchy-staple area

2
10
30
50
90

Per cent of
starchy-staple area

1
4
15
30
70

MILES
0   100   200   300

Adapted from P. Gourou, *La Densité de la population rurale au Congo Belge* (Brussels: 1955), pp. 145, 146. Map: Food Research Institute.

MAP 1-6

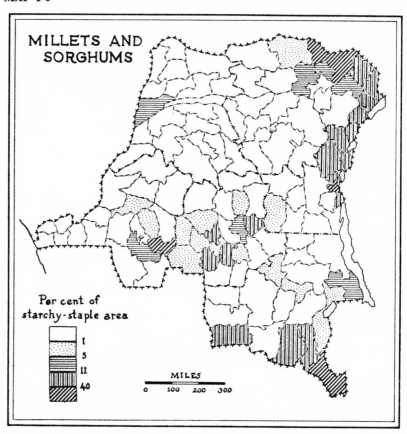

MILLETS AND
SORGHUMS

Per cent of
starchy-staple area

1
5
11
40

MILES
0   100   200   300

Adapted from P. Gourou, *La Densité de la population rurale au Congo Belge* (Brussels: 1955), p. 147.

10

MAP 1-7

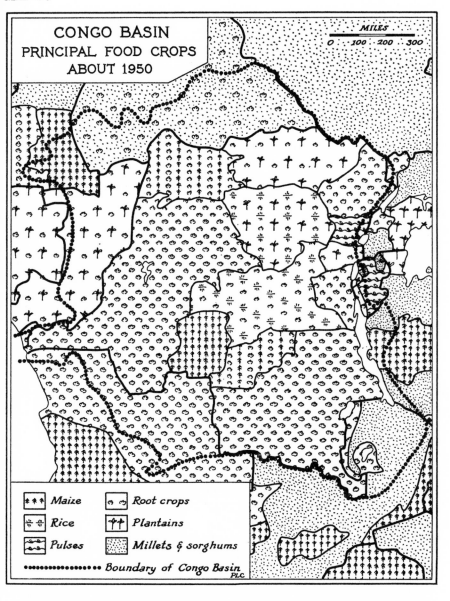

Data from B. F. Johnston, *The Staple Food Economies of Western Tropical Africa* (Stanford: Stanford University Press, 1958), p. 72; and from Appendix, below. Map: Food Research Institute.

MAP 1-8

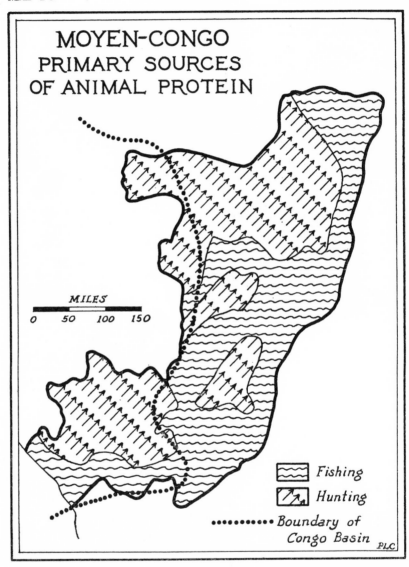

MOYEN-CONGO
PRIMARY SOURCES
OF ANIMAL PROTEIN

MILES

0   50   100   150

Fishing

Hunting

••••••••• Boundary of
Congo Basin

Data from P. Bascoulergue and J. Bergot, *L'Alimentation rurale au moyen-Congo*, Fr. Equat. Afr., Service Commun de Lutte contre les Grandes Endémies, Section Nutrition, 1959. Map: Food Research Institute.

MAP 1-9

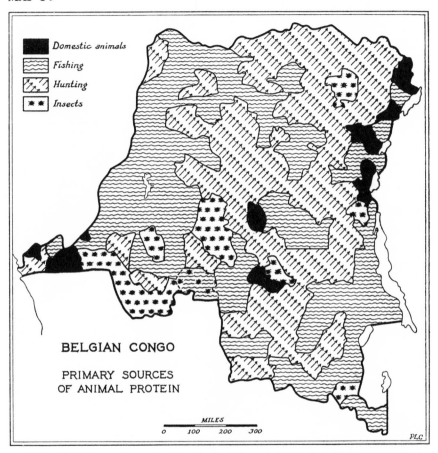

Legend:
- Domestic animals
- Fishing
- Hunting
- Insects

BELGIAN CONGO

PRIMARY SOURCES
OF ANIMAL PROTEIN

MILES

0   100   200   300

PLC

Data from P. A. Gomez, R. Halut, and A. Collin, "Production des protéines animales au Congo," *Bull. Agr. du Congo Belge,* Aug., 1961. Map: Food Research Institute.

MAP 1-10

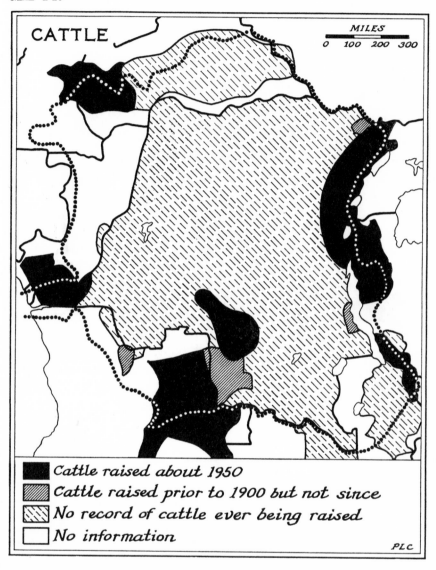

CATTLE

MILES
0   100   200   300

■ Cattle raised about 1950
▨ Cattle raised prior to 1900 but not since
▧ No record of cattle ever being raised
☐ No information

PLC

Data from sources cited in text in discussion by tribes and from Gaston Derkinderen, *Atlas van Belgisch Congo en Ruanda-Urundi* (Brussels: Elsevier, 1955), Map 10, p. 106. Map: Food Research Institute.

14

MAP 1-11

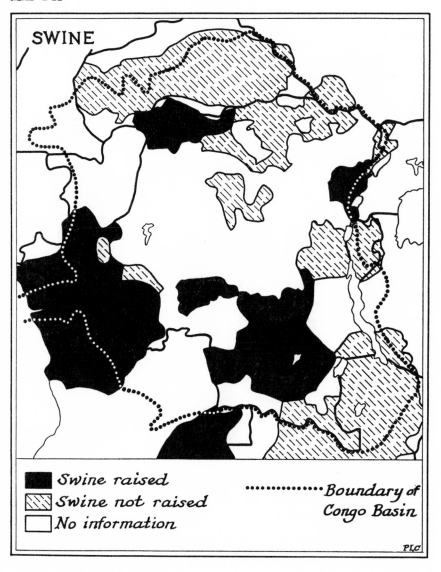

SWINE

■ Swine raised
▨ Swine not raised
☐ No information

•••••••••••••• Boundary of
Congo Basin

PLC

Map: Food Research Institute.

MAP 1-12

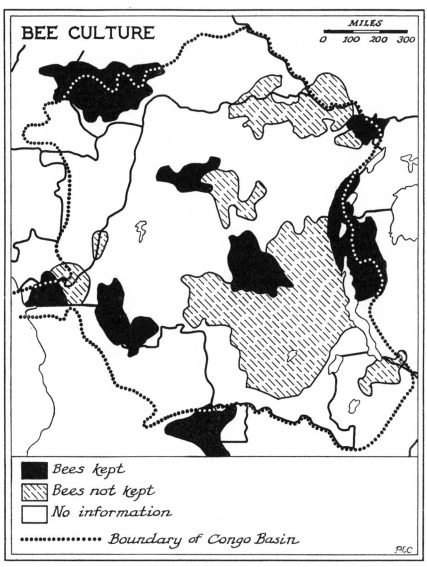

Map: Food Research Institute.

MAP 1-13

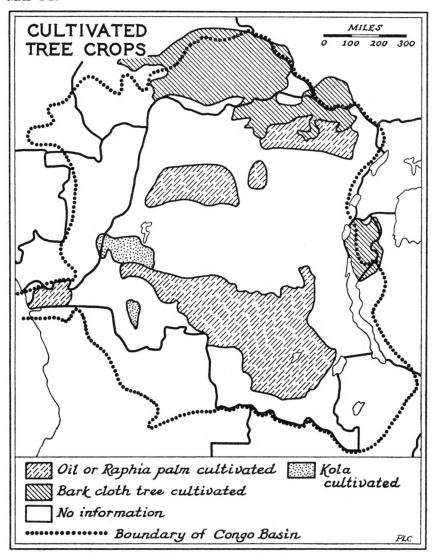

MILES
0   100   200   300

CULTIVATED
TREE CROPS

Oil or Raphia palm cultivated   Kola cultivated
Bark cloth tree cultivated
No information
•••••••••••••• Boundary of Congo Basin

PLC

Map: Food Research Institute.

tainment — as the outline of consumption, investment, and production that follows will suggest.

Although the primary economic activity everywhere is production of food and drink, there is great variation in the number of products available and in how they are derived. The most direct method is merely to harvest useful products of the forest or grassland, whether plant or animal, and to consume them raw on the spot. At the opposite pole is complete reliance on domestic plants and animals, with foodstuffs passing through several stages of processing before they are consumed. Neither of the extremes is found in the traditional economies of the Congo Basin. Even some pygmies who rely largely on hunting, fishing, and gathering subject some of the foodstuffs so obtained to considerable processing; and in the most complex tribal economies some food is still obtained by hunting, fishing, and gathering, although the level of agricultural production may be fairly high relative to needs.

Crops

Most tribal economies are predominantly agricultural and produce a wide range of commodities.[1] The Azande of the northern Congo Basin were growing at least fifty-two different crops in 1945 (*108*, ch. 5). The Banda had sixty cultivated plants in 1953 (*346*, pp. 212–57). Thirty crops were cultivated by the Mandja in 1911 (*150*, p. 211). Sixteen crops are listed for the Bas-Congo area for 1948, and the same number for the Bemba of Northern Rhodesia in the 1930's (*121*, pp. 798–806; *305*, pp. 407–8).

The main agricultural effort is usually for production of staple foodstuffs, probably by far the major source of calories, as Table 1-1 shows. Quantitative data are lacking for other parts of the Congo Basin, but qualitative information suggests that the relative importance of staple foods is approximately that found in consumption surveys.

The nine major staple foodstuffs or foodstuff groups cultivated in the Congo Basin — manioc (or cassava), millets-sorghums, maize, bananas-plantains,[2] sweet potatoes, pulses, rice, yams, and taro (or cocoyams) — vary greatly in importance from one region to another. In the northwestern corner of the Belgian Congo maize was estimated to represent over 90 percent of starchy-staple crop acreage in the 1950's, while manioc represented over 75 percent of area in starchy-staples in several parts of the southern and western Belgian Congo (Map 1-4). In other areas, such as Bumba territoire, neither of these crops represented as much as 2 per-

TABLE 1-1 Relative Importance of Starchy-Staples and Pulses in Diets, in the Congo Basin or Areas Adjacent to It

Area or tribe	Date	Starchy-staples and pulses as a percentage of total caloric intake
		(Percent)
Lala	1947–48	94.8–95.0
Northwestern corner of the Congo Basin	1956–57	90–93
Azande just outside the Congo Basin	1947–48	91.8
Central Ruanda-Urundi	1956	87
Bas-Congo	1946	85.3–87.5
Sundi and Dzem	1956–58	71.7–88.9

Data from, or derived from, V. Drachoussoff, "Essai sur l'agriculture indigène au Bas-Congo, *Bull. Agr. du Congo Belge* (Sept. 1947), pp. 545–46; P. Bascoulergue and J. Bergot, *L'Alimentation rurale au Moyen-Congo* (French Equatorial Africa, Service Commun de Lutte contre les Grandes Endémies, Section Nutrition, 1959), pp. 29, 31, 34, 46; R. Masseyeff, M. L. Pierme, B. B. Bergeret, *Enquêtes sur l'alimentation du Cameroun, II. Subdivision de Batouri*, No. 4173 (I.R.C.A.M., 1958), pp. 93–95; Betty P. Tompson, *Two Studies in African Nutrition*, Rhodes-Livingstone Papers, No. 24 (Manchester, 1954), App. 7; G. M. Culwick, *A Dietary Survey among the Zande of South-western Sudan* (Sudan, Min. Agr., 1950), pp. 139–41; and P. Leurquin, "Économie de subsistance et alimentation au Ruanda-Urundi: Quelques cas concrets," *Zaïre*, No. 1, 1958, pp. 16–28, cited in W. O. Jones, *Manioc in Africa* (Stanford, Calif., 1959), pp. 145 and 243.

cent of staple crop area, and rice acreage was over 70 percent of the total. Official data for Ruanda-Urundi in 1948–49 show pulses (mainly beans) to occupy 62.3 percent of staple-crop acreage [3] in Bushiru, one of the twenty-two agricultural zones of the country; but in another zone, Budaha, pulses accounted for only 10.1 percent of staple-crop acreage, while the share of millet-sorghum was 35.2 percent (*45*, p. 354).

Root crops, and mainly manioc, are most frequently the staples of greatest importance in the Congo Basin according to acreage estimates, but large areas are dominated by maize, rice, or bananas-plantains (Maps 1-4 to 1-6). In the northern and southern extremes of the Basin millet-sorghum reigns, while in the highlands of Kivu and Rwanda and Burundi, pulses hold first place. (Map 1-7. See Appendix for details of construction of this map.)

Animal Husbandry

Data on the importance of animal husbandry in the Belgian Congo are provided by P. A. Gomez, R. Halut, and A. Collin. On the basis of estimates by local administrators and agricultural researchers, Gomez and his associates compiled a map showing the amount of protein per capita coming from hunting, fishing, the collection of insects, and from animal husbandry about 1957 (*153*). Although rough, and unreliable as indicators of absolute amounts of protein available, these data probably portray fairly faithfully the primary source of nonvegetable protein in each territoire.

Food consumption surveys made between 1956 and 1958 by Bascoulergue and Bergot provide information on sources of protein in five rural areas and Brazzaville in Moyen-Congo, former French Equatorial Africa (Map 1-8). In each village studied, the sample of families surveyed was drawn equally from families with two to four, with five to eight, and with nine or more members. For each family observed, food consumption was measured for a week — except at Kibouendé, where surveyors were in the village fifteen months and every family was surveyed twice, for a week each time. Except to note that 258 families were studied in 35 villages, the authors do not give details as to the size of the samples drawn.

Unless available data are consistently very much in error, fishing — in areas near the major rivers and lakes — and hunting elsewhere are typically the major sources of animal protein in the Congo Basin (Maps 1-8 and 1-9). Insects — mainly caterpillars — come third. Domestic animals are outstanding only in a few areas along the eastern edge of the Congo (Kinshasa), in three territories in Kasai, and in a portion of Bas-Congo (Map 1-9).

How animal husbandry compares with crop production cannot be determined from available statistics, but J. S. Hathcock has estimated that the areas dependent on livestock around Lake Albert are the only ones in the Belgian Congo where herding is more important than crop production (*172*, p. 25).

Less information is available on which domestic animals are important, but relatively few tribes in the Congo Basin keep cattle, except in Rwanda-Burundi, a zone of high altitude extending along the rim of the Basin from Lake Kivu to Lake Albert, and scattered areas in the west, northwest, and southwest (Map 1-10). Goats, sheep, and chickens are found widely, although prior to European rule several tribes kept no goats or sheep. Swine are commonly raised in the southwest portion of the Basin, in parts of Katanga, and in some of the north-central and eastern portions of the Congo watershed (Map 1-11). Several tribes in the Congo Basin raise dogs for eating; the Poto and Azande deliberately fatten them (*330*, p. 176). Cats are considered a delicacy at least among some of the southwestern Kongo (*267*, 1:208). Pigeon keeping antedated European rule in much of the south-central portion of the Basin.

Beekeeping

Throughout most of the Congo (Kinshasa) certainly, and possibly more widely, bees are robbed. In parts of the northwestern Congo Basin, along much of the eastern edge of it and in scattered areas elsewhere there is record of Africans constructing hives for their bees (Map 1-12). Most accounts are too sketchy to determine what other practices are followed, but at least in Rwanda-Burundi not only are hives built but they are kept near the villages and swarms of bees are brought to them.

Factors of Production

Various types of communal land tenure are found in the tribal economies. Systems of property rights vary greatly from one area to another, but in general land is allocated by some tribal authority — e.g. a group of elders, the chief, or the lineage head — and may be used as long as it yields a product. Rights to lands fallowed are lost as soon as the last harvest is reaped. In some cases the rights to lands enriched while in use — e.g. village sites fertilized by household wastes and human excrement — continue during fallow periods; and trees planted usually can be owned even though the land they grow on cannot. As a rule livestock and all material goods are also owned.

In most cases land for staple food crops is actually allocated to women because under polygyny, found throughout the Congo Basin, each of a man's wives and her children constitute a separate household. The amount of land a woman receives tends to be determined by both her needs and ability.

The most common method of obtaining labor to supplement that in the household is to organize a working bee (or a beer-work party). The individual organizing the bee offers beer or food for all willing to help with a particular task, such as hoeing or weeding. Neither wage labor nor sharecropping, now of considerable importance in the tribal economies of some other parts of tropical Africa, is reported in the literature for the Congo Basin, and there is nothing to suggest that either is of more than slight importance.

Specialization and Markets

Everywhere there is specialization in the tribal economies of the Basin, and in some areas production is highly specialized. Viscount Mountmorres, who toured parts of the Basin in 1904 to investigate allegations of maladministration of the Congo Free State, says of the Bondjo on the Ubangi River: "Their towns are all divided into three sections devoted respectively to the warriors; the manufacturers; and the food producers. This last class is, on the river, composed of the fisher folk; inland, it consists of the agriculturalists" (*271*, pp. 18–19).

Léon Guiral noted in 1881 that the Tio (Teke) around the present city of Kinshasa (formerly Leopoldville) had little agricultural production and were obliged to buy considerable quantities of foodstuffs — particularly manioc, their staple (*165*, p. 239). C. Liebrechts, writing of his sojourn in the Congo Basin from 1883 to 1889, says the Yanzi — who traded some commodities with the Tio and others around Kinshasa even though they are located some 200 miles away — grew only manioc, buying all other necessities in marketplaces (*236*, p. 72).

Fernand Nys, in a book published in 1896, emphasizes the specialization among the Abarambos and neighboring peoples located some 250 miles northeast of Kisangani (formerly Stanleyville) (*279*, p. 135). A. de Calonne-Beaufaict too, in a study published in 1912, underscores specialization and exchange among the Babwa (also found northwest of Kisangani), and notes that the neighboring Azande came regularly to Babwa marketplaces to buy staple foodstuffs such as finger millet, sorghum, and manioc (*95*, p. 77).[4]

Livingstone vividly described the markets of Nyangwé on the Lualaba River. He estimated there was a market every 8 or 10 miles; every fourth day was market day in any one location. People walked up to 25 miles to these markets. He reckoned there were 3,000 people — mostly women — at one market and 1,500 at another (*405*, p. 377).

Stanley found markets all along the Lualaba River from Nyangwé to Stanley Falls, and suggested that commerce was sizable (*333*, pp. 126–256). In eastern Kivu, markets attended by 3,000 people were reported by early European observers (*69*, pp. 793–94).

Lieutenant Storms estimated that 1,000 people daily attended the market at Ujiji on the eastern shore of Lake Tanganyika when he was there in 1882, and he reported that commodities came from as much as 400 miles away (cited in *409*, p. 161).

The Kuba area some 300 miles west of Nyangwé is described by Jan Vansina as having had markets since at least the seventeenth century, some attended by 1,000 people or more (*392*, pp. 193, 195).

Lieutenant Gorin, in an article published in 1894, describes active marketplaces east of the Kuba in the Kwango. He gives no estimates of attendance but does talk of "big markets" and mentions that thirty to forty goats and pigs and two head of cattle were often slaughtered by market butchers on market days (cited in *222*, p. 113). If such meat was as expensive relative to other foodstuffs sold in tropical African marketplaces then as now, attendance may well have exceeded 700 people.

A. J. Wauters, in a book published in 1885, suggests there was considerable commerce then on the lower Congo River: "one frequently sees arrive at Stanley Pool little fleets of 10 to 20 dugout canoes heavily laden, directed by the Wabouma, river people of Kwango. There they unload their merchandise, their voyage by water being forcibly interrupted by the Ntamo Falls, and they continue by land toward San Salvador" (*409*, p. 162).

Lieutenant Lemaire, in a book published in 1895, estimates as many as 1,500 people in some of the marketplaces around Stanley Pool (*222*, p. 112).

Although there were no marketplaces, trade appears to have been active between the Uele and Ubangi rivers (Map 1-1) prior to European rule (*303*, p. 538, and *214*, 2:103). Belgian agricultural officials reported considerable trade for this area in 1913 and described the Africans as "natural traders" (*152*, p. 597). In the southeastern portion of the Congo Basin too there was a sizable amount of marketless exchange.

The Unga of the Bangweulu swamps in the southeastern Congo Basin had no markets, but from the number of commodities they traded commerce appears to have been considerable (*206*, pp. 4–5). G. Gouldsbury and H. Sheane reported a "fair amount" of trading done among the nearby Bemba (*157*, p. 288).

Katanga also lacked marketplaces until they were started by the first officers of the Congo Free State (*396*, p. 148); but there was a heavy trade through caravans, some of which are said to have numbered over 1,000 people (*51*, p. 89).

Investment

Categories of investment vary considerably. Tools consist principally of various hoes (Figure 1-1) or digging sticks, hatchets, spears, bows and arrows, and knives made locally or bought. Other common capital goods are mainly nets and traps of various sorts; sometimes looms; grindstones, wooden or ivory pestles and mortars, pots, baskets, canoes, fences, granaries, and temporary shelters built in fields. In most areas, exchange of commodities for wives is also a form of investment, for they increased the household's labor supply and hence its production. In precolonial times slaves were also a means of increasing the labor supply.

Consumption

Staple foodstuffs are transformed into a number of products. The principal one is a bland, starchy, doughlike paste that is broken into chunks with the fingers and dipped into a tasty stew of such things as meat, fish, insects, and vegetables. Alcoholic beverages are the second most important group of products from this source.

Although stews — often referred to in the literature as relishes — are

FIGURE 1-1 Some Traditional Hoes

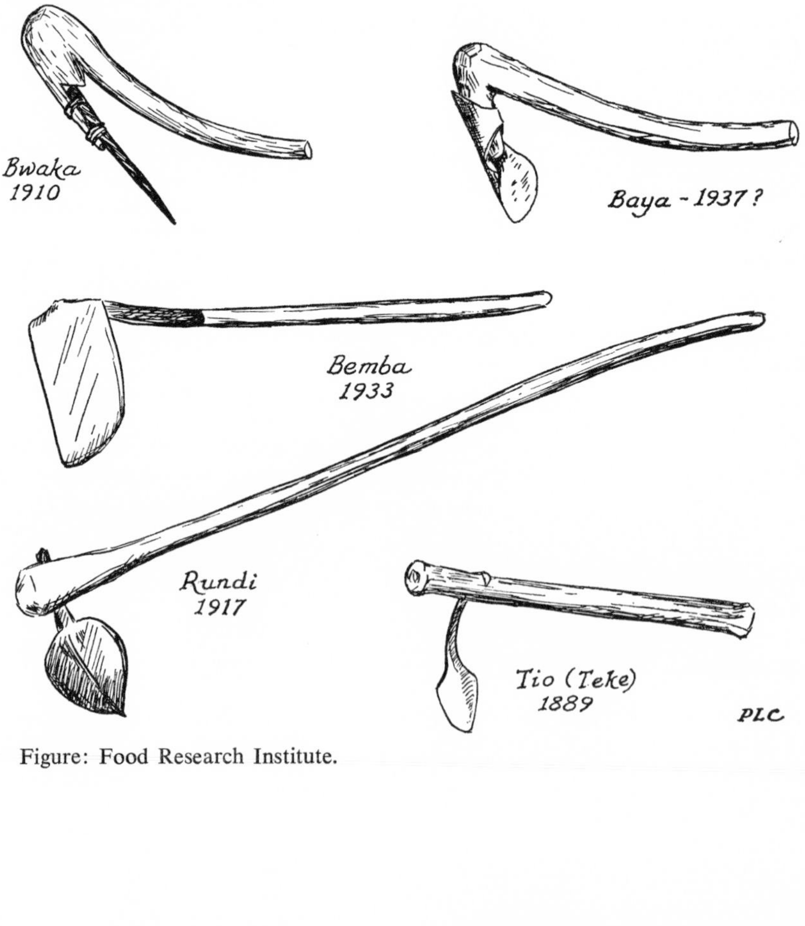

Figure: Food Research Institute.

relatively small contributors of calories, they are important sources of proteins, vitamins, and minerals; and they permit a great variety of diet. Even where there is little variation in the dough-porridge that serves as the staff of life,[5] the fare of African households is far from monotonous because of the variety of relishes eaten with the staple food. In Malawi, adjacent to the southeast corner of the Congo Basin, almost half the plants used for food (55 of 124) are important partly for the use of their leaves in the kitchen (*423*). Few tribes have all 55 kinds of leaves available, and the relative importance of these foodstuffs varies considerably; however, all the careful studies of African diets in the Congo Basin support the conclusion that many different relishes are typically eaten.

The Bemba of Zambia have 4 types of dough-porridge, at least 38 relishes, 36 or more cooked foods other than relishes and porridge, and at least 6 foods consumed raw, and 9 drinks (Table 1-2). The neighboring

TABLE 1-2 Principal Bemba Dishes

Item	*Foodstuff*	*Method of preparation*
Finger millet porridge	*Eleusine coracana*	flour made into porridge[a]
Sorghum porridge	*Sorghum* spp.	" " " "
Maize porridge	*Zea mays*	flour from immature ears used for porridge
Manioc porridge	*Manihot utilissima*	flour made into porridge[b]
Peanut relish	*Arachis hypogaea*	pounded into sauce and added to various other ingredients to make relishes[b]
Peanut relish	" "	peanuts ground and cooked into a cake, then stamped hard with salt
Bean relish	*Phaseolus* spp.	fresh pods boiled with salt[b]
Bean relish	" "	dried beans stewed to form a puree; salt is added[b]
Bambara nut relish	*Voandzeia subterranea*	half-dried pods cooked with water[b]
Cowpea relish	*Vigna uncuiculata*	fresh leaves stewed (may be added to peanut sauce)[b]
Pea relish	*Pisum sativum*	dried leaves stewed with locally made soda (may be added to peanut sauce)[b]
Pea relish	" "	dried leaves softened with locally made soda and cooked on potsherds with salt and water
Pumpkin relish	*Curcubita* spp.	fresh leaves stewed[b]
Mpwa	*Solanum naumanii*	fruit stewed

Table 1-2 *(Continued)*

Item	Foodstuff	Method of preparation
Wild greens[a]		
Pupwe relish	Unidentified	fresh leaves stewed with peanut sauce and salt, or dried leaves stewed with locally made soda[b]
Candabemba relish	"	"
Lusakasuka relish	"	"
Kapalala relish	"	"
Cinsanki relish	"	"
Tata relish	"	"
Caonde relish	"	"
Kaboswe relish	"	"
Wild orchid relish	*Orchis mabembo*	stewed with peanut sauce and salt[b]
Edible fungi relish (30 kinds)	—	stewed alone or with peanut sauce
Finger millet scones	*Eleusine coracana*	flour made into scones (for journeys only)
Boiled sorghum	*Sorghum* spp.	whole grains boiled
Roasting ears	*Zea mays*	green ears of maize boiled or roasted on the cob[b]
Shya miyeye	" "	very young ears boiled and eaten cob and all
Pounded maize	" "	dried grains boiled and pounded
Boiled maize	" "	dried maize boiled
Maize blancmange	" "	mature maize pounded and added to water; this liquid is then boiled and left to set into blancmange
Roasted manioc	*Manihot utilissima*	roots roasted in chunks (dipped into peanut sauce before being eaten)
Boiled sweet potatoes	*Ipomoea batatas*	sweet potatoes boiled (eaten alone)[b]
Roasted sweet potatoes	" "	sweet potatoes roasted in hot ashes[b]
Nsemwa	" "	dried sweet potatoes boiled with salt[b]
Boiled Livingstone potatoes	*Coleus esculentus*	boiled tubers (eaten alone)
Stewed Livingstone potatoes	" "	tubers stewed with peanut sauce[b]
Heated peanuts	*Arachis hypogaea*	kernels are heated on a potsherd
Bean or pea cake	*Phaseolus* spp. or *Pisum sativum*	puree of stewed dried beans or peas pounded into a cake and cooked with very little water and salt[b]

Table 1-2 *(Continued)*

Item	Foodstuff	Method of preparation
Parched peas	*Pisum sativum*	fresh peas cooked in a pot without water
Parched Bambara nuts	*Voandzeia subterranea*	fresh nuts cooked in a pot without water
Boiled pumpkin	*Curcubita* spp.	boiled (eaten alone)[b]
Boiled cucumber	*Cucumis ficifolius*	small cucumber boiled whole[b]
Cooked cucumber	" "	cucumber skins cooked with locally made soda
Stewed wild meat (7 principal types)	—	meat stewed slowly[b]
Roasted wild meat	—	meat roasted on sticks (used mainly on journeys)
Ukusalula	—	wild or domestic meat cooked dry on a potsherd
Stewed fish	—	stewed slowly[b]
Roasted fish	—	cooked dry on a potsherd
Cooked caterpillars (6 principal types)	—	slowly stewed with peanut sauce or cooked dry
Roasted termites	—	cooked dry
Roasted locusts	—	" "
Roasted crickets	—	" "
Cucumbers	*Cucumis sativus*	eaten raw
Peanuts	*Archis hypogaea*	" "
Wild plums	*Anisophyllea* sp.	" "
Loquats	*Uapaka Kirkiana*	" "
Mpundu fruit	*Parinarium mobola*	" "
Sorghum stalks	*Sorghum* spp.	stalks chewed raw
Finger millet gruel	*Eleusine coracana*	flour made into a thin gruel[b]
Finger millet beer	" "	flour made into beer
Sorghum beer	*Sorghum* spp.	" " " "
Maize beer	*Zea mays*	flour from immature maize made into beer
Peanut gruel	*Arachis hypogaea*	nuts heated, pounded, and cooked with water
Cucumber gruel	*Cucumis ficifolius*	cucumbers boiled to make a hot drink
Plum drink	*Anisophyllea* sp.	made into a drink; method not described[b]
Loquat drink	*Uapaka Kirkiana*	" " " " " "
Mpundu drink	*Parinarium mobola*	" " " " " "

Data from, or derived from, A. I. Richards, *Land, Labour, and Diet in Northern Rhodesia* (Oxford University Press: Oxford, England, 1939), Appendix A.

Note: Negligible amount or none:—

[a] Several types are not listed here.

[b] One of the most common methods of preparation.

Lala appear to have about the same number of relishes but possibly fewer other cooked foods.

In Rwanda-Burundi a minimum of 8 types of porridge are made; there are 5 wild tubers sometimes consumed; and at least 36 relishes, 16 fruits, and 6 drinks are known.

The Mandja of the northern Congo Basin have 2 staples and 52 non-staple dishes. Around Lake Leopold II at least 61 insects or wild plants enter the diet; and in the Kwango area a conservative estimate is 55 relishes, 14 fruits, and 10 drinks.

The Luvale know at least 4 porridges and 65 relishes. They include the 18 most common types of caterpillars, the 19 principal fungi, and the 7 chief wild greens. In addition, a minimum of 23 wild and 11 domesticated fruits are consumed (*417*, pp. 6–16).

Relish production involves little processing except where preserved fish or insects are used, or when locally made salt — sometimes derived from the ashes of plants especially cultivated for this purpose — is substituted for imported salt as a flavoring.

Shelter and clothing, the second major category of consumption goods, vary greatly. Huts with mud, wattle, or thatch walls and thatched roofs are found everywhere, but they may be elaborate affairs which are maintained a generation or more or hastily built structures used only a year or two. Cotton, bark cloth trees, and raphia palms are grown to provide raw materials for clothing in many areas (Map 1-13); body coverings are also made from collected grass and leaves, from the skins of wild or domestic animals, and from cloth obtained in trade.

PART II Techniques of Production

2

Shifting Cultivation
in the Congo Basin

Shifting cultivation[1] is a vague concept generally used to cover any agriculture in which the boundaries of farmers' most important fields shift from one cultivation cycle to the next. (A cultivation cycle is completed when a field has been cultivated, then fallowed.) Although some authors restrict the term "shifting cultivation" to the practice of shifting the homesite as well as fields, and refer to the shifting of field boundaries around a fixed homesite as field rotation, the wider concept is the one commonly encountered.

The main reason field boundaries shift is that the principal method of restoring soil fertility lost through cultivation is not only to rest land periodically but to allow regrowth of natural vegetation during fallow periods. Because natural vegetation is uncontrolled during fallow periods, which usually must be longer than periods of cultivation for restoration of fertility, a thick growth of vegetation results, particularly in the tropics, and field boundaries easily become blurred.

For analysis of problems of economic development, the most important feature of this type of agriculture is heavy reliance on nature, rather than on means involving human effort, to restore soil fertility. The degree of this reliance on nature can be expressed in terms of the length of fallows, provided information is available on the quality of soil and the size and

31

character of human effort involved in restoring soil fertility. Frequently only the relative length of fallow periods is known, but in the tropics field boundaries seem always to shift when fallow periods exceed cultivation periods. We therefore classify any system in which either field boundaries are known to shift or the fallow is longer than the period of cultivation as one of shifting cultivation, recognizing that in some instances systems characterized by a reverse fallow-cultivation ratio may belong in this classification.

Distinguishing between systems in which homesites shift and those in which they do not is economically meaningful because of the capital destroyed and the labor cost required in shifting a homestead. However, in tropical Africa at least, moving the homesites may be prompted by superstition or fear of witchcraft as well as for economic reasons such as to reduce the distance between the homesite and fields. Moreover, farmers who shift their homesites conceivably could have just as high productivity per acre or per unit of labor as neighboring groups that have fixed home-sites. Groups whose houses are easily dismantled and moved — like the Kuba and Lele in the Southern Congo Basin, whose hut walls are made of woven mats — may move their houses when the distance to fields exceeds, say, x yards, whereas those with more permanent dwellings might walk much farther to fields rather than incur the cost and waste of moving their homesteads. Finally, there is no fundamental difference in the method of restoring soil fertility when homesites are not shifted. Some farmers with fixed homesites are completely dependent on nature for restoration of soil fertility. Therefore we include as part of shifting cultivation farmers with shifting fields but permanent homesites.

Nor do we restrict the term shifting cultivation to certain types of land tenure, as is sometimes done. Frederick J. Simoons limits it to situations where rights to cultivate a particular plot of land expire once the plot is abandoned to lie fallow. He points out that in at least one part of Africa, northwestern Ethiopia, farmers may retain rights to particular plots even when they are fallowed for many years, coming back to the same fallow once it can be cropped again, while in other parts of the same area rights to cultivate fallow land are not defined in terms of specific fields or plots previously worked by the cultivator (*329*, p. 72).

This is an economically interesting distinction because, where rights to a particular field are retained through fallow periods, cultivators have incentive to make improvements that will increase productivity even if these only reduce the fallow period and do not allow complete escape from use of fallows. However, the difficulty of maintaining the identity of fallows in most of the tropics may give the distinction limited relevance. In the hot and humid parts of the tropical belt, growth of natural vegetation is so rapid and dense that field boundaries often begin to disappear before the last crops in the cultivation cycle are harvested. There is no suggestion in the literature that the identity of main field fallows is maintained anywhere in the Congo Basin.[2]

Shifting cultivation is common in the tropics and not unknown in temperate areas. It probably was common at one stage of the agriculture of most of North America and Europe and was found in parts of Finland and in northern Russia — beyond the upper Volga River — as late as the nineteenth century (*92*, p. 208). It has been documented at one time or another in northwestern Spain, in portions of the Hercynian highlands of Germany and central Europe, and in parts of the uplands of Japan, China, and Korea (*408*, p. 77). Shifting cultivation is still widely found in the tropics, extending over some 36 million square kilometers (14 million square miles) and involving some 200 million people (*145*, p. 160).[3] Tropical Africa has, by a wide margin, more of it than any other continent. Almost no permanent field agriculture is found in a broad, continuous belt running across the middle of the continent that includes all of the Congo Basin and most of tropical Africa.

Looking at economic development from the beginning of agriculture to the present, we are almost certain to find any tropical economy characterized by shifting cultivation at some early phase of development. It can be expected whenever 1) soil rapidly loses its fertility once cleared of natural vegetation, 2) fertilizers are unavailable or expensive, and 3) land is sufficiently abundant, for a given size of population to be supported from it, to permit use of a long fallow. All three of these conditions are characteristic of the Congo Basin and most of the rest of tropical Africa.

Fertility

In the tropics, unlike many temperate areas, land which will support lush forest, and from the growth of natural vegetation appears highly fertile, loses its fertility very rapidly once it is cleared and planted to annual crops. Under the conditions of high rainfall found in much of the tropics, soils are ever subject to leaching, and most plant nutrients not tied up in vegetation are leached out.

Burning is practiced almost everywhere that shifting cultivation is found. In forest areas it serves to eliminate an abundance of felled vegetation that is in the way; in savanna areas it helps kill unwanted plants, particularly grasses. In both areas it is also done because the ashes are valued for the nutrients they add, and perhaps because of other beneficial effects, such as killing weed seeds and making the soil less acid in reaction or more friable. Once natural vegetation is cut and burned, the nutrients it holds are either liberated as gases (nitrogen and sulphur) or deposited in the form of ash on the soil surface.

Crops planted on the cleared areas rapidly deplete the weak concentration of nutrients found in the soil before clearing, and much of the nutrients from the felled vegetation is soon lost through leaching. In addition removal of vegetation exposes the soil to destruction by sun and rain. Hence there is a toll of fertility through both erosion and oxidation of humus exposed by burning (*184*, p. 179; and *278*, p. 10).

During the fallow period the process is gradually reversed. There is initially a rapid growth of vegetation from new seedlings and from the root system of the felled vegetation. Nutrients are brought up from the rooting zone and stored in the increasing volume of vegetation. At the same time, erosion is reduced by the dense natural cover that is developing, and leaching is reduced by a layer of litter that begins to accumulate from falling leaves and twigs. Biotic activity on the soil surface quickly decomposes much of the litter; nutrients are thus added to the top soil, and humus is increased as some of the carbon of the litter is incorporated into the soil (*184*, pp. 160–61 and 178–79; and *278*, pp. 9–10).

Total nutrients stored during the fallow increase rapidly at first, then at a slower rate. Research at the Yangambi experiment station in the heart of the humid forest near Kisangani shows that well over half of the most important nutrients were accumulated during the first five years of an 18- to 19-year fallow (*184*, p. 160; and *203*, p. 222):

Length of fallow (*Years*)	*Nutrients stored in vegetation*			
	N	*P*	*K*	*Ca and Mg*
	(*Kilograms per hectare*)			
2	190	22	169	160
5	570	32	420	421
8	580	35	670	668
18–19	700	108	820	822

When land is cleared or partially cleared and planted with tree crops — such as rubber, oil palms, coffee, or cocoa, which like wild trees and shrubs can capture soil nutrients as they percolate through the soil — fallows are not necessary, and permanent field cultivation can be practiced.

Unavailability of Fertilizers

Where annual crops are grown, the rapid loss of soil fertility can be offset by use of fertilizers; but in a large portion of the Congo Basin cattle cannot be kept because of the tsetse fly; goats and some poultry are commonly kept, but neither their manures nor others available (e.g. night soil) are widely used. Chemical fertilizers are unfamiliar and expensive; they must be imported, and most farmers are located long distances overland from the nearest port.

Land Abundance

If soil rapidly loses its fertility once cleared, and the option of using fertilizers is ruled out, the long fallow is the only means of restoring fertility left, given the goal of yields near those on newly cleared land. Failure to allow land a long enough fallow to restore fertility means that when it is cleared again it will give even lower yields; hence either increasingly large amounts of land must be cleared to compensate, the level of other economic activities increased, or the level of consumption reduced. For a community at its minimum physiological level of living any reduction of the level of consumption will, by definition, reduce its population.

Thus for a given per capita level of living and a given degree of reliance on crop production there is some critical ratio of population to the land it has claim to, for shifting cultivation to be workable. A denser population can be supported only if there is less reliance on crop production or a change in agricultural methods.

Tools and Division of Labor

Shifting cultivation can be practiced with a wide range of tools from digging sticks to tractors, but in the Congo Basin it is usually characterized by little use of capital equipment. Everywhere fire is employed either to help remove vegetation so there will be room for crops, or to reduce vegetation to fertilizer (ash). The tools employed are usually machetes or similar long-bladed knives, hatchets, and hoes. The plow was not used in pre-European agriculture and is still rare. Hatchets or fire are used to kill or fell undesirable trees. Useful trees, such as the oil palm and trees which bear edible fruit, are left standing. Very large trees, or those of exceptionally hard wood, are usually killed by ringing with a band cut in the bark through the cambium layer, or debris may be piled around the base and ignited. Small trees, bushes, and vines may be cut with either a long-bladed knife or a hatchet. Hoes, long-bladed knives, or fire are used to remove grass.

Everywhere men clear the soil of trees and large bushes; but with the exception of relatively small areas in the eastern Congo Basin and along the upper Congo River, data available suggest that the other production operations are left to the women and children (Map 2-1).

The diversity of the role of men in crop production is particularly noteworthy because of the implications for the effect of transferring labor from the agricultural to the industrial sector and because it is contrary to a common assumption that the role of men in agriculture is everywhere the same in tropical Africa (see, for example, *37*, p. 72; *49*, p. 169; *429*, pp. 132–33; and *34*, p. 169).

Length of Fallow and Frequency of Shifting Homesites

In the Congo Basin the period land is rested is usually more than twice as long as it is cropped, and not infrequently much longer. Usually some fields are cleared each year and some are abandoned. Fields are made as near the homestead as possible,[4] but after a few years the only new land left may be a long walk from the hearth.

Unless some other consideration prompts a move sooner, the homesite is deserted and a new one nearer uncleared land is chosen when the distance between homestead and fields becomes intolerable. Land around the old homestead, especially areas that have been enriched by the accumulation of household wastes, may continue to be cultivated for several seasons.

Not all tribes in the Congo Basin shift their homesites, but all alternate their fields between a short period in crops and a longer period in bush or grass fallow. How frequently the homesite is shifted depends on the fertility of the soil, the crops grown, the production techniques employed, and the density of population, as well as the cost of moving or rebuilding housing. The Azande of the southern Sudan shift homesteads roughly every ten years, the Banda of the Central African Republic every eight; the Bemba and Lala of the southeastern Congo Basin were moving their homesteads every five years or so in the 1930's; and in Rwanda-Burundi homesteads are not shifted.

Field production is supplemented by gardens in which cultivation is

MAP 2-1

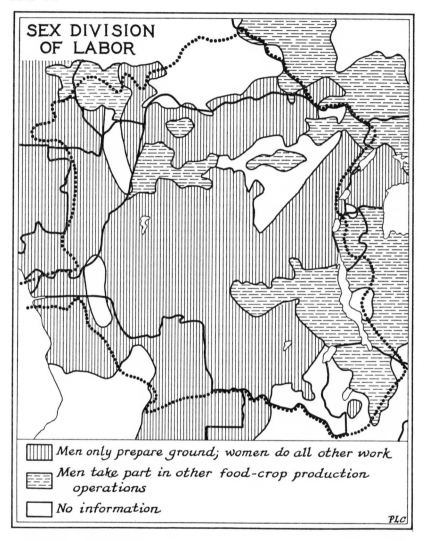

SEX DIVISION
OF LABOR

Men only prepare ground; women do all other work

Men take part in other food-crop production
operations

No information

Data from sources cited in text and from H. Bauman, "The Division of Work According to Sex in African Hoe Culture," *Africa* (July, 1928), p. 302. Map: Food Research Institute.

more intensive; here the soil is usually not rested until the homesite is shifted. Gardens that are rested are generally given a relatively short fallow. Gardens adjacent to the homesite usually receive household refuse and sometimes compost or animal manure. Distant gardens are typically made in relatively fertile valleys whose soil requires rest less frequently than that of upland fields.

Classification of Agricultural Systems

The distinguishing feature of shifting cultivation is, as we have noted already, that cultivators rely heavily on nature to restore soil fertility. In extreme cases the cultivator makes no attempt to conserve or replenish soil fertility. He merely clears land, plants crops until yields fall below the level he considers satisfactory, then turns to another portion of un-cleared land available. If population is sparse enough he may always clear land that is virgin in the sense that it is carrying its climax vegetation.[5] On the other hand population pressure may force him to clear any given area before its climax vegetation can develop. At the opposite extreme are agricultural systems in which soil fertility is maintained solely by the efforts of man.

Much of agriculture in the less developed countries (and nearly all of that of tropical Africa) is nearer the first limiting case than the second. Man makes some effort to maintain or restore soil fertility but relies con-siderably — sometimes heavily — on nature for help, either because he does not know of alternative techniques or because they are too expensive.

In general, the less the reliance on nature by cultivators, the greater the skill in controlling the crop environment, and the greater the density of population that can be supported, or the greater the production surplus available for exchange with other areas in the same economy or for export. Because of its relevance for analysis of economic development, the degree of reliance on nature by cultivators is the basis for classification of the agricultural systems of the Congo Basin used in this book.

The complexity and extreme diversity of agricultural systems in the Basin present a number of problems of classification. Most tribes have three or four types of fields and plots, and these are rarely well enough described to establish differences in the importance of secondary fields and plots. Farmers who make no effort to enrich main fields may have gardens in special environments — for example near the homestead or along a stream — which are irrigated or given refuse and fertilizers. The

MAP 2-2

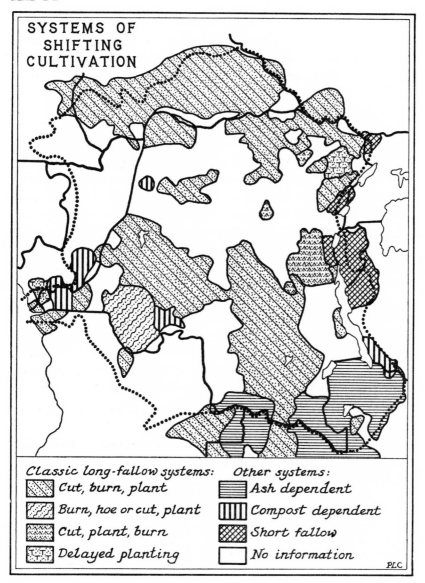

SYSTEMS OF
SHIFTING
CULTIVATION

Classic long-fallow systems: *Other systems:*
Cut, burn, plant   Ash dependent
Burn, hoe or cut, plant   Compost dependent
Cut, plant, burn   Short fallow
Delayed planting   No information

P.L.C

Data from sources cited in text and from Central African Republic, Mission Socio-Économique Centre Oubangui, *L'Emploi du Temps du paysans dans une zone de l'Oubangui Central 1959–60* (Paris, Nov. 1961) p. 67.

harvest from these may be only a small proportion of total crop production or may be sizable, conceivably nearly as large as that from the main fields in some instances. The difficulties of classification presented by secondary plots may not be serious, however. For most of the tribes of the Congo Basin for which there are any data on agricultural methods, main fields are planted with the principal starchy-staples in the diet; and in total, as noted earlier, starchy-staples usually account for from 80 to 95 percent of calories consumed. A classification based on main fields may serve fairly well to distinguish agricultural systems.

Another problem is lack of data on some practices. For most tribes the only evidence on attempts to maintain or restore soil fertility is what can be inferred from descriptions of clearing land and preparing it for planting. Perhaps equally relevant in some areas is the amount of labor devoted to control of weeds and pests, but unfortunately such data are not available for any of the tribes under study.

Information is lacking on the agricultural techniques of a number of tribes in the Congo watershed, and we have undoubtedly missed some of the literature; however, the data assembled below seem to represent all the major climatic zones of the Congo Basin, and they probably suffice to outline the major agricultural systems found.

Four major systems of agriculture, ranging from those in which restoration of soil fertility is left almost entirely to nature to systems characterized by practically no dependence on fallow periods, are found in the Congo Basin; and a number of subtypes can be distinguished (Map 2-2):

Class I   Classic tropical long-fallow systems — the most frequently reported.

Class II   Ash-fertilizer-dependent long-fallow systems — found only in the southeastern corner of the Basin.

Class III   Compost-dependent long-fallow systems — found only in savanna areas.

Class IV   Short-fallow systems — the only systems reported that rely heavily on animal manures or irrigation; restricted to the eastern rim of the Basin.

These four agricultural systems, and the variations found within them, are the subject of the next six chapters. Chapter 9 focuses on animal husbandry, which, except in the short-fallow systems, is usually not related to techniques of crop production. Chapter 10 discusses methods of storage and processing.

3

Classic Tropical
Long-Fallow Systems

By far the most common and most diverse of agricultural systems in the Congo Basin are the long-fallow systems, in which little or no effort is made to maintain or renew soil fertility in main fields. In the simplest of these the soil is not worked; the natural cover is cut and burned and the crop is planted in holes made in the ash.

This simplest case is close to the description of shifting cultivation found in general discussions of the phenomenon in the tropics. But in fact it is only the limiting case of shifting cultivation in the Congo Basin and not widely reported. There are at least eleven other types of shifting cultivation in long-fallow systems employing little or no fertilizer, as well as other types of shifting cultivation (discussed in other chapters) in which some effort is made by cultivators to restore soil fertility.

The twelve classes we distinguish within the category of classic long fallow are ranked according to the kind and amount of effort in main fields and the sequence of field operations, as follows:

Class   1.   Cut, plant, burn (forest).
Class   2.   Cut, plant,wait one season, finish planting (forest).
Class   3.   Cut, burn, plant (forest).
Class   4.   Cut, burn, hoe, plant (forest).
Class   5.   Cut, burn, hoe, plant (savanna).

41

Class   6.   Cut, burn, plant, hoe.
Class   7.   Burn, hoe and cut, plant.
Class   8.   Hoe and cut, then burn, or burn, then hoe and cut.
Class   9.   Hoe and cut, burn, clean, plant.
Class 10.   Hoe and cut, clean, burn, plant.
Class 11.   Cut, burn, clean or level, hoe, plant, followed by repeated
            hoeings.
Class 12.   Cut, plant tree crops (forest).

We have ranked the system of planting tree crops on newly cleared land as the most intensive of the twelve classes because of its potential for allowing cultivators largely, if not entirely, to eliminate fallow periods — although this potential appears not yet to be realized among any of the tribes relying on the technique.

Techniques of cultivation might be expected a priori to differ considerably in forest and savanna areas. The savannas have less vegetation and therefore less stored nutrients for deposit through ashes resulting from use of fire in clearing operations; uncontrolled fires may sweep through savanna fallows frequently, disrupting the process of restoration of soil fertility and making the soil vulnerable to rain and sun; and the abundance of noxious seed and the mat of grass and weed roots near the surface of the soil at the time of clearing necessitate both better preparation of the seedbed (usually at least one hoeing) and more frequent and thorough weedings once crops are established.

Data available confirm that there are indeed differences in methods employed by peoples living entirely in one zone and peoples in the other, as well as in methods used for savanna and for forest areas by tribes having access to both. In general, the simplest techniques, and probably those requiring the least labor per cultivator, are found only in forest areas; all the savanna systems involve hoeing and weeding, and some include a good deal of cleaning, ridging, or mounding.

For only one or two groups in the Congo Basin is there reasonably complete coverage of all aspects of the agricultural techniques. For some groups fairly good descriptions are available on one or two facets of agricultural methods, such as crop associations or clearing techniques; for others perhaps only the agricultural calendar or crop sequences are covered; while for still others accounts may focus on mounding or weeding practices. Frequently observers have not reported clearly what they do discuss.

In the remainder of this chapter and the three that follow we have included all available information on agricultural systems — even if some of it is too fragmentary to support inferences yet about variations in agricultural methods — because of its potential value for comparative work on shifting cultivation elsewhere in Africa and in other parts of the world. Where observers have been vague we have quoted them directly rather than attempt to guess the meaning intended.

Class 1: Cut, Plant, Burn (Forest)

The cut, plant, burn technique is the only system in which fields are burned after crops are growing. It is reported only in forest areas or areas near the forest belt which possibly would still be forest except for the activities of man. Usually the crop occupying the field when it is fired is bananas, plantains, or manioc.

Clearing is often done over a relatively long period, and crops are planted as soon as the smaller vegetation has been cut. By the time all trees to be removed have been felled, the planted crops have established themselves, and the field is given a burning, which apparently inflicts little or no damage on the growing crops. This practice has the advantage of allowing the cultivator to spread his labor over a long period. It also provides an established crop before the creation of a layer of ash, so that crops may capture some of the nutrients that would later be leached.

Kasongo Area

A cropping method described about 1913 (*339*) for the area around Kasongo, on the Lualaba River, is exceptional in being the only instance of reported burning of debris in fields after manioc has been planted, and the only account of burning planted fields in the savanna zone, although the practice is not uncommon in the forest belt.

All vegetation is cut with a hoe in September or October; manioc cuttings are planted on the flat; then the felled vegetation is burned. When the newly planted manioc stems begin to produce leaves, maize is planted in a furrow made with a hoe, four or five kernels being dropped every 8 or 10 cm. (*339*, p. 207).

Rice fields are prepared at about the same time as manioc cultivations, but debris is removed or burned before planting. About two months after the field is cleared the rice is planted, timed to ripen when birds are busy nesting, and will do it less damage.

Cultivation of millet and sorghum is mentioned but is not described. Tobacco gardens around the huts are fenced and fertilized with manure of small livestock or with ashes.

For the Medje, Rega, and Lengola, there are descriptions of burning fields after bananas-plantains are planted.

The Medje

The Medje occupy an area of the northern Congo (Kinshasa) adjacent to part of the Congo Azande and the Mangbetu that lies almost entirely within the forest. The population density is between five and fifteen persons per square kilometer (*377*, Annexe 6). The Medje do not have cattle, although goats, sheep, and poultry are kept. Manioc is reported now to be the base of the diet (*251*, p. 379). Maize, bananas-plantains, and sweet potatoes are of secondary importance.

The most thorough description of Medje agriculture — an article published in 1918 by M. Lacomblez, then the government agronomist for the Medje area — reports the number of varieties of crops grown to have been as follows (*208*, pp. 103–8):

Crops of Medje	*Number of varieties*
Bananas-plantains [a]	27
Yams and related crops	22
Bulbous yams	10
Sweet manioc	5
Bitter manioc	2
Maize	7
Sweet potatoes	4
Taro	3

[a] Lacomblez uses the French term *banane*, which as we have said can refer to either bananas or plantains. Since other sources show the Azande to have both, and since there is evidence of considerable exchange of food crops between the Azande and Medje, I have assumed that the Medje had both at the time Lacomblez wrote. Moreover, Casati's description of the varieties he observed in 1881 suggests that the Medje grew both (*70*, p. 177).

In addition, Lacomblez cites four varieties of gourds, three varieties each of sugarcane and oil palms, two varieties each of peanuts, sesame, tobacco, smoking hemp, and raphia palm. Rice, finger millet, Irish potatoes, beans, Bambara nuts,[1] castor beans, pepper, tomatoes, amaranth, and broom sorghum are also mentioned, but without data on the number of varieties grown.

Lacomblez distinguishes between plots near the village and paths and those in the forest; and among crop associations he distinguishes fields in which bananas-plantains are grown from fields in which they are absent. Little specific information is provided; however, discussion of crop associations contains a statement that "the various crops are generally grouped in the same plot and associations of most diverse plants are found in each field" (*208*, p. 102); that bananas-plantains are grown in almost every field; that maize or sweet potato associations are among the field types that may not contain bananas-plantains; and that maize is always interplanted with vegetables (*208*, pp. 102, 105).

Since there is almost no month without rain, bananas-plantains can be planted at any time; usually, however, fields are prepared between December and March, the months of least rain. The men begin by cutting the underbrush with axes and machetes. As soon as a portion of the field is thus cleared — and before trees are cut — women start planting bananas-plantains shoots 15 to 20 cm. long amid the debris, making holes in the untilled soil with sticks or possibly elephant tusks. After all the field is planted the trees are partially cleared; trees left are those of great size or especially hard wood, and those of value: oil palms, raphia palms, and three other varieties of oil-bearing trees for which only African names are given,[2] and trees with leaves liked by caterpillars. "When the tree felling has been terminated, a general burning of the field is done on a dry day, and then one proceeds to plant manioc interplanted with various annual crops. The incineration, like the cutting of trees, is not complete and affects only the new undergrowth and debris on the ground" (*208*, p. 101). Manioc planted through bananas-plantains is spaced widely, cuttings 20 to 25 cm. long being set in holes 2 to 3 meters apart.

Nothing is said of weeding, except that it is women's work. Organic fertilizer is applied by some villages of the Mabodu group of the Medje. Weeds are piled around the base of bananas-plantains plants "with the goal of providing compost" (*208*, p. 101). Lacomblez estimates that fields are left in bush fallow not more than four or five years.

The Rega

Data on the Rega come primarily from observations made by Commandant Delhaise in 1906 and 1907 when he was in charge of the Rega sector of what was then Orientale Province, Belgian Congo. The Rega are forest people who grow bananas-plantains as their principal staple food. Other crops are maize, yams, manioc, sweet potatoes, peanuts, sugercane, tobacco, and, in the extreme east, beans. Although they live in the forest, the Rega have no oil palms. Sheep, goats, and chickens are found; cattle are not kept.

Delhaise describes clearing operations as follows (*102*, pp. 127–28): "The men clear the land with a small hatchet and a native knife. The roots are left in the ground. Trunks of trees are used for fuel and cut up and collected for this purpose by the women. The branches and leaves are burned in place . . . when the Warega wish to establish a banana grove, they leave the felled trees in place and immediately plant bananas. Then the field is burned. The fire does not destroy the bananas; on the contrary, according to the Warega, it strengthens them."

Bananas-plantains and manioc can be planted[3] any time during the year; other crops are usually planted from October to April. Usually there is little or no hoeing: "they are content to stir the earth a little around the spot where the plant is to be planted. Most often, once planting is finished, no further attention is paid to the field. Sometimes one or two weedings are given if weeds develop too much" (*102*, pp. 127–28).

Delhaise gives no information on gardens, and only says that it is not customary to alternate crops.

The Lengola

Among the Lengola, land is only half cleared for bananas-plantains; the vegetation is cut and bananas-plantains shoots set out; about a month later the field is burned (*338*, p. 157).

Class 2: Cut, Plant, Wait One Season, Finish Planting (Forest)

The Yombe, found near the mouth of the Congo River, the Lese and the southern Mamvu, located in the northeastern corner of the Congo Basin, partially cut vegetation, plant bananas-plantains, then wait a season before finishing the clearing operations and planting other crops among the established bananas-plantains.

Like the cut, plant, burn method, this technique allows cultivators to distribute their labor over a long period. In the area of the Lese and southern Mamvu, at least, fields are only partially cleared initially and plantains planted, then a season later the field is burned and other crops interplanted. The Yombe, however, burn the field before planting plantains, then finish clearing, and burn the field a second time when companion crops are planted. The Yombe collect and pile debris for the second burning, not allowing fire to sweep uncontrolled through growing crops as with the cut, plant, burn method. Lese and southern Mamvu burning techniques are not clearly described, but information available suggests that uncontrolled burning may be practiced and that the only difference from the cut, plant, burn system is the practice of delaying the interplanting of secondary staples one season.

The Yombe

C. Van Overbergh, in a monograph on the Yombe published in 1907, provides the following information (*386*). The Yombe inhabit forest country broken by small expanses of parklike savanna. The population density is estimated at some twenty persons per square kilometer. Van Overbergh suggests that the northern Yombe living in the forest zone grow bananas-plantains as their major staple, with yams in second place; but although yams are second in production, they may rank behind manioc in the diet, for the forest Yombe trade bananas-plantains for manioc with the savanna Yombe. The savanna Yombe rely on manioc as their primary source of calories, with sweet potatoes and bananas-plantains of secondary importance. Van Overbergh does not clearly distinguish agricultural techniques followed in the two zones, except to note that in forest areas peanuts are not often grown, and beans are sometimes planted before bananas-plantains (*386*, p. 181). Minor crops in both areas are taro, maize, beans, peanuts, gourds, tomatoes, eggplant, amaranth, cabbage, red peppers, watermelons, sugarcane, tobacco, papayas, mangos, and citrus fruit. Goats, sheep, swine, chickens, ducks, and occasionally pigeons are kept.

The general description of land preparation appears to relate to both savanna and forest. Undergrowth is cleared in the rainy season with a small hatchet that has a blade 7 to 10 cm. wide and a handle 40 to 50 cm. long.[4] Some of the debris is piled around the base of larger trees where it is left to dry until the field is burned in the middle of the dry season (*386*, pp. 176, 182). Some time after the burning, probably after the rains begin, the clearing is hoed with a small hoe which has a handle 30 to 40 cm. long; then bananas-plantains are planted and the plot is apparently left for a year. "A year later when the plantains begin to bear," says Van Overbergh, "they begin to develop the land: the brush is cut, collected in small piles and burned; the soil is then hoed and when the rains come the field is planted" (*386*, pp. 182–83). What is planted at this time is not clear, but at another juncture Van Overbergh suggests that bananas-plantains are interplanted with manioc, maize, and other minor crops. Local agricultural officers listed the following crop associations in 1953 (*47*, p. 52): manioc or bananas-plantains/yams/maize; manioc/peanuts/maize (and sometimes sweet potatoes); bananas-plantains/beans/maize; bananas-plantains/rice; maize/beans; manioc/maize; manioc/maize/sweet potatoes; and manioc/bananas-plantains.[5]

Yams and manioc are planted both on mounds and on the flat. Yams are not weeded; manioc is weeded one to three times; peanuts, beans, and sweet potatoes are weeded only once; rice is weeded continually (*47*, p. 53).

Tobacco is planted at the end of the rainy season in small unfenced plots near the village; it is harvested at the end of the dry season.

The two common crop sequences are beans, manioc/bananas-plantains/maize, manioc/bananas-plantains, bananas-plantains, bananas-plantains, bananas-plantains, followed by fallow for six to seven years and maize/peanuts, beans/bananas-plantains, then beans or peanuts/maize, or manioc/bananas-plantains (*47*, p. 54).

In the north, around Dindji, the following nine-year sequence is sometimes found (*47*, p. 54):

Year	*Crop*
1	Yams
2–4	Bananas/beans
5–7	Manioc/beans/maize
8	Aerial potatoes or maize
9–16 or 17	Fallow

Around Seke-Banza, beans/maize are followed by three years of fallow, then beans/maize are planted again (*47*, p. 54).

The Lese and Southern Mamvu

Lacomblez, while agricultural officer for the Lese and southern Mamvu, described their agricultural system in an article published in 1924 (*209*). Forest is found throughout the domain of both peoples; plantains are the dominant starchy-staple, followed by manioc and yams — of almost equal importance according to Lacomblez; maize and sweet potatoes are tertiary crops; and beans are of considerable importance. Eighteen varieties of bananas-plantains, sixteen of yams, seven of sweet potatoes, six each of manioc and maize, and four of sugarcane are known (*209*, pp. 329–31):

Crops of Lese and southern Mamvu	Number of varieties
Plantains	16
Bananas	2
Yams	8
Bulbous yams	7
Poisonous yams	1
Sweet potatoes	7
Sweet manioc	4
Bitter manioc	2
Maize	6
Sugarcane	4
Beans	?
Taro	?

Lacomblez implies that several varieties of both beans and taro are found, but because they were not named by the Lese he does not enumerate them. No cattle are found, although small livestock and chickens are common (*209*, p. 332).

A large knife, a hatchet, and a small knife are the principle tools used in field work. Hoes apparently were not known prior to contact with Europeans, and were little used as late as 1924 (*209*, p. 331).

Fields are only partially cleared, initially. As the dry season approaches, underbrush is cut and plantains are set out. Clearing continues until only about a third of the large trees are left standing; then, at the beginning of rains, the field is burned and other crops are interplanted with the growing plantains (*209*, p. 327). Mounds are made for sweet potatoes but not for manioc.

Crop associations are not described, but Lacomblez states that beans are grown in almost every field, and rice is grown in pure stand, usually on fallow. Maize may be grown alone, but is usually grown with plantains and is weeded frequently. A few bunches of sugarcane, gourds, and amaranth are found in some fields. A. P. Merriam says the Lese and Mamvu "are noted for their cultivation of the oil palm . . . ," but he does not give details (*251*, p. 387).

Sugarcane and tobacco are singled out as crops grown mainly in gardens near the hut. No other information is given on gardens.

Class 3: Cut, Burn, Plant (Forest)

Throughout the heart of the forest zone, clearing is done over a long period, and the soil is worked little, if at all, prior to planting. The cut, burn, plant technique — reported for the Turumbu, the Bumba area, the forest Kongo and Tio (Teke), the northern Mongo, the Bali (a group of the Ndaka), the Budu, the forest peoples of Ubangi District of the former Belgian Congo, the Tetela, and the Vili [6] — is the most common mode of preparing forest fields that is described in the literature.

Crops are planted in the ash immediately after burning, in all the areas in the heart of the forest zone reporting this technique. However the Tetela, located on the southern fringe of the forest zone, clean fields of unburned litter after the burning.

The Turumbu

O. E. Elskens and M. Tharin furnish data which make possible a brief sketch of agriculture of the Turumbu, a northern group of the Lokele, during the second decade of this century. Completely in the forest zone, the Turumbu grow manioc as their principal starchy-staple; bananas-plantains are of secondary importance. The only other information about crops is that neither rice nor oil palms are grown (*127*, p. 709; *338*, p. 172).

Land is usually cleared in the dry season (December to March), but manioc can be planted throughout the year and some clearing may be done at other times. The first operation is to cut all the underbrush with a knife.[7] After a wait of several weeks, the farmer fells most of the trees with a hatchet, then trims off their branches (*126*, p. 768). There is a second wait of a few weeks to let the debris dry. Then on a sunny day the debris is piled "around certain trees" and burned. The burning finished, small holes about 20 to 30 cm. apart are made in the soil with a knife, and manioc cuttings 30 to 40 cm. long, taken from the lower part of the manioc stalk, are stuck in the holes at an angle, two or three stems in each hole. Soil is packed around them with the foot. After manioc, bananas-plantains are sometimes planted every 3 meters or so among the manioc.[8]

Weeds do not develop for four or five months if the field is well burned, because seeds in the soil are killed. When the manioc plants are about a meter tall, weeds are pulled up or cut down with a knife; hoes are never used in weeding. At the same time soil is pulled around the base of the plant. This operation is repeated once sometime later — Elskens does not say when — and the field is given no further attention until harvest, except possibly to break off some stalks now and then if plants become too bushy, so as to facilitate circulation of air and penetration of sunlight. Some leaves are gathered from the field every day for cooking, and this helps to keep plants from growing too tall. Elsken's informants also thought this helped the roots to develop (*126*, p. 769).

Manioc is harvested by first cutting the stems 30 or 40 cm. up, then removing some of the earth from the roots with a knife,[9] and finally pulling the roots free. The crop is harvested gradually according to needs.

Information is not provided on techniques used in cultivation or harvest of other crops.

The Bumba Area

Use of the cut, burn, plant method is suggested for the area around Bumba. E. Pauquet, in an article published in 1955, describes rice cultivation there and notes that rice is usually grown interplanted with maize, bananas-plantains, manioc, and gourds (*284*).

Clearing begins in the dry season (February to March); first, thickets and small trees are cut with a machete, then the larger trees are felled with a hatchet. Cleared plots are burned as soon as all clearing has been finished and the debris has dried a "few days." Sowing follows immediately. The men make holes about 30 cm. apart with sticks; the women and children place around ten grains of rice in each. Weeding is begun as soon as sowing is finished and is continuous for about two months, or until the rice plants are 50 to 60 cm. tall.

As the field starts to ripen, tree branches are tied on vines so that they can be pulled from a distance to frighten away birds. Once the grain is ripe, men, women, and children move over the field picking off the rice heads and dropping them in baskets. Harvested grain is immediately sun-dried, cleaned of straw, and threshed with a stick. A winnowing tower 2 to 4 meters high is constructed, and the threshed grain is poured from the top.

The Forest Kongo and Tio (Teke)

The peoples inhabiting the forest areas around Kisantu on the lower Congo River were estimated about 1922 to have fifteen to twenty times as much land in forest as was cropped; thus, they cleared any plot once every fifteen to twenty years (*374*, p. 222). Fully regenerated forest is cleared in three, and secondary forest in two, stages (*372*, p. 538).

In the first stage, shrubs and creepers are cut with a knife or machete at the beginning of the dry season, in order to form a bed for felled trees to lie on; tree trunks are more easily burned if a layer of finer vegetation is lying under them. The second stage is cutting down all trees except very large or useful ones. Trunks are cut off some 60 to 80 cm. above the ground, and branches are removed to facilitate burning. In secondary forest, burning is the next step, for no large undesirable trees are found. In fully regenerated forest, the large trees which are not useful are killed by ringing, so that they will not shade crops. All debris is then left to dry until the end of the dry season. On the day of burning the field is ignited at several points along its windward side (*372*, p. 540). It is then planted, with no preliminary hoeing.

The Northern Mongo

D. Van Moesieke, a Belgian agronomist, describes the agriculture of the northern Mongo in an article published in 1929.

The northern Mongo live entirely in the forest. Estimates of population density are not available for 1929, but in the late 1950's the area was in the category of two to five persons per kilometer (*377*, Annexe 6). Bananas-plantains and manioc are the principal staple foodstuffs. Goats and poultry are raised throughout; sheep and pigeons are found in the southeast (*368*, p. 53). There are no cattle.

Fields may be cleared at any time, but usually in the dry season (December to March). As with most other forest tribes, very large trees, those of extremely hard wood, and useful trees are left standing; all others are cut and the field is burned on a dry day. Then shoots of bananas-plantains — obtained by pulling the suckers away from the base of mature plants — are set out. They may be planted as soon as separated from the mother plant, or they may lie in a heap for two or three days until the leaves begin to grow (*384*, p. 534).

Van Moesieke does not discuss crop associations except to state that "there is no rule for the type of associations followed" (*383*, p. 423), and to comment that maize is always planted with bananas-plantains, while peanuts and rice are usually grown alone.

He gives little information on planting techniques. Rice fields are apparently cleared in the same manner as bananas-plantains fields except that the plot is usually burned twice in order to get a more complete burning of vegetation. Holes for planting maize are usually made with a stick or the hands, possibly because of a shortage of tools. Van Moesieke makes a general statement about the lack of tools in the district, but he does not mention maize specifically (*383*, p. 395). Sweet potatoes are always mounded; manioc and yams may be grown on mounds, but other crops apparently are not (*384*, pp. 534–50). Sugarcane and gourds are often planted on termite hills. Oil palms are planted in abandoned fields and along paths and roads. As the accompanying tabulation shows, planting distances vary considerably (*384*, pp. 534–50):

Crop	Number of varieties grown	Planting distances (meters)	Number of seeds, shoots, or cuttings per hole	Number of weedings
Bananas-plantains	53	1.5–3.0	8–12	0
Manioc	5	1.5–2.0	1	. . .
Sweet potatoes	"several"	0.2–0.3	1	0
Yams	4	. . .	1	. . .
Rice	. . .	. . .	1	"several"
Maize	. . .	2.0–3.0	2–3	"several"
Peanuts	. . .	0.05–0.15	2–3	"several"
Sugarcane	5	0.3–0.4	1	0
Oil palms	. . .	. . .	1	0

Note: Information not available: . . .

Manioc, bananas-plantains, and maize are relatively widely spaced, while peanuts and sugarcane are planted closely. Except for rice, maize, and peanuts, a single seed, shoot, or cutting is set in each hole.

The number of times the field is weeded varies from none for bananas-plantains, sweet potatoes, sugarcane, and oil palms to "several" times for rice, maize, and peanuts. In some areas maize is not weeded at all, in others it is "weeded constantly" (*384*, p. 545). Peanuts and rice are weeded carefully until they are large enough to overpower weeds and grass.

Manioc is pruned when the plant is 50 to 75 cm. tall, to obtain leaves for stews. Yams and peanuts may be pruned if the vines or stems become "too long," because it is believed that tubers will not develop with an excess of leaves. Van der Kerken reports that oil palm trees are cultivated, but he does not describe the technique (*368*, 1:53).

Bananas-plantains, peanuts, tobacco, chilies, and various vegetables are grown in gardens in or near the village. Compost is made in the village from household wastes, but no information is given about how or where it is used.

Bananas-plantains can be harvested throughout the year; the central stalk, a trunklike stem, is cut down at harvest in order to bring the fruit within reach and also to prune the plant so that suckers that have formed at the base of the central stem will grow more rapidly. Yams are harvested twelve to fifteen months after planting, although they are not fully mature for another three months (*384*, p. 541). The tuber is cut just below the top, and the smaller portion with the vine attached is immediately replanted. Information is not given on other crops.

Ubangi District

C. Léontovitch, agricultural inspector for the Belgian Congo in 1933, described agricultural techniques of Ubangi District; and E. Mestdagh, a Belgian administrator, provided a description of maize culture in the district bearing that name in 1913, a considerably smaller area. Both areas have the Bwaka people as their most numerous population. The Banza, Ngbandi, and Gobu are the other principal tribes, but reference is also made to the Gombe, Mono, and Togbo. Léontovitch estimates the Bwaka at 165,150 and the total population of the district as 357,089 (*224*, p. 51). Recent population estimates place the population density of the district between five and fifteen persons per square kilometer (*377*, Annexe 6). In the north, stretches of parklike savanna are found, but most of the district is forest.

The principal food crops are maize, manioc, and in parts of the forest zone, bananas-plantains. Léontovitch reports that the Ngbandi prefer bananas-plantains and manioc; the Banza, manioc and maize; and the Bwaka, maize (*224*, p. 51). Livestock production is limited to goats, sheep, and poultry.

Mestdagh's article on maize covers mainly the Bwaka and peoples along the southern bank of the Ubangi River between Dongo and Banzyville. Both Mestdagh and Léontovitch suggest that maize is the principal crop in this zone.

Mestdagh states that the land is cleared, leaving large trees, and the debris is burned; then, without any preplanting cultivation, maize is planted in small holes 70 to 80 cm. apart that are made with a hoe (*256*, p. 884).[10] Three or four kernels are placed in each hole. Fields are guarded for several days after planting, to keep birds away. No weeding or hoeing is done; instead, cucurbits are planted among the maize plants to conserve moisture and to choke out weeds. Other crops, such as rice, manioc, taro, and bananas-plantains, may also be scattered throughout the maize field. The earliest maturing of the four varieties of maize may be harvested three months after planting; the latest maturing variety is ripe about a month later. After stalks are dry, the ears are twisted off and the stalk is pulled up and left to lie on the ground. Two crops per year are grown, but the second one gives a considerably lower yield.

The Bali and Budu

H. Van Geluwe's compilation of information on the Bali (a group of the Ndaka) and related peoples provides a little information on the agriculture of the Bali and Budu. The following description of the Bali is from material published by P. Schuebesta and A. Moller between 1934 and 1936 *(318, 266)*. Information on Budu agriculture comes from data published in 1924 by Czekanowski *(90)*.

Both the Bali and Budu live in the forest and rely mainly on bananas-plantains; maize and manioc are of secondary importance. The only domesticated animals are a few sheep and goats and some chickens.

The Bali fell the large trees, which crush the smaller vegetation as they fall. Then the field is burned, and bananas-plantains are planted. Harvest is ten months later *(318,* pp. 28–29; 266, p. 36, cited in *380,* p. 52).

Budu methods are described as roughly the same as those of the Bali, except that the largest trees of the forest are not cut in some areas *(90,* p. 286, cited in *380,* p. 53).

The Tetela

A few notes on Tetela agriculture are given by M. W. Hilton-Simpson in a book published in 1911, and by E. Mestdagh in articles published in 1912. The Tetela occupy mainly forest, with some savanna. Hilton-Simpson cites millet, maize, rice, manioc, sweet potatoes, bananas-plantains, peanuts, beans, and onions as Tetela crops, without indicating their relative importance *(179,* p. 59). Schmitz, in a 1912 publication, lists bulrush millet as the primary staple *(317,* p. 49). Mestdagh suggests that rice is grown in only some of the villages; he describes four varieties grown *(253).*[11]

Land is cleared and the debris burned, then unburned litter is cleaned from the field *(253,* p. 353). Holes for planting rice are made with a hoe in the unworked soil 20 to 30 cm. apart; and five to ten kernels of rice are dropped in and covered. Later maize is planted between the rice plants.

When the rice crop is mature, the heads are cut off, dropped in a basket, and transported to a circular mud-and-wattle crib about 2 meters high and wide. Heat generated in this pile of rice heads helps to separate the kernels from their husks. After three or four days the rice is spread on the ground and threshed by beating with long sticks.

Class 4: Cut, Burn, Hoe, Plant (Forest)

This method is characteristic of the Sakata and some of their neighbors; of the Kuba and part of the Kongo tribe [12] on the forest zone's southern fringe; and of the Bongo on its northern fringe. It is also found in high forest areas around Uvira on the northeastern edge of Lake Tanganyika. The technique differs significantly from the cut, burn, plant method in that the seedbed is worked after fields are burned. This almost certainly requires considerable labor, a good portion of which must be crowded into a fairly short period between the time that felled vegetation is dry enough to burn and the beginning of rains. Thus the total amount of land a cultivator can crop is much more likely to be restricted by labor bottlenecks than with other forest techniques.

The Sakata and some of the adjacent peoples in the western part of the Kasai River–Lake Leopold II area not only work the soil before planting but make mounds. Mounds are clearly not made in the eastern part of the Kasai River–Lake Leopold II area or the high areas around Uvira; the account of the Bongo is vague on this point.

The Sakata

The Sakata occupy both savanna and forest; around Lake Leopold II, and north and east of it, forest prevails; south and west of the lake the vegetation changes to parklike savanna. The population density of the territoire of Kutu, an administrative unit containing mostly Sakata, ranged from 3.4 persons per square kilometer in 1947 to 3.6 in 1951 (*306*, p. 654).

The following account of Sakata agriculture, provided by C. B. Ngondo (*274*) applies to his home village, Kutu, which lies in the forest zone.

The staple crop of the area is manioc, but considerable amounts of yams are also planted. Minor food crops are plantains, maize, and sweet potatoes. Oranges, lemons, avocados, papayas, mangoes, pineapples, guavas, and bananas are the principal fruits cultivated. Goats, sheep, and poultry are raised, but no cattle.

Fields are cleared in the dry season, from July to September. The first operation is to cut underbrush with a hatchet or machete. Next trees are cut down, leaving those of especially hard wood that are difficult to cut, very large trees, and trees that bear products of value. The debris is let dry two weeks or so and burned where it lies.

In burning a field, the oily residue from palm oil processing is ignited to start the fire. If bananas-plantains are to be grown, the windward side of the field is lit first so that the fire will move rapidly over the surface and only partially consume the debris. For manioc, the fire is started on the leeward side to ensure a complete burning. If manioc is to be planted, mounds are made to reduce the depth that must be dug in harvesting the mature roots. Immediately following the first rain after the burning, mounds about a meter in diameter at the base and half that at the apex are made with a short-handled hoe that has a blade about 25 cm. wide. The cultivator steps one pace from the last mound and begins to pull earth on top of her foot, rotating as she works so that when finished she has a mound formed around one leg. She lifts her leg out, takes another pace, and repeats the process.

As soon as mounds are made, manioc is planted; three cuttings three or four nodes long are spaced equally around the sides of each mound. Bananas-plantains, maize, and tobacco are usually interplanted with manioc, plants being placed here and there throughout the field. None of these companion crops is placed on mounds, and the ground is not hoed before planting bananas; a hole is dug with a small hoe, the rhizome is set in it and covered with soil. Maize and tobacco can be planted at any time of year except during the dry season, July to September. Usually several plantings are made, a few weeks apart. Manioc harvest begins twelve months or so after planting and may continue ten to twelve months longer, thus several plantings of maize and tobacco can be made during the life of one manioc plot.

As soon as weeds become troublesome, the field is hoed between mounds with a small hole. Weeds on mounds are pulled by hand to avoid damaging the manioc roots. Manioc is harvested by digging a little earth away from the roots, then grasping the stalk and pulling it and all attached roots free. Roots that are broken off are then dug out. Bananas-plantains are harvested by cutting down the stalks of the plant and then cutting the bunch of fruit free from the stem. After harvest, manioc stalks are piled in a shady place on one side of the field where they rest, without drying out too much, until the next planting.

Sugarcane, yams, and rice are grown in special fields, often in pure culture. Sugarcane is established by planting sections of stalk in holes or trenches. As yams are consumed, the ends containing buds are sliced off and placed in a shady, moist place near the hut where they are kept until planting time. After yams have been planted, stakes are placed by the young yam plants to provide support for the vines. The only rice grown is unirrigated, but details of its culture were not known to Mr. Ngondo. Neither surgarcane, yams, nor rice is planted on mounds. Weeding is done continually, so long as needed. Sugarcane soon develops enough leaves to choke out weeds. Yams are harvested in the same manner as manioc; sugarcane is harvested with a knife.

Around huts small, sometimes fenced, gardens are made and planted with vegetables, maize, tobacco, bananas-plantains, and sweet potatoes. Behind the hut a refuse pile composed of sweepings, leaves used for wrapping food and other objects, and other wastes is maintained. Periodically this pile is burned and a new one started. Part of the ash and compost left after its burning is spread on crops in garden plots near the hut, and the site of the old refuse heap is planted with bananas-plantains.

The Kasai River–Lake Leopold II Basin

Observations by J. Maes in 1913–14 provide a few notes on the agriculture of the Lake Leopold II basin and the northern portion of the Kasai watershed. Accounts by two Belgian agronomists — articles by J. Ghys in 1934 and by J. L. Robert in 1952 — provide additional data. Ghys discusses the Teke, Tende, and Boma, all savanna tribes; while Robert discusses these and the Sengere, Dia, Sakata, Bobaie, Mbelo, Bidjem-kamba, Ipanga, Imoma, Yembe, Bolendu, Bolia, and Ekonda peoples as a group.

The Kasai River–Lake Leopold II basin is savanna in the south and forest in the north. Manioc is the staple food, while bananas-plantains, and in places maize and peanuts, are of secondary importance. Only a few domestic animals — goats, chickens, and dogs — are kept.

Ghys suggests that there is a good deal of difference in the number of varieties of major crops grown among the Teke, Tende, and Boma (*151*, pp. 125–27):

Crop	Teke	Tende	Boma
Bitter Manioc	4	7	5
Bananas-plantains	9	12	. . .

For these three tribes as a group, he lists 4 varieties of sugarcane; 2 each of peanuts, yams, and sweet potatoes; 23 of vegetables and spices, and 6 kinds of fruit trees: native lemons, oranges, safou,[13] bananas-plantains, papayas, and pineapples. Kola nuts are grown around Mbé; and in the vicinity of Bolobo, on the Congo River, one finds the mandarin orange, lemon, avocado, Brazil nut, guava, mango, granadilla, passion fruit (*Passiflora edulis*), and bullock's-heart (*Annona reticulata*).

Robert does not discuss the varieties of crops planted, but he does sketch crop associations for the whole of Lake Leopold II District, distinguishing between forest in the north and east and the parklike savannas in the south and west. In general, the forest peoples grow little if any peanuts or sesame but rely instead on palm oil. The savanna people possibly grow less yams; and in the eastern part of the savanna — but nowhere else in the district — maize is a major crop. Bananas-plantains are only a minor crop except in the northeastern part of the forest zone (*306*, p. 682).

In the forest areas there are two principal field types: the main one is manioc interplanted with bananas-plantains, maize, yams, and tobacco; the second is sugarcane in pure stand.

To clear fields for the main association, men clear the brush and pile it at the base of the large trees, where they burn it in order to bring the tree down. Around Lake Leopold II and north of it manioc is then planted on mounds about 30 cm. high that are made after the first hoeing; mounds are not made in the eastern areas (*306*, p. 682). Where bananas-plantains are grown, refuse is piled at the base of those grown near the village, and it is common, says Maes, to "go into the bananas-plantains groves to answer the calls of nature" (*241*, p. 39).

Maize is not important in the diet anywhere, and east of Tolo "seems to be completely unknown." Among the Teke (along the Congo River), "large fields of maize" are found. "It is well to note, however, that the intense cultivation of maize in that region was not due to any direct use of it by the native, but to the hope of selling it profitably to the traders and workers of Leopoldville-Kinshasa" (*241*, p. 40). Maize is planted in holes 30 to 60 cm. apart. When the seeds first sprout, the field is easily damaged by birds, so children are sent to guard plantings for four or five days. "Maize is neither hoed nor propped" (*241*, p. 40).

Rice is grown by peoples of the Bena Dibele–Kole region. It is sown in holes and is weeded two or three times during the first stages of growth. The field must be guarded constantly from flowering to harvest (*241*, p. 40).

The general sequence is a cycle of two or three years of crops followed by six to seven years of fallow. This is usually repeated two or three times;

then the plot is abandoned for sixty to a hundred years, during which time the village is moved (*47*, p. 59).

Within the period of crop cultivation, some forest people — the Bolia, for example — follow manioc with peanuts, but others grow few peanuts. In savanna areas the first crop on newly cleared land is usually peanuts or Bambara nuts that are later interplanted with manioc, maize, gourds, and yams.

In gardens near the villages vegetables, tobacco, and sweet potatoes are interplanted with manioc.

The Bongo

According to Maes and Boone the Bongo are located between the Ngbandi and Ubangi rivers, which would place them in the northern edge of the forest zone (*242*, p. 216). E. Torday verifies that they occupy areas that are mainly forest (*193*, 1:367). The only description of their agriculture is his account, published in 1908 (*193*, 1:368–69):

The necessities of life have compelled these natives to gather together in immense villages, separated from one another by considerable stretches of uninhabited country.

•   •   •   •   •

The Bongo villages are fortified by felled timber, pits, or *moats*. Not far from the villages stretch the plantations. At the cost of enormous labour great clearings are opened in the forest. Everything is beaten down or cut short. Next, fire burns up the leaves and small dry wood. The men do this preliminary work. Then the women and slaves dig up the ground, roughly cleanse the soil, setting themselves particularly to the task of getting rid of parasitic growths. After this they plant pell-mell and almost at the same time maize, manioc, bananas,[14] pumpkins and other vegetables, a reasonable space being left between the plants. The plantation thus produces in succession crops of maize, vegetables, then bananas, and finally manioc.

The Bongo peoples do not weed their fields except during the first half of the year for the crops of maize and vegetables. At the end of five or six months, banana trees and manioc plants struggle against the weeds which grow afresh without ceasing, and they are with difficulty disentangled from time to time. These plantations, of neglected appearance, bristling with tree trunks and obstructing every step by all kinds of remains, . . . give a stranger the feeling of the work of giants careless of the petty details of vegetation. By this method, the Bongo obtain the maximum of produce and are lavishly rewarded for their toil. They never plant in natural clearings; the soil there is not rich enough.

High Plateaus around Uvira

G. Weis provides some information of agriculture on the high plateaus (about 2,700 meters) around Uvira on the northwestern tip of Lake

Tanganyika, in an article published in 1959. No information is provided on the dominant staple, but maize and peas are both listed as important. Cattle are kept, but in small numbers. Only about 0.06 animals per capita were reported (*413*, p. 219). Both goats and sheep are also raised.

To clear fields, the forest is cut and the debris piled and burned. Sometimes after the first burning unburned logs and branches are repiled and fired again for a thorough burning. After all debris is burned, the field is hoed and is ready for planting. Unlike neighbors at similar altitudes in Rwanda and Burundi (discussed in Chapter 6) these people apply no animal manures; neither do they irrigate (*413*, p. 203).

Usually maize, peas, or tobacco is planted in pure stand after clearing. There is no mention of crop associations or sequences.

Class 5: Cut, Burn, Hoe, Plant (Savanna)

This technique is characteristic of tribes widely separated: the northern Bira on the eastern rim of the Congo Basin near Lake Albert, the Songe found between the Lualaba and Sankuru rivers in the south-central part of the region, the Luba of Katanga, the Holoholo on the western edge of Lake Tanganyika, the Unga near Lake Bangweulu on the southeastern edge of the Congo Basin, peoples of the Brazzaville area, most of Thysville territoire of the former Belgian Congo, the Vili near the mouth of the Congo River, and the Holo of extreme southern Kwango and northern Angola.

The technique appears to differ from the cut, burn, hoe, plant method of the forest zone in several ways. Less nutrients are stored in vegetation cut when fields are opened, therefore less nutrients are supplied to crops through ashes when fields are burned. Crop associations differ in a number of ways, but particularly in that bananas-plantains, of major importance in forest areas using this method, are largely replaced by other starchy-staples such as maize, manioc, and sorghum in the savannas. Mounds are made in some variants of the forest technique but not in others, whereas they are a major part of the technique in all but one of the ten savanna areas using this technique.[15]

The Northern Songe

Data on the northern Songe come from materials written before 1908 and compiled by C. Van Overbergh. The northern Songe are in the transition zone between forest and savanna; some of them occupy forest, others occupy a parklike savanna. The population density falls in the range of two to five persons per square kilometer in the east but five to fifteen persons in the west. The northern Songe live in large villages, at least one of which was estimated by E. Laurent to have 10,000 inhabitants in about 1897 (cited in *387*, p. 194).

Manioc is the dominant staple foodstuff, but maize,[16] beans, and bulrush millet are important. Other crops grown are rice, sweet potatoes, yams, Madagascar potatoes, bananas-plantains, Bambara nuts, peanuts, beans, sugarcane, pineapples, gourds, chilies, tomatoes, castor beans, tobacco, and hemp. Goats, sheep, chickens, ducks, and pigeons are common; a few cattle are found.

The principal tools are a small hatchet and a short-handled hoe.

Only a rough sketch is given of techniques of cultivation. According to R. Schmitz, fields are cleared by the collective effort of the men, who cut all vegetation, leave it to dry eight days, then burn it (*387*, p. 213). Later,[17] in August or September, the women collectively hoe the soil and plant maize on the flat, or make mounds and plant manioc on them; often both are done, the two crops being grown together. Maintenance of fields is done individually, but the crop is harvested collectively by the women.

Two crops of maize can be grown annually. The first crop is harvested in February or March; the date of the second harvest is not given.

Crop associations are little discussed. Other than the maize/manioc field already mentioned, Schmitz shows, in a map of Dibue village, fields of millet/maize, manioc, maize, millet, and beans. Crop sequences are not discussed.

Gardens are cultivated near the huts; plants like sweet potatoes, bananas-plantains, gourds, sugarcane, pineapples, payayas, tomatoes, chilies, hemp, and tobacco are grown. Tobacco plots, the only gardens enclosed, are fenced with pickets placed in the soil and tied together with creepers (*387*, p. 198).

The Southern Songe

Vermeesch provided an account, published in 1924, of a group of the southern Songe, called the Bekalebwe, that occupies most of the area between Kabinda and Tshofa. This is entirely in the tall-grass savanna zone. The dominant staple food appears to be maize; manioc and bulrush millet are of secondary importance. The relative importance of other crops and livestock appears to be the same as for the northern Songe. The principal tool of the southern Songe is a hoe with a blade 10 to 12 cm. wide and a handle 1.4 to 1.5 meters long (*400*, p. 20).

During the dry season new fields are cleared, apparently by cutting brush and hoeing down grass; then the debris is burned. As soon as the rains begin, in September, cowpeas are broadcast and left without further attention until harvest in November. After they are harvested, mounds are made, all litter being buried in the center of the mounds, and maize is planted in holes 1 to 1.2 meters apart. Four or five seeds are dropped into each hole and covered by pushing the soil over them with the foot. Maize is usually weeded twice; after the second weeding the field is thinned, only the best plants being left at each place. Maize is harvested at the end of the rainy season (May), and the field is left until the following September, when new mounds are made in the same manner and maize is again planted, this time mixed with manioc (*400*, p. 13). Alternatively, the field may be started toward the end of the rainy season, or in the dry season; if so, beans or bulrush millet are planted the first year and maize not until the second year (Figure 3-1).

FIGURE 3-1 Southern Songe Crop Sequences, 1924

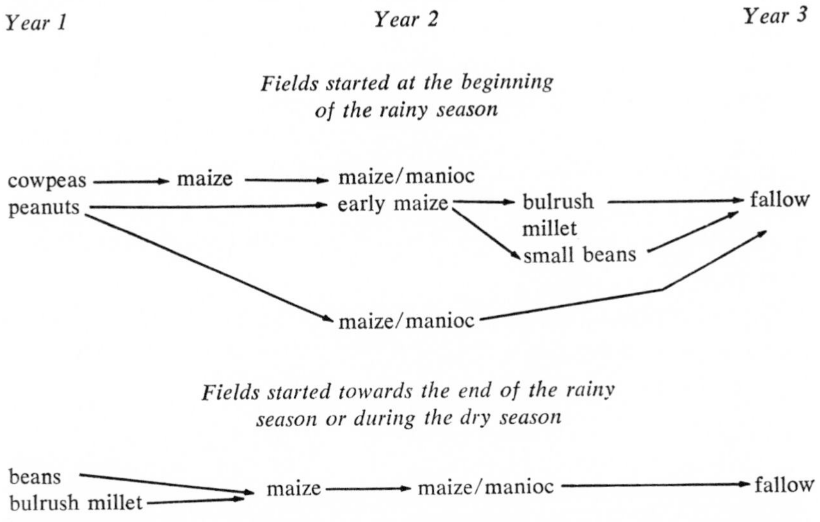

Year 1   *Year 2*   *Year 3*

Fields started at the beginning of the rainy season

cowpeas ——→ maize ——→ maize/manioc
peanuts ————————————→ early maize ——→ bulrush ————————→ fallow
                                         millet
                                         small beans
                              maize/manioc

Fields started towards the end of the rainy season or during the dry season

beans
bulrush millet ——→ maize ——→ maize/manioc ————————————→ fallow

Bulrush millet and peanuts are weeded once or twice; no reference is made to weeding other crops, except maize. With the exception of cowpeas, small beans, and peanuts, all field crops are grown on mounds. A few mounds of sweet potatoes and gourds are usually planted in the main field.

Tobacco plots are prepared by a variant of the ash-dependent method of field preparation of the Bemba of Zambia (discussed in Chapter 4). A large pile of wood is collected — preferably near a big termite mound — and burned. Tobacco seedlings have already been started in special beds. When the young plants have from four to six leaves, they are transplanted to mounds made in the ash left from the burned wood (*400*, p. 18).

The fact that leguminous plants help to restore soil fertility is said to be appreciated by Songe farmers, and legumes are reportedly grown in fields for this reason (*400*, p. 21).

Surveillance is given millet fields as they mature, to protect them from birds. Other fields are apparently not watched, but fences are built around peanut and tobacco plots. Another practice is to dissolve the manure of small livestock in water and brush the solution on the leaves of plants to be protected. This is said to repel animals which might otherwise forage in the fields (*400*, p. 21).

Beans and peanuts are dried on the ground after harvest. Tobacco leaves are dried on a net before the hut, then stacked together and wrapped with a banana leaf to encourage a slight fermentation.

Maize and gourds are sometimes grown in valley gardens during the dry season. Except for these, gardens are located near the village. Bananas-plantains are often planted behind the hut, where they receive refuse from the household. Other crops grown around the hut are maize, beans, yams, sugarcane, African sorrel, shallots, eggplant, chilies, small tomatoes, and African vegetables. Maize and beans are usually planted together, maize serving as support for the beans. A few yams are grown at the base of bushes.[18]

Oil and raphia palms are planted around the edge of villages. Mature palms are a characteristic feature of settlements, since villages are moved only for an "exceptionally grave" reason (*400*, p. 14).

The Luba

The population density in Luba country is from two to five persons per square kilometer in most territoires, but in parts of the northern areas up to fifteen persons per square kilometer is recorded, while at the eastern and western extremes of Luba occupation the density drops to less than two persons per square kilometer in some areas (*377*, Annexe 6).

Manioc is the principal crop, and maize is of secondary importance; [19] information on the importance of other crops is not given. Goats, sheep, swine, a few cattle, chickens, ducks, and pigeons are raised.

The principal tools, according to P. Colle, are a hoe with a blade 15 to 20 cm. long and a handle some 50 to 60 cm. in length, and a hatchet with a handle about half as long as that of the hoe (*83*, 1:185).

Apparently the Luba practiced some sort of ash-dependent agriculture at the time of Colle's observations for one crop — finger millet grown for beer — but relied on other methods of cultivation for the production of staple foodcrops. Usually, Colle states, a ring is cut through the bark of the trunks of large trees to kill them; they are felled by fire — by kindling wood staked around the base of the trunk — only if branches are needed to produce ash for cultivation of finger millet. J. Wilmet, in a study based on field work done in 1958, states that the Luba practice a "primitive Bantu" type of cultivation, i.e. some form of the classic long-fallow system; but he does not provide detail, although he discusses ash-dependent systems found among southern neighbors and clearly indicates none of them is found among the Luba (*426*, pp. 17 and 27).

In the main fields, all vegetation is cut in the dry season and burned. The next operation is construction of small mounds, probably not done until after the first rains so that the soil will be easy to hoe, but Colle does not specify the timing. In October and November, as the rainy season begins, manioc stems 20 or 30 cm. long are planted on mounds about 80 cm. apart. Maize, finger millet, peanuts, and bananas-plantains are set out between the manioc cuttings (*83*, 1:207). Verhulpen, in a study published in 1936, states that sorghum and peanuts are interplanted with manioc, and that millet, sorghum, and sesame are found only in some regions (*399*, p. 316). Whether separate fields of these companion crops are also established is not clear, but Colle does say that sweet potatoes and sugarcane are grown in valley bottoms (*83*, 1:209, 212).

Colle reports two annual crops of maize. The first is planted in October and harvested in January, the second is planted at the time of harvest of the first and is harvested in May or June. Maize is said to be planted by making a hole in the soil with the toe and dropping in two or three seeds,[20] then stepping on the hole with the heel to cover the grain (*83*, 1:208). Plantings of other crops are spaced throughout the rainy season (*83*, 1:208–11; *399*, pp. 322–23):

Crop	Planting time	Harvest time
Sesame	October–November	January–February
Sweet potatoes	December	April
Peanuts	February	June–July
Finger millet	February–end of March	June–July

Sesame is broadcast in unmounded portions of manioc fields.

Tobacco and perhaps other crops are grown near villages (*83*, 1:218). Thorn bushes are cut and laid over the young tobacco plants to protect them from the goats and chickens; other operations are not described. Verhulpen says that maize is grown mainly in gardens near streams and is interplanted with beans (*399*, p. 16). The sweet potato and sugarcane plantings in valley bottoms that Colle refers to are almost certainly gardens.

The only information on crop sequences is Colle's reference to the soil being "abandoned for a while" after a crop of manioc.

The Holoholo

Robert Schmitz described Holoholo agriculture in a study published in 1912. The Holoholo, in the savanna zone, rely on sorghum as their primary staple. Maize and manioc are secondary crops, while rice, sweet potatoes, yams, taro, bananas-plantains, peanuts, Bambara nuts, sesame, chilies, oil palm, amaranths, tobacco, cotton, cucurbits, peppers, sugarcane, thorn apples, bottle gourds, castor beans, *Pedicellaria pentaphylla*, and *Solanum Bojeri* are of tertiary or minor importance (*317*, pp. 13–14). Cattle, goats, sheep, chickens, and Barbary ducks are raised. It is clear that cattle are of little importance, but the significance of other domestic animals cannot be determined from Schmitz's account.

Cultivation of fields is started in August, before the rains begin; new fields are cleared by felling trees and pulling out grass (*317*, p. 108). When the debris is dry, it is burned where it lies and mounds are made with a long-handled hoe. In October maize is planted, in holes made with a hoe. Fields are then interplanted with manioc, cowpeas, gourds, peanuts, or sesame. Maize is harvested in January and sorghum is broadcast among the dry maize stalks. About the same time a new field of maize is planted. As sorghum harvest approaches, a small hut is constructed on stilts in each sorghum field; the guards who are sent to protect the field from birds rest here. The second maize harvest is in April; in May sorghum is harvested. To reap sorghum, men march across the field holding a pole before them which breaks over sorghum stalks. The women follow and cut the heads from the fallen stalks (*317*, p. 67).[21]

Schmitz does not specifically discuss crop sequences or associations, but he implies that a maize, sorghum, maize sequence is known, whatever other sequences may be practiced (*317*, p. 108).

During the dry season, maize and gourd gardens are made in valleys where the soil is moist. Small fenced gardens near the village are planted with yams, bananas-plantains, castor beans, and tobacco (*317*, p. 93).

The Northern Bira

The northern Bira occupy savanna area and keep cattle. Bananas-plantains, maize, sorghum, manioc, sweet potatoes, rice, beans, peanuts, sugarcane, and gourds are listed as the principal crops grown, but no information on their relative importance is given (*378*, p. 52). Tobacco, cabbage, tomatoes, and Irish potatoes are also named, with the implication that they are minor crops.

To clear land, vegetation is cut with a large knife and burned; then the soil is hoed. No information is given on other agricultural practices.

The Unga

W. V. Brelsford, formerly district commissioner of the administrative area containing the Unga, the tribe inhabiting the swamps around Lake Bangweulu, published a description of their agriculture in 1946. C. G. Trapnell adds information on certain points.

The population density is high, reaching 106 persons per square kilometer in some areas (*5*, p. 13). The Unga apparently keep no livestock and are only part-time cultivators. They rely mainly on fishing for their livelihood, but in June of each year migrate from fishing grounds to their gardens where manioc, finger millet, sweet potatoes, pumpkins, gourds, and beans are planted. From June until rains begin in October, the Unga live in temporary grass shelters near their gardens; in October or November they return to their villages.

Manioc, the main crop, is cultivated on mounds about 4 feet high and 5 feet in diameter (*57*, p. 124). Manioc planting begins in June and may last until November. Beans are planted on manioc mounds in June or July and are harvested in October or November. A pumpkin/gourd association and sweet potatoes alone are planted on mounds, the first in July and the latter in August; these crops ripen in November and December, respectively. Finger millet is not grown everywhere, but where it is, the tall grass is cut down or hoed up in October. In November dirt is knocked out of the grass roots with a stick and all debris is burned. The crop is sown the same month, and the field is left without attention until the harvest in April (*360*, p. 69). In some areas pumpkins and sorghum are planted on anthills, but neither Brelsford nor Trapnell describes the techniques employed. Nor is weeding, fertilizing, or harvesting discussed, but apparently some crops are weeded, for Brelsford speaks of women being left to do the hoeing after planting, while men drift off to fish.

Only one crop sequence is mentioned by Brelsford — two to four years of manioc followed by a year of fallow. At the end of the fallow period, mounds are remade and any vegetation on them is turned into the soil with a hoe. Trapnell mentions this sequence and adds that a finger millet, manioc, finger millet sequence is sometimes also followed for several years (*360*, p. 69).

Trapnell describes gardens near the village where "mounds are made after burning grass and reeds in November or by turning under large heaps of grass in April, when any *Phragmites* reeds are first cut out" (*360*, p. 69). Mounds made in November are planted the following month with manioc, some sweet potatoes, beans, and a little maize. Mounds made in April are planted to manioc and sweet potatoes. Harvest of manioc begins eighteen months later, the whole plant being removed and new cuttings set in its place.

In dried spots near the village, old manioc mounds may be spread and planted with peanuts; separate beds are sometimes also made for sweet and Livingstone potatoes. A third type of garden is made in areas some of which are as much as 2 feet below water level during the high-water season, and therefore must be protected by dikes.

In diked gardens, grass and reeds are burned in October; then the roots and surface litter are hoed into heaps and soil is spread over them to make mounds which are planted with manioc, some beans, and possibly a little maize. Maize and sweet potatoes are harvested before the March floods; whatever manioc roots have formed may also be harvested at this time if heavy floods are expected. If manioc is harvested after the March flood, cuttings are planted at the same time. When the rise of water is normal, manioc is left until March of the second year, seventeen months later. Diked gardens are planted to the same crops indefinitely.

Around villages some sorghum, sugarcane, pineapples, and "other minor crops" are grown. Trapnell also includes *Trichilia* trees for shade,

Melia azedarach, and the physic nut (*Jatropha curcas*), from which curcas oil is produced among village crops (*360*, p. 69).

According to Trapnell, Unga occupying sandbanks have a much simpler system of agriculture, in which stunted manioc is "the sole crop of importance" (*360*, p. 69). Mounds as much as 3.3 meters across and 1 meter high may be made and planted with manioc from December until the following October, when the farmers migrate to areas that will support finger millet. Manioc is often harvested twelve months after it is planted. After a crop or two of manioc, plots are fallowed for two or three years.

Usually nothing is planted with manioc. Some maize and sorghum, a few sweet potatoes, beans, edible gourds, pumpkins, or watermelons, which are reportedly about the only other crops, may be planted near the village or on an old village site; and a few pineapples or some plants of pigeon peas, tobacco, castor beans, or physic nut may be grown in the village itself (*360*, p. 70).

The Brazzaville Area

In an article published in 1957 P. Vennetier provides data on the area around the city of Brazzaville. Here vegetation is cut or pulled up and burned at the end of the dry season; then the soil is hoed into mounds 50 cm. in diameter and 10 to 20 cm. tall for manioc, or into "small" mounds or beds for peanuts (*395*, pp. 136–38).

Thysville Territoire, Former Belgian Congo

In Kimpangu, Noa, Loanga, Kimpese, Kyende, Lunzadi, Gungu, and Tumba sectors of Thysville territoire, vegetation is cut, piled, and burned if peanuts or beans are to be planted; for bananas-plantains or manioc, the piling is omitted (*47*, p. 80).

Most crops are planted on mounds or raised beds. Peanuts are either sown broadcast or placed in holes; no other crops are broadcast. Fields are usually weeded twice — once in November or December, and again two months later. Weeds pulled in manioc fields are often left between the growing plants to form a mulch. Other field operations are not described.

"Palms, fruit trees, and oil-bearing trees of the forest" are planted in lines around or near the villages and are cultivated "several years." On hillsides the lines of the orchard are made "parallel to the slope." Wherever located, annual crops may be interplanted with tree crops (*47*, p. 79).

The principal motive for making these orchards is said to be the desire to create an inheritance for future generations of the maternal clan (*47*, p. 80).

Kimpese, Kyende, Lunzadi, and Gungu sectors are said to have no crop sequences. Crop sequences elsewhere are shown in the tabulation (*47*, pp. 78–79):

Sector	Crop Sequences
Tumba (Masangu area)	Irish potatoes/bananas-plantains, manioc/peanuts
Kimpangu (forest areas)	1. Peanuts/bananas-plantains or beans/bananas-plantains, beans/manioc/peanuts
	2. Beans, beans, manioc/peanuts. Gourds/maize/manioc, beans or peanuts
Kimpangu (savanna areas)	Beans/maize/bananas-plantains, manioc/peanuts, beans, peanuts, Irish potatoes, bananas-plantains, beans
Loanga	1. Gourds/maize or peanuts/maize, beans, manioc for two years, fallow two or three years
	2. Peanuts, manioc/maize, manioc, fallow three or four years, manioc/pigeon peas or peanuts
	3. Beans/bananas-plantains/maize, bananas-plantains for five years, peanuts/manioc, manioc, fallow six years

The Vili of the Congo (Kinshasa)

The Vili in the Congo (Kinshasa) inhabit both forest and savanna, but the region is usually classified as savanna. Vegetation is cut and burned. Then, in savanna areas, mounds are made; in forest areas holes are made in the soil and crops are established without any further operation.

Four crop sequences are commonly followed in savanna areas, with pulses usually first and manioc last; in forest areas only two are usually found, with manioc generally first (*47*, p. 7; Figure 3-2 in text).

The Holo

The Holo of northern Angola and Kwango, as described by Jacques Denis in an article published in 1962, inhabit a savanna characterized by

FIGURE 3-2 Vili Crop Sequences

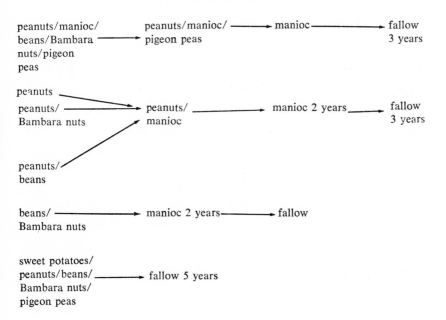

Savanna areas

Forest areas

unusually weak soils. They typically cultivate newly cleared land only one season before it is returned to natural vegetation (*103*, p. 20). The cattle they formerly raised were eliminated by a disease epidemic about the turn of the century (*103*, p. 25). They now raise goats, swine, and poultry.

Clearing of new fields starts at the beginning of the dry season, with the men cutting trees and bushes which the women pile and burn. The women then hoe the field and make mounds for manioc, the dominant staple. The manioc is planted at the beginning of the rainy season and weeded the first time two months later; it may be weeded again at the end of the rainy season in years when the growth of weeds is heavy. Maize, beans, peanuts, Bambara nuts, and oilseed gourds are the other field crops mentioned, but the only information on crop associations is that some maize, beans, and peanuts are grown with manioc (*103*, p. 21).

The Holo maintain small gardens near the homesite which are devoted to condiments such as thyme, common black pepper (*Piper nigrum*, and chilies (*Capsicum frutescens*), some cotton, and tobacco.

Class 6: Cut, Burn, Plant, Hoe

This technique is found among the western Kaonde and the Luvale, located in the savanna on the southern edge of the Congo Basin. It is the only savanna technique in the classic long-fallow systems in which starchy-staple food crops are planted without working the soil the first season after clearing. The second and third seasons, mounds are usually made.

The Luvale

The main features of the Luvale agricultural system were described by C. M. N. White, then African land tenure officer in Northern Rhodesia, in a paper published in 1959. The Luvale inhabit a grassland savanna with belts of woodland that stretches from the edge of the Congo Basin in western Angola to the upper Zambezi Valley in Zambia. The principal crop is manioc, but a wide variety of other crops is grown (*416*, pp. 19–20).[22] Cattle are raised, although White emphasizes that they are less important than crops; goats, sheep, and swine he says are "much more numerous" than large animals. Swine are fairly important in some areas. In 1957 White estimated that there were half as many swine as goats in the Kabompo area, but they were unimportant in Balovale (*417*, p. 20):

Animal	Balovale	Kabompo
Goats	3,410	6,500
Sheep	1,117	3,500
Swine	296	3,500

Chickens, Muscovy ducks, and pigeons are kept, and "a considerable number of eggs" are produced.

Field cultivation of the poorer soils is described by Trapnell and Clothier: "Roughly spread piles [of brush] are burnt over large patches without complete destruction of trunks and stumps" (*361*, p. 32). Bulrush millet is broadcast alone the first year, but the second or third year mounds may be made and manioc, roselle, and cucurbits are interplanted with it. If manioc is planted the second year and bulrush millet is to be resown the third year, the manioc bushes are pruned back to allow space for the millet crop. After manioc has been planted, the field is usually left in that crop for another two or three years, and then returned to bush. On the better soils an additional planting of manioc is made before the plot is abandoned.

Small gardens near the hut contain "cassava, maize, etc." (*361*, p. 33). Other gardens, made in areas where underground water keeps the surface relatively moist, are planted with such things as manioc, tobacco, cucurbits, and rice (*361*, p. 34).

The Western Kaonde

Among the western Kaonde, the area to be sown with sorghum, the main crop, is cleared and hoed during the early rains, felled trees and brush being piled in the field and burned. Maize is planted in the burned patches, and the entire plot is broadcast with sorghum interplanted with small amounts of sesame, cowpeas, and cucurbits (*361*, p. 27). Maize and sorghum may be repeated the second or third years, the boundaries of the original field being extended each year. The field is then usually abandoned, but may be planted to finger millet for one year first.

Near villages small garden plots are hoed into mounds and planted with manioc, sweet potatoes, and a little maize (*361*, p. 28). In valley bottoms maize gardens are made. Usually the grass is hoed off and burned; then maize, beans, and here and there pumpkins are planted on small mounds. Maize gardens may also be made on anthills.

Class 7: Burn, Hoe and Cut, Plant

The burn, hoe and cut, plant system, a form of fire farming, is reported only in savanna areas where fire effectively eliminates most of the vegetation. Except for the reversal of the burning and hoeing operations, this method of agriculture is much like the cut, burn, plant system. The Class 7 method is characteristic of the peoples of Kwango (roughly the region between the Kwango and Kwilu rivers), with the exception of the Pende, and of the savanna areas around the northeastern end of Lake Tanganyika.

The Kwango Area

A good deal of general information is available on the agriculture of the area of the Congo (Kinshasa) lying between the Kwango, Kasai, and Loange rivers because much of the southern portion of the region is characterized by poor soils and lack of an exportable cash crop. In an effort to learn more about its problems and potential E. L. Adriaens, then chief of the Laboratoire de Recherches Chimiques du Ministère des Colonies (Belgium), was directed in 1948 to make a study of the diet and nutrition of the area, a study of six months' duration (*3*, p. 228). Adriaens' report provides a general comparison of crops grown, data on crop introductions, and details on techniques of food processing among certain tribes.

A second major source is a special study of soils and vegetation that was made in 1955 by R. Devred and R. Hardy, both agronomists. This article provides a general account of crop associations and crop sequences. A. Rassel, also an agronomist, gives detailed information on bulrush millet and Bambara nuts for the whole region.

The Kwango is entirely in the savanna. In the north, the more humid area, the characteristic vegetation is tall grass and oil palms. In this part of the area, the density of population is relatively high for the Congo Basin — as much as twenty-two persons per square kilometer — and, except for Kenge territoire, is at least three times greater than in the southern areas (*110*, p. 1395):

Territoire	Major tribes found	Population density about 1957 (persons per sq. km.)
Northern Kwango		
Kenge	Yaka, Mbala	6.28
Gungu	Pende, Bunda	14.85
Idiofa	Pende, Bunda	11.70
Kikwit	Mbala, Bunda	22.52
Masi-Manimba	Mbala, Yanzi	15.05
Southern Kwango		
Kasongo-Lunda	Yaka, Holo	4.59
Feshi	Suku, Pende	3.98
Kahemba	Chokwe, Lunda	2.77

In the south the oil palm tends to disappear, except in some valleys, and the grass is generally shorter and less dense. Throughout its length the Kwango is divided into a series of plateaus by several almost parallel rivers and streams running from south to north.

Bulrush millet and manioc appear to be the major starchy-staples throughout the region. Maize and Congo jute (*Urena lobata*) are the principal cash crops in areas where cash crops are grown. A large number of crop varieties are grown even in the south, where soils are poor over much of the region, the population density is relatively low, and people generally appear poor compared with other areas of the Congo (Kinshasa). For the whole region Adriaens lists manioc, yams, taro, sweet potatoes, millet, maize, twenty-one varieties of vegetables,[23] eight fruits, and seven condiments (*4*, pp. 476–511). Cattle are not common but sheep, goats, and poultry are generally kept.

In the valleys one finds gallery forest with oil or raphia palms; the microclimates are relatively moist and the soil is comparatively good. Maize and Congo jute are grown as cash crops. The main crop association is maize interplanted with manioc, gourds, and sometimes peanuts, although peanuts are more often grown in monoculture (*110*, pp. 1397–98). In some areas Bambara nuts are also a cash crop, small plots of them being mixed with peanuts or planted alone. If maize and urena are planted with peanuts, the field is fallowed from two to four years after each harvest, but no other crops are ever planted with them (*301*, p. 13). If only maize and urena are grown, these crops are planted year after year until the soil must be abandoned a few years to rest.

A manioc/bulrush millet association[24] is said to be the main field type on the plateaus. The first operation in establishing a field is to burn the grass during the dry season and then to dig any remaining refuse into large mounds about 35 cm. high, placed following the slope. At the beginning of the main rains in September, manioc cuttings are thrust into the mounds at about 1 meter intervals. At the same time, Bambara nuts are interplanted. Usually fields are given a single weeding (*301*, p. 14). Bambara nuts are harvested gradually from the fourth to fifth month after planting. Harvesting of manioc begins about eighteen months after planting and may continue through the twenty-fourth month. As soon as manioc has been harvested, the tops of the mounds are hoed; after the first heavy rain the following season (around March) bulrush millet is broadcast and the mounds are hoed again to cover the seed (*300*, p. 14). As the grain begins to mature, children are dispatched to guard the fields from depredations by birds. Harvest is about the middle of the dry season (July). This harvest is usually followed by a "long fallow" (*300*, p. 14); thus the sequence of crops usually involves only one cycle of two seasons.

Adriaens suggests that gardens are found around villages, but there is possibly considerable variation from tribe to tribe. M. W. Hilton-Simpson's account in 1909 of the agriculture of the Bunda, whom he visited while exploring parts of the southern Congo Basin, suggests that they then had no gardens near the hut (*179*, pp. 262–63): "we found villages very different from any that we had yet visited. Instead of building their huts in a group, the Babunda live in the midst of their plantations, and accordingly the villages cover a great many acres of ground, some even extending to a couple of miles in length. . . . The huts themselves, dotted about with their fowl-houses and granaries in the millet fields, are square, and they have their doors so high above the ground that a little platform is built outside the entrance, by means of which the occupants can climb into the hut . . . ."

The only full description of gardens in Kwango is for the culture of Bambara nuts, a crop that may be of considerable significance in some parts of Kwango. Rassel notes that in the Congo (Kinshasa) Bambara nuts are important in the diet or as a cash crop only in Leopoldville Province; almost all the production comes from Kwango and Kwilu districts (*301*, p. 3). Bambara nuts grown in gardens are sown in pure culture near the hut, mixed with peanuts on old village sites (one seed per hole in holes placed 40 cm. apart), or, among the Chokwe and Lunda, mixed with manioc, sweet potatoes, cowpeas, and coleus potatoes.[25]

Tobacco is sown in special beds, then transplanted to mounds made near the hut (*47*, p. 71).

Savanna Areas around Uvira

At lower altitudes around Uvira the principal starchy-staples are manioc, beans, sweet potatoes, and bananas-plantains. Peanuts are the only secondary crop mentioned. Fields are first burned, then hoed and planted. Information is not available on crop associations or sequences, but sequences are apparently short. Weis notes that, except for unusual pockets of good soil, fields must be fallowed after each crop (*413*, p. 201).

Class 8: Hoe and Cut, Then Burn, or Burn, Then Hoe and Cut

In two sectors of the area inhabited by the Kongo tribe, hoeing may either precede burning or follow it, depending on the season fields are being cleared. Data on the agriculture of the Kongo come mainly from a detailed agricultural study of Bangu and Inkisi, two sectors of Thysville territoire, former Belgian Congo, that was made in 1945 and 1946 by V. Drachoussoff, a Belgian agronomist.

Bangu Sector

Bangu, both forest and savanna zones, had a population density of about eleven persons per square kilometer in 1944 (*120*, p. 506). Cattle are not raised, but swine, goats, sheep, and poultry are found in most villages.

The principal source of calories is manioc, followed by beans and peanuts. Bananas-plantains, maize, and rice are minor starchy-staples. Drachoussoff made estimates of food consumption for two groups of villages: one group, designated as Lambo, was centered on Manilonde village; the other, the Sanga group, centered on Lukamba village (Table 3-1).

TABLE 3-1   **Estimates of Average Daily Caloric Intake of Principal Foods, Bangu Sector**

	Lambo		*Sanga*	
Foodstuff	*Calories*	*Percent of total calories*	*Calories*	*Percent of total calories*
Manioc				
Flour	368	13.6	736	26.3
Chickwangues	820	30.2	984	35.1
Fresh	63	2.3	63	2.2
	1,251	46.1	1,783	63.6
Beans (dried)	684	25.1	171	6.1
Peanuts	274	10.1	274	9.8
Palm oil	180	6.6	180	6.4
Maize	74	2.7	74	2.6
Bananas-plantains	47	1.7	47	1.7
Rice	—	—	69	2.5
Meat or fish	6	0.2	6	0.2
Other[a]	200	7.4	200	7.1
	2,716	99.9[b]	2,804	100.0

Data from B. F. Johnston, *The Staple Food Economies of Western Tropical Africa* (Stanford, Calif., 1958), p. 202, and V. Drachoussoff, "Essai sur l'agriculture indigène au Bas-Congo," *Bull. Agr. du Congo Belge* (Dec. 1947), pp. 545–46.

[a] An arbitrary figure sufficient to bring the total caloric intake to about 2,800 calories, the amount Drachoussoff assumed to be required by a normal adult.

[b] Does not add to 100 because of rounding.

The estimates were based on personal observations and questions to Africans. Drachoussoff thought them good approximations of actual consumption, except that they failed to include fruits and vegetables cultivated around the homestead.

The reason for the considerable difference in the importance of manioc and beans in the two areas is not clear. Both groups of villages are in the savanna, only some 20 kilometers apart. Part of the reason may be that these groups do not have the same varieties of crops available to them. Only for gourds and Bambara nuts, among the crops for which Drachoussoff lists varieties, did two or more villages have the same varieties; and differences in the importance of crops were positively correlated with differences in the number of varieties available.

Manilonde village, which belongs to the group of villages deriving an estimated 46.1 percent of calories from manioc, has only five manioc varieties available, whereas Lukamba village, in the group that obtained an estimated 63.6 percent of calories from manioc, has seven manioc varieties, three of which are not known in Manilonde (*121*, pp. 798–805): Similarly, Manilonde village, in the group which got 25.1 percent of total

| | *Varieties* | |
Crop	*Manilonde*	*Lukamba*
Bitter manioc	*nsielele*	*nsielele*
	mputampembe	*mputampembe*
	mputandombe	*songololo*
		poko
Sweet manioc	*ntomi*	*ntomi*
	lundala	*lundala*
		kengele
Plantains	*bubi*	*bubi*
	zengani	*zengani*
	nsasa	*nsasa*
	kinbuamba	*kinbuamba*
	pongo	*ndongila*
Bananas	*kinsiesie*	*kinsiesie*
	dinkondo dia mputa	*kimbangala*
	ntiba	*kivuazi*
Yams	*ngufu*	*ngufu*
	menga-menga	*menga-mengc*
	dioko	*kuamukongo*

	Varieties	
Crop	Manilonde	Lukamba
Sweet potatoes	*longa*	*kwamulenge*
		lodi
Gourds	*malenge*	*malenge*
	nsundia	*nsundia*
Peanuts	*kongo*	*kongo*
	wuungu	*wuungu*
	malunguba	*malunguba*
	mputu	*mputu*
Bambara nuts	*kongo*	*kongo*
Beans	*ndamba*	*ndamba*
	diniania	*diniania*
	carte	*carte*
	kandua ntu	
	lombo mvula	
	loanza	
	bamba	
	zangi	
	mazi mankala	
Maize	*menga-menga*	*menga-menga*
		mpumbu
		nsizi

calories from beans, has six more bean varieties than Lukamba village, a member of the group getting only 6.1 percent of calories from beans.

The considerable variation in the availability of crop varieties between Manilonde and Lukamba villages seems to be generally characteristic of the Bangu and Inkisi areas as a whole, and there are also other differences between the two sectors. Table 3-2 shows the number of varieties of major crops, in the five villages studied in the Bangu area, to range from two to four for bitter manioc; from two to six for plantains; from one to four for peanuts; and from one to nine for beans. For most crops the total number of different varieties known in the sector exceeded the number of varieties grown in any one village.

Intersector differences were greater, as a rule, than differences within

TABLE 3-2 The Number of Varieties of Major Crops Grown in Selected Villages, Bangu and Inkisi Sectors, Former Belgian Congo, 1945–46

Village	Bitter manioc	Sweet manioc	Plantains	Bananas	Yams	Taro	Sweet potatoes	Gourds	Peanuts	Bambara nuts	Beans	Pigeon Peas	Sesame	Maize	Tomatoes	Tobacco
Bangu																
Vunda-Nkama	2	1	2	4	5	1	2	2	3	1	2	1	0	4	4	2
Congo-Botongo	3	3	6	5	5	1	3	2	4	1	1	0	0	3	0	0
Lukamba	4	3	5	3	3	0	2	2	4	1	3	0	0	4	0	0
Manilonde	3	2	5	3	4	0	0	2	4	1	9	0	0	2	0	0
Kisende	2	1	5	1	2	0	0	2	4	1	8	0	0	2	0	0
Range for sector[a]	2	2	4	4	3	1	3	0	1	0	8	1	0	2	4	2
Entire sector	7	5	8	5	7	1	3	2	7	1	11	1	0	9	4	2
Inkisi																
Banza-Nsundi	5	2	4	3	4	2	2	4	2	1	2	0	2	3	2	2
Kinkewa	7	5	7	3	4	2	1	4	2	1	1	1	1	3	2	2
Sumba	4	1	2	3	3	0	3	4	2	1	2	1	0	2	3	1
Kilumbu	6	3	5	3	4	2	2	4	3	1	1	1	0	2	2	3
Range for sector[a]	3	4	5	0	1	2	2	0	1	0	1	1	2	1	1	2
Entire sector	9	5	9	7	5	4	6	4	3	1	2	1	2	5	3	6
Number of varieties common to both sectors	1	2	6	3	3	0	2	2	2	1	2	1	0	2	2	1

Data from V. Drachoussoff, "Essai sur l'agriculture indigène au Bas-Congo, *Bull. Agr. du Congo Belge*, Sept. and Dec. 1947.

[a] The difference between the highest and lowest numbers.

sectors. Inkisi farmers have the greater number of varieties of bitter manioc, taro, sweet potatoes, plantains, bananas, gourds, sesame, and tobacco; Bangu farmers have the greater number of varieties of yams, peanuts, beans, tomatoes, and maize; and the number of varieties the two groups of farmers have in common is typically considerably less than the total number of varieties grown in either area.

Whether the greater variation in known crop varieties reflects more than the fact that Drachoussoff was particularly interested in intervillage differences in varieties grown — while most observers of African agriculture are not — cannot be determined; but at least one other study in the Congo Basin has given similar results. C. M. N. White, who spent several years among the Luvale, located in eastern Angola and western Zambia, says of manioc in that area (*417*, p. 19): "The Luvale recognize by name a very large number of different types of cassava. . . . There is constant interchange of types, and great interest is taken in their real or imaginary virtues. One or other type will often assume temporary popularity on this account. Thus a man at Musekelembwa remarked that they had no *kapumba* variety at his village, but he went and got some from a village twenty miles away . . . ."

Three main field types are distinguished by season. Normally they are, in decreasing order of importance, those in which planting begins in October, those planted in April; and the dry season cultivates in valleys, which are started the end of May or the first of June. Rice, urena, Irish potatoes, maize, gourds, beans, yams, and a mixture of manioc and peanuts are planted in the October to December planting period; manioc grown alone or mixed with peanuts is planted during the season beginning in April; peanuts, beans, maize, tobacco, and Irish potatoes are grown in the dry season.

Different methods of clearing fields are employed in forest and savanna areas. To clear forest, undergrowth is first cut, then small trees are felled. Certain large trees, *Chlorophora excelsa* and others which are of value, are left standing; the remaining large trees are killed by piling wood around them and burning. The field is then burned to eliminate debris. Any small branches remaining are collected in piles and burned; logs are left in the field, and after the field is hoed crops are planted around them. All hoeing is apparently done with what Drachoussoff calls a "Ceylon hoe." He gives no description of tools.

Two methods of clearing are used in savanna areas. The field may be hoed and then burned, or burned before hoeing. Hoeing first is often practiced on fields with a heavy growth of grass if they are to be planted in April, a time when uncut grass burns poorly. However, it is also used for the other main planting period, the October planting, in two villages surveyed, Manilonde and Vunda-Nkama.

Postclearing operations are the same in savanna or forest. The main planting season begins with peanuts and maize planted in October. For peanuts a small hole is scooped with the hand on wide, flat-topped mounds made parallel to the slope; a seed is placed in the hole and covered with soil. Less commonly, peanuts are sown broadcast and covered with a light hoeing. Holes for maize are made with the end of a machete and receive from one to four kernels. Gourds are the next crop planted, then plantains, and finally yams and manioc. The last two are usually planted on mounds not later than the end of December. In some savanna areas manioc is planted on the flat, but if grown with peanuts it is planted on the peanut beds (*121*, p. 817). At Lukamba village two cuttings of manioc stem are placed on mounds, one cutting on each side; at Congo-Botongo three cuttings are planted in a straight line; at Vunda-Nkama either two or three cuttings may be planted, depending on the size of the mound. Irish potatoes are planted on ridges; beans, urena, maize, and probably rice are planted on the flat. Beans are planted by making a small hole with a machete and dropping in one to three seeds. With rice ten to fifteen grains are placed in each hole.

Drachoussoff does not describe how weeding is done, and does not discuss all crops, but he does give data showing considerable variation in the number of weedings given major crops (*121*, p. 818):

Crop or association	*Number of weedings*
Manioc grown alone	Usually 2; sometimes 1
Manioc and peanuts	Usually 1; sometimes a second one after harvest of peanuts
Peanuts grown alone	1 at Lukamba, Vunda-Nkama, and Manilonde; elsewhere 2
Beans grown alone	1 at Kisende and Congo-Botongo; elsewhere 0
Beans and manioc	1
Rice	1–2, depending on season
Urena	1–2, depending on season
Irish potatoes	1

No fertilizers are applied in fields; but around the huts gourds, taro, bananas, and fruit trees are often planted in holes that have been filled with household wastes (*121*, p. 814). No other information is provided on gardens near the homestead.

Hedges are maintained around some fields to protect them from village livestock.

Crop associations and sequences vary greatly also; in fact, no two villages were closely similar, as Figures 3-3 and 3-4 show. Almost every combination of the major crops is found, except beans and peanuts. Manioc is found in most fields, and maize is frequently present.

The cropping cycle is short. On poorer soils, the land must be left fallow for a short period after the first harvest, and for a longer time after the second. The typical length of long fallows varies from five to nine years, according to village. Drachoussoff emphasizes that these are esti-

Village

Bas-Congo, 1945-46

Main fields

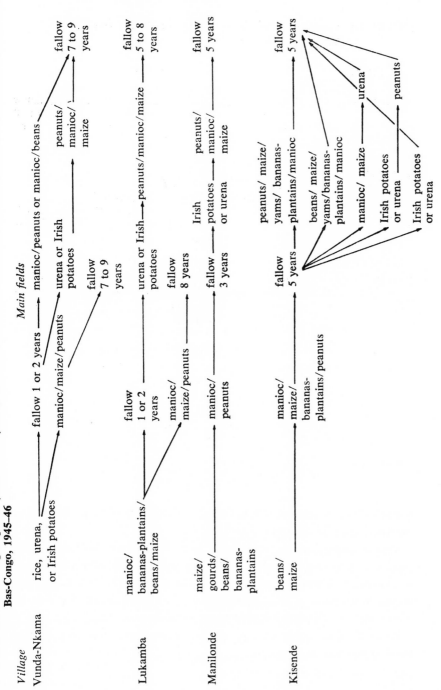

FIGURE 3-4   **Garden Crop Sequences, Forest Zone, Bangu Area, Bas-Congo, 1945–46**

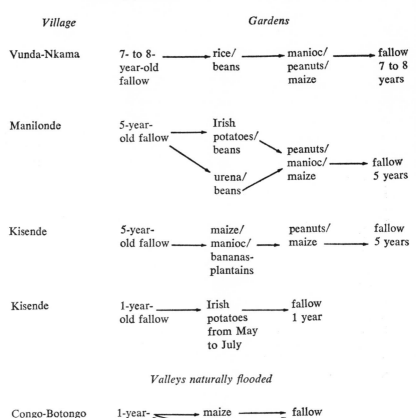

Village   *Gardens*

Vunda-Nkama   7- to 8- ————→ rice/ ————→ manioc/ ————→ fallow
                 year-old   beans   peanuts/   7 to 8
                 fallow   maize   years

Manilonde   5-year-   Irish
                 old fallow ——→ potatoes/
                                beans ——→ peanuts/
                                            manioc/ ————→ fallow
                                urena/   maize   5 years
                                beans

Kisende   5-year-   maize/   peanuts/   fallow
                 old fallow ——→ manioc/ ——→ maize ————→ 5 years
                                bananas-
                                plantains

Kisende   1-year- ————→ Irish ————→ fallow
                 old fallow   potatoes   1 year
                                from May
                                to July

Valleys naturally flooded

Congo-Botongo   1-year- ←——→ maize ————→ fallow
                 old fallow ——→ beans ——— 1 year
                                peanuts

mated average lengths of fallow, and says the long fallow can be as much as twenty years in duration (*121*, p. 811).

Where valley gardens are made, the crop sequences are usually less complex. In flooded valleys, there is only a one-year fallow; peanuts, beans, or maize are planted in September and harvested in December. The field is naturally flooded in December and let lie fallow for twenty-one months, after which it is planted with one of the same three crops.

In the savanna zones no crop sequences are found. The crop associations are apparently the same in all villages Drachoussoff surveyed; he lists the following (*121*, p. 811): (a) peanuts planted alone, (b) manioc planted alone, (c) peanuts/maize, (d) peanuts/manioc/maize/vegetables.

Inkisi Sector

The Inkisi sector is almost all savanna. The population density was about sixteen persons per square kilometer in 1945, somewhat higher than in Bangu, which had about eleven persons per square kilometer around the same time. No cattle are kept, and small livestock production is similar to Bangu.

Inkisi is traversed by the railway connecting Kinshasa and Matadi, and produces a considerable amount of foodstuffs for the Kinshasa market. Manioc and peanuts are the most important crops in this trade, but vegetables, condiments, poultry, sheep, goats, and swine are also produced for the urban markets.

Methods of clearing fields are the same as for Bangu,[26] but some variation in planting is found. Bangu farmers usually hoe fields before planting peanuts; at Inkisi this is only rarely done (*121*, p. 816). All major crops are usually planted on ridges at Inkisi, instead of on mounds, although mounds are sometimes made on slopes. At Bangu the order of planting is peanuts and maize, gourds, bananas-plantains, manioc and yams, while at Inkisi it is maize and beans, then bananas-plantains, yams and gourds, and finally manioc and peanuts. In some parts of Inkisi sector beans, peanuts, and maize are planted simultaneously; or peanuts, manioc, and sesame are planted simultaneously, and beans three weeks later (*121*, p. 817).

The only differences in planting techniques that Drachoussoff records are in the number and placement of manioc cuttings. At Sumba and Kilumbu villages, two cuttings are placed parallel on the ridge. At Kinkewa and Banza-Nsundi manioc is planted on mounds — four cuttings placed to form a square at Kinkewa and two cuttings set opposite each other on round mounds at Banza-Nsundi.[27] Weeding, harvesting, and storage operations appear to be the same in Bangu and Inkisi.

Crop associations are considerably different from those of Bangu. A maize/manioc/beans association or successions of either maize/manioc-beans or manioc-beans are grown at the head of the sequence at Inkisi, but not at Bangu (Figure 3-5). Sesame is found in one association at Inkisi, but not Bangu; while urena, Irish potatoes, and bananas-plantains are not found in Inkisi associations although they are of some importance at Bangu.[28] Garden associations differ from those of main fields at Bangu, but not at Inkisi, although savanna plateaus at Inkisi have special associations. Finally, more crops are found in associations grown in naturally flooded valleys at Inkisi than at Bangu (Figures 3-4 and 3-5).

FIGURE 3-5   Crop Sequences, Inkisi Area, Bas-Congo, 1945–46

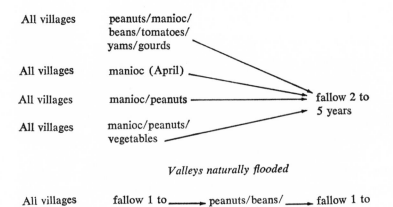

Village	*Main fields*

Banza-Nsundi   "old fallow" ——→ manioc/maize/ ——→ sesame/ ——→ fallow
                                                    beans   peanuts/   3 to 4
                                                                                       manioc   years

Banza-Nsundi   manioc/ ——————→ beans/yams/
                          maize   vegetables

Kinkewa   maize/   manioc if pre-   fallow 3 to
                          peanuts/ ——————→ ceding harvest ——→ 4 years
                          manioc   is good; other-
                                                             wise fallow

Sumba   manioc/   manioc if pre-   fallow 3 to
                          peanuts/ ——————→ ceding harvest ——→ 4 years
                          yams   is good; other-
                                                             wise fallow

Kilumbu   manioc-   manioc (planted   fallow 3 to
                          beans (planted ——→ in October) if ——→ 4 years
                          in April)   preceding har-
                                                             vest is good;
                                                             otherwise fallow
                                                             one season, i.e.,
                                                             until the following
                                                             April, then manioc

Fields on savanna plateaus

All villages   peanuts/manioc/
                          beans/tomatoes/
                          yams/gourds

All villages   manioc (April)

All villages   manioc/peanuts ——————————→ fallow 2 to
                                                                                         5 years
All villages   manioc/peanuts/
                          vegetables

Valleys naturally flooded

All villages   fallow 1 to ————→ peanuts/beans/ ————→ fallow 1 to
                          3 years   maize/tobacco   3 years

Crop sequences are less complex at Inkisi, as a rule, and the length of the fallow is typically only about half as long. Also, there is more use of a one-year fallow after the first crop, if the first crop yields poorly. And a longer fallow is practiced in valleys that are periodically flooded: one to three years after each crop at Inkisi, one year at Bangu.

Class 9: Hoe and Cut, Burn, Clean, Plant

This technique is the one employed by the Azande, the Logo, and possibly the Alur, all found in the savannas of the northern and northeastern edge of the Congo Basin. The Alur cannot be clearly classified with data available, but what information is at hand suggests that their techniques may be similar to those of the Logo and Azande.

The distinctive feature of this system, compared with other savanna techniques, is careful cleaning of fields after they are planted — the Azande clean their fields twice. Heavy use of labor in weeding is also clearly a feature of this system, but whether the weeding effort is usually large for savannas cannot be judged until better data are available for other savanna techniques.

The Azande

The Azande were the subject of the most detailed agricultural survey in tropical Africa yet published — a study of six villages by Pierre de Schlippe from 1948 to 1951 while he was senior research officer at the Yambio experiment station (*108*, pp. 29–31). The Azande are found mostly in the Congo Basin; but only two of the four portions of the tribe that De Schlippe discusses, the Azande of French Equatorial Africa and of the Congo (Kinshasa), live there; the other two groups — the ones he studied most intensively — occupy an area adjacent to the Basin on the north. De Schlippe suggests, however, that the agricultural systems of the Azande he surveyed in extreme southern Sudan traditionally were basically similar to those of the Azande within the bounds of the Congo Basin.

Trained African observers placed in the villages being surveyed were instructed to record the daily activities of each able-bodied adult found on a handful (from eight to twenty) of farms. De Schlippe regularly reviewed the records and himself visited farms with the most interesting fields and activities to inquire further about how various activities fitted into the Azande agricultural system. Observers were paid surprise visits from time to time, too, and informants were cross-questioned in an attempt to ensure that records were reliable.

The Azande are the third largest tribe in the Congo Basin in terms of the area they occupy, ranking behind the Banda and Luba. The density of the Azande population which De Schlippe studied in the Sudan varies from six to fifteen persons per square kilometer. The Azande have never kept cattle, nor do they have goats or sheep. The only domestic animals are small dogs and poultry. The focus of economic activity is in individual homesteads rather than in villages.

Azande Crops. Finger millet (*Eleusine*) is the most important crop in the diet, followed by maize, which possibly held first place as late as 1915 (*108*, p. 228). Two starchy roots, manioc and sweet potatoes, are fairly important. Sorghum, bulrush millet, and upland rice, a crop said to be recently introduced from the Congo, are minor grain crops; yams and taro are minor roots and tubers. Oilseeds and pulses are peanuts, sesame, hyptis,[29] cucurbits, cowpeas, mung beans, climbing cowpeas and their relatives, climbing lima beans, Bambara nuts, pigeon peas, and soybeans, a crop which has almost disappeared after an unsuccessful attempt at introduction by the Sudan Medical Department (*108*, p. 57). The principal fruits and vegetables cultivated are pineapples, papayas, bananas, plantains, mangoes, maize (for immature maize ears), cucumbers, bottle gourds, calabash gourds, okra, roselle, tomatoes, eggplant, and sweet sorghum.

In addition to these cultivated plants, "many more fruits, roots and fruity vegetables" are gathered from the bush and gallery forests (*108*, p. 72). Specifically mentioned are two cereals: *Hyparrhenia edulis* and *Loudetia* sp.; three wild sources of oil: the oil palm (*Elaeis guineensis*), the shea butter tree, *Butyrospermum parkii* var. *niloticum* and *Lophira alata*; and six weeds whose leaves are used as vegetables: *Bidens pilosa, Sesamum indicum, Celosa* spp., *Portulaca* sp., *Conyza Aegyptica*, and sesame of the ridge (unidentified).

Crops used for purposes other than food are Deccan hemp, common or smoking hemp, bark cloth tree, cotton, tobacco, red pepper, and climbing sponge gourd.

Field Types in the Southern Savanna. De Schlippe distinguished two ecological zones among the Azande of the southern Sudan, which will be designated here the northern and southern savannas. The southern, more humid, savanna is a belt extending across the southwestern end of the

Sudan; the northern savanna comprises most of northern Azande country, merging into the Sahara in the north.

The Azande reduce short-run declines in soil fertility by a system of crop alternation that De Schlippe calls a crop sequence rather than a crop rotation because the pattern varies so widely. Longer term declines in yield are avoided, after a point, by shifting the homestead. Within the general crop sequence are two connected subsequences — one for garden plots and one for fields — which have as their first stage the establishment of a new homestead.

A new homestead may be established for several reasons: death of a wife,[30] crop failure by an epidemic of crop pests, repeated illness followed by conviction that witchcraft is involved, or declining soil fertility. If none of these causes has been experienced by the time the soil is exhausted, search for a new homesite is prompted by declining crop yields and appearance of certain weeds, such as *Bidens pilosa, Eleusine indica, Commelina benghalensis, Pennisetum pedicelatum,* and *Chloris* spp. Apparently reasons other than declining fertility often prevail, for De Schlippe found in discussions with informants that they typically did not anticipate ever moving, although when questioned they admitted having moved in the past once every eight to twelve years or so, on the average. When a homesite is abandoned, the courtyard and gardens may still be cultivated a while before being left to revert to bush.

The location of the new homestead is decided upon by consulting an oracle, but the exact site is chosen for its proximity to water, absence of crop predators, and the fertility of the soil.

The move is usually made in the dry season (November to April), and at first only temporary huts are constructed. During the first year almost no gardening is done at the new site and the principal cultivations are the main finger millet association or the peanut-finger millet succession. Fields come up to the edge of the hut, and there is no courtyard.

In October, after most crops have been harvested, a courtyard is marked off. The topsoil removed from it is distributed at its outer boundary; this forms a ridge from 20 cm. high and 60 cm. wide to 50 cm. high and 2 meters wide, depending on the size of the courtyard and depth of the topsoil.

The courtyard, the ridge, a band adjacent to the outer edge of it, and plots adjacent to the band receive more frequent attention than the fields; they are referred to here as the garden (Figure 3-6). Thus the garden

FIGURE 3-6   The Azande: Location of Principal Fields, 1948

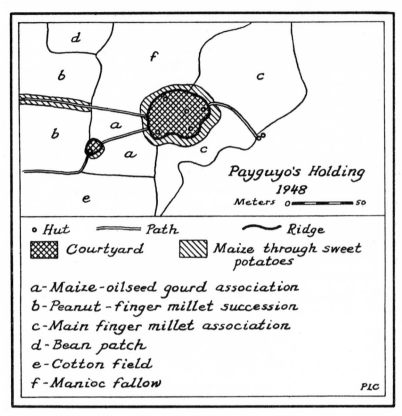

Payguyo's Holding
1948
Meters 0 ━━━━━ 50

• *Hut*   ═══ *Path*   ⌒ *Ridge*
▨ *Courtyard*   ▨ *Maize through sweet*
                                    potatoes

a- Maize-oilseed gourd association
b- Peanut-finger millet succession
c- Main finger millet association
d- Bean patch
e- Cotton field
f- Manioc fallow   PLC

Based on Pierre de Schlippe, *Shifting Cultivation in Africa* (London, 1956),
p. 112. Figure: Food Research Institute.

sequence is initiated after one of the field types has been established in the
garden spots.

De Schlippe notes twenty-one categories of field and garden plot types
that are clearly recognized by the Azande. Eleven special environments —
each utilized with a different crop or crop association — are found in the
courtyard around the hut; the ridge defining the outer bound of the courtyard and the band adjacent to the outer edge of the ridge are two other
categories. The remaining eight categories are fields or plots away from
the courtyard (Figure 3-6).

The most important field types are two finger millet ones here called
the main finger millet association and the peanut-finger millet succes-

sion. A third finger millet association which is of lesser importance is designated as finger millet-through-grass.

The Main Finger Millet Association. Typically this association is started on land that has already been cultivated one or more seasons. From May — almost a month after the beginning of the rainy season — to July, the field is opened with a hoe fashioned to a short L-shaped handle (*108*, p. 81): "The cultivator stands bent forward, the hoed land being on one side, the unhoed grass on the other, and as he works he goes slowly back along the grass frontage like a man harvesting oats with a sickle. The hoe in his right hand cuts away tuft after tuft of grass with slices of soil just under the root, whilst the left hand collects them. . . . Then he rises slightly, beats the earth from the roots of the grass . . . and throws it a metre or so away. . . . Next he bends again, and before resuming the first movement, he swings his hoe from side to side to break any clods that remain."

About three weeks after this hoeing the clearing is burned over and at the same time, or immediately following, is hand-cleaned, sticks and bunches of grass spared by the fire being piled into small heaps, which in turn are burned.

In a completely grassless forest, hoeing is replaced by slashing the undergrowth with a machete (Figure 3-7). On land that has not been cropped for several seasons, trees are felled or killed by fire before the opening hoeing, and the lag between hoeing and burning is generally longer.

Whether felling must be done or not, on the day of burning, or very soon after, maize is sown in holes 1.5 to 2 meters apart; on land cultivated the previous season, some manioc cuttings may be interplanted with the maize. With a hoe in his right hand the cultivator makes a hole and throws the seeds (or sticks in the manioc cuttings) with his left, closing the hole with his foot as he moves forward one step for the next hole.

Once this planting operation is completed, there is a second wait of fifteen to twenty days before the finger millet is broadcast. Finger millet is sown alone or mixed with some ratooning sorghum, sesame, hyptis, or possibly Deccan hemp, oilseed watermelons, or cucumbers. The seeds are thrown in small pinches from above the shoulder.

Sowing is immediately followed with a hoeing[31] to mix the seeds with the soil: "The left hand remains unemployed, except to collect odd branches, or either the hoe is taken by both hands. The soil may be so

FIGURE 3-7 The Azande: Principal Tools Used about 1950

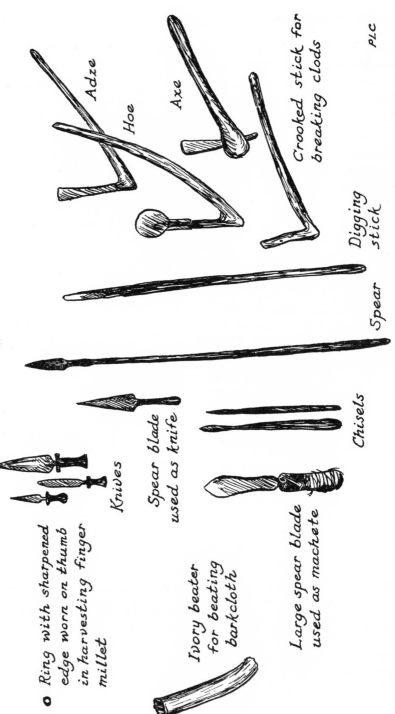

Ring with sharpened edge worn on thumb in harvesting finger millet

Knives

Spear blade used as knife

Adze

Hoe

Axe

Crooked stick for breaking clods

Digging stick

Spear

Chisels

Ivory beater for beating barkcloth

Large spear blade used as machete

PLC

Based on Pierre de Schlippe, *Shifting Cultivation in Africa* (London, 1956), Plates 11 and 12. Figure: Food Research Institute.

loose that the hoe is dragged through it without lifting it up at each stroke" (*108*, p. 82).

About a week later — two to four days after the finger millet germinates — the second hand-cleaning of the field is done. The small piles of debris may be burned; sometimes they are not.

Some two and a half months after the finger millet is sown, the maize harvest begins. Maize is harvested by hand, the ear being broken off the stalk. Harvesting is gradual and may extend over several weeks.

About two weeks or so after the first maize is harvested — by mid-September — the finger millet is given the only weeding it gets. Since this weeding is performed so late, the vegetation to be removed is large enough to be pulled by hand, and hoes are not used. Tall grass and climbers are pulled; shoots are broken off of stumps. Because the finger millet is thickly planted and there is no room for rubbish in the field, some debris is piled outside the field and some on the taller tree stumps; it is believed that "Seeing grass high up on the stumps, eleusine will try to imitate it and grow tall" (*108*, p. 122).

Finger millet ripens from mid-October to mid-November, and is harvested without delay once ripe, to avoid damage by late rains. To harvest, the stalk is grasped just under the head with the thumb and index finger, and is cut with a sharp-edged ring worn on the thumb.

Sesame, harvested in November and December, and hyptis, harvested in January, are reaped with a small knife. The knife is held in the right hand and the stalks are pressed against the sharp edge of the blade with the thumb. A large knife is used on sorghum (harvested in December and January).[32]

Unlike most of the other fields, the main finger millet field is not guarded once the crops are ripe. It is usually quite a distance from the hut, and its maize is often not considered worth the trouble involved in protecting it from monkeys, which may do a good deal of damage. The other crops in the association have no molesters — except sorghum, which may be bothered by birds if their food is in short supply.

The Peanut-Finger Millet Succession. In this field type finger millet is sown while the peanut crop which preceded it is being harvested. Clearing the field starts as early as mid-March and is accomplished in the same manner as described for the main finger millet association. (According to informants, clearing began earlier "in times gone by." The opening hoeing on some fields was then done as early as January and February — before the main hunting and fishing season [*108*, p. 125]. The reason for this change in timing is not given.)

Immediately after burning the cleared field, peanuts are planted: "the cultivator opens the holes one after the other in neat rows moving slowly backwards. In this case he often takes the hoe in both hands. After completing a row, he sows his seeds and closes the holes in a forward movement" (*108*, p. 83).

Maize or manioc may be associated with peanuts in this field type, the maize being sown a few days before, simultaneously, or considerably after the peanuts, depending on the weather. Since maize is less drought-resistant than peanuts, it is not sown until the cultivator thinks the rains have begun in earnest. Manioc is planted in May or June, soon after the peanuts come up.

Peanuts are the only Azande crop requiring protection prior to the harvest period. Jackals, guinea fowl, and squirrels may all dig up seeds. Branches are placed over the field immediately after planting to reduce damage. After germination of the seed no further protection is provided until about three weeks before harvest, a period when there is danger that jackals and pigs by night, and monkeys, squirrels, and guinea fowl by day, will unearth the ripening peanuts. From this time until well after harvest — since pigs continue for some time to damage the finger millet while looking for peanuts — a man armed with spear and torch sleeps in the field.

Peanuts are weeded only once, usually from thirty to fifty days after planting, the period when they are in blossom. Either hand weeding or hoe weeding is practiced, and the refuse is placed on stumps as with the main finger millet association.

Harvesting begins at the end of June on early fields and continues until September. The bulk of the harvest is in August and September. Finger millet is always sown as the peanuts are harvested: "First the eleusine is broadcast; then the groundnuts are pulled with the left hand, the right hand swinging the hoe, which helps the pulling and searches for those nuts which may have broken away and remained in the soil . . . ." (*108*, p. 83).

The pulled peanut plants are left lying on the ground in the field a few days to be washed by rain, then are piled to dry, and finally are removed from the field so they will not obstruct the germinating finger millet. The pods are pulled from the piles of peanut bushes, and the denuded plants are deposited on stumps, rocks, or termite mounds.

Once the finger millet is sown, the crops associated and field operations parallel the main finger millet association. However, maize is less likely to be planted, and sesame and hyptis are often not planted at all; it is too late for them, because the broadcasting of finger millet with the harvesting of peanuts comes at least ten days later than the sowing of finger millet in the main finger millet association. In fact, De Schlippe reports that prior to a fairly recent introduction of an early-maturing variety of peanuts, sesame was never grown in the peanut-finger millet succession (*108*, p. 125). Ratooning sorghum, Deccan hemp, oilseed watermelons, and cucumbers also may be associated with finger millet in the peanut-finger millet succession; but fairly frequently finger millet sown as part of the harvest of peanuts is left to grow alone and is given very little weeding. The Azande do not bother to remove the typical weed of these fields, a plant of the *Eragrostis* family.

Finger Millet-through-Grass. The third finger millet field type involves no cultivation before sowing and is found only on fields which have been cropped at least once since being cleared. From mid-June to mid-August finger millet and sesame or hyptis are broadcast through the grass that grew after the last crop was weeded — grass that is typically a stand of *Panicum maximum* or *Rottboellia exaltata* which has reached a height of 0.5 to 1 meter at the time finger millet is sown. More sesame is sown with finger millet than in the main finger millet association, and sometimes sesame is sown in pure stand. If the sesame variant is followed, there is no variation in planting practices, except that sowing is near the first part of the mid-June to mid-August planting period. Whatever the proportion of sesame sown, it is broadcast; and the field is hoed and cleaned as in the main finger millet association, except that the cleaning is not so thorough — a thin mulch is left.

No weeding is done; in fact, there is a belief that the crop will become diseased if it is weeded.

Bean and Cowpea Fields. Fields of beans, cowpeas, and green grams (*Phaseolus angularis*) are usually opened like the finger millet-through-grass type, except that broadcasting is not followed by hand cleaning; bean and pea sprouts are strong enough to push through the mulch. No weeding is practiced.

Sometimes cowpeas — but never green grams — are planted after the plot is opened by the hoe and burn technique, and are planted in holes as peanuts are. Cowpeas so planted must be weeded. They may also be grown on termite mounds, presumably after the mounds are flattened, but De Schlippe does not say.

Beans are gathered from mid-September to the end of November. They are not guarded.

Ridge Cultivation. The remaining crop associations are found in small patches near the homestead. Ridges are made or repaired in February or March, immediately after the relatively light rains that fall at the end of the dry season; and maize and pumpkins are sown the same day, or the next, in one or two rows made along the crest of the ridge. Sweet sorghum may be added to the ridge plantings any time between March and June, and its stalks are consumed for their sweet juice from May on.

Weeding, by either hoe or hand, is started at the end of April and continues for about a month. Okra may be grown from April to June. In June and July cuttings of sweet potatoes are planted on the outside slope of the ridge (the pumpkin vines creep down the inside slope). Over the same period, maize is harvested while still slightly immature and is consumed as a vegetable. A second planting of maize may be made in July or August.

In September and October sweet potatoes are weeded. In October pumpkins begin to ripen, and in December sweet potato harvest begins and proceeds at a pace consistent with the needs of the kitchen, often not terminating before April.

Ridges are the only Azande field type receiving fertilizer. Sweepings from the courtyard containing some kitchen refuse, residuals from crop processing, and ash are applied to the ridge. Chaff from threshing hyptis is spread on the ridge and burned in January. Refuse from salt processing (leached ashes from salt plants) is also deliberately spread on the ridge. Other refuse from processing is not used immediately, but thrown on a pile in the bush some 10 to 30 meters from the kitchen and left two or three years to decompose; then the pile is planted with such things as bananas, maize, taro, early vegetables, sesame, and cucurbits.

In addition to the courtyard ridge, ridges are sometimes made along important paths, but these are usually planted only with sweet potatoes and a manioc hedge, and are not fertilized.

Other instances in which crops are grown on raised earth are vegetables started on special ridge seedbeds, and yams and bananas grown on mounds made inside the courtyard.

Maize-through-Sweet Potatoes. A band 1 to 10 meters wide that is parallel to the outer edge of the courtyard ridge, and sometimes runs along paths, is devoted mainly to sweet potatoes; the last of these are harvested in March just before the beginning of the rainy season. At this time the soil is well pulverized from harvesting operations. With the first rains in April, the area is cleaned — but usually not cultivated, although it is often given a summary weeding — then planted with maize, and frequently manioc as well. This patch of maize is weeded once, presumably in the same manner as ridge maize, although De Schlippe does not make this clear. The maize ripens from the end of July to September, a month to six weeks after harvest of ridge maize.

In the meantime, sweet potatoes have grown again from pieces of vines and roots left at harvest, and the ground is well covered with sweet potato foliage by the time maize is removed. Weeding is done from September to March. These sweet potatoes, like the ridge sweet potatoes, are harvested as needed.

When manioc is associated with maize it forms enough shade the second year to prevent regrowth of the sweet potatoes, and the ridge band reverts to pure manioc for a year or so. After that it may be reopened as a maize-through-sweet potato plot or a maize/oilseed gourd association.

Maize/Oilseed Gourd Association. Extending from the ridge band are small patches planted simultaneously with maize and oilseed gourds. This field type always is initiated on land cultivated the previous season; preplanting preparation of the soil is slight, consisting merely of a hand cleaning to remove trash, and sometimes a light hoeing in addition. In late March or early April maize and oilseed gourds are sown simultaneously, spaced well apart. Sometime between April and July they receive a hoe weeding, and maize is harvested from July to August. Gourds are gathered in September and October.

Manioc Fallow. Manioc, as has been noted, is interplanted from May to August in both of the principal finger millet and maize field types. The following year the land is left unattended, manioc alone occupying it (by this time the manioc is usually large enough to eliminate most weeds and grass with its shade). Manioc is harvested according to need during the first two years of fallow, but frequently a large portion of the crop is never harvested; that remaining is gradually eliminated by regrowth of shrubs and trees.

Cotton Fields. Cotton fields are not part of traditional Azande agriculture since cotton is a newly introduced crop. It is grown without companion crops. The techniques followed appear to be largely those recommended or imposed by local agricultural officers.

Crop Sequences. A rigid order of field type succession cannot be achieved because unpredictable factors such as labor availability, weather, ritual obligations, and illness defeat careful planning. The Azande cultivator must continually improvise.

The following are general objectives which are achieved if possible. The main finger millet association always is planted as either the first or second association on newly cleared land; the peanut-finger millet succession may be sown in the first, second, or fourth season; finger millet–through–grass may be planted the second, third, or fourth season but is grown the fourth season only if it was also planted the season before; the maize/oilseed gourd association is planted only in the second and third seasons; the only association to be found in the fifth season is maize/sweet potatoes with manioc; manioc is the crop most frequently occupying the field when it is abandoned (Figure 3-8). The garden sequence consists of alternation of finger millet-through-grass, maize-through-sweet potatoes, and maize/oilseed gourds, with short interruptions in cropping when the plot is given to an unweeded manioc fallow or to grass fallow.

Production of Crops in Special Environments. Cultivated fruits, vegetables, rice, yams, taro, condiments, and tobacco are outside the crop sequences; each of these is in a small environment especially favorable to it. Oilseed watermelons, tomatoes, mock tomatoes *(Solanum* sp., grown only for their leaves), roselle, eggplant, red peppers, mangoes, and papayas are grown in the courtyard, where they are free from weeds and are fertilized by ash and refuse. Bananas are grown on small mounds; and okra, yams, peanuts (as a vegetable), and various vegetables are grown on broken ridges in the courtyard. Rice, bananas, taro, sesame (as a vegetable), maize, and other crops are grown on old refuse heaps. Moist, shady spots under the kitchen eaves are used as tobacco nurseries. Ash accumulations found outside the courtyard, especially those resulting from the burning of stumps during clearing of a field, are used for tobacco and various vegetables. At the base of trees that have been killed, climbing varieties of cowpeas, lima beans, and oilseed gourds, plus bottle gourds and calabashes, are planted. Living trees are used to support yams. Uninhabited termite mounds are flattened and planted with white sorghum, rice, and cowpeas.

Minor crops requiring the same ecological conditions as crops in one of the field types may be planted as an adjacent patch or as a border to a field. Examples are manioc and okra hedges around, and patches of

FIGURE 3-8 Azande Crop Sequences

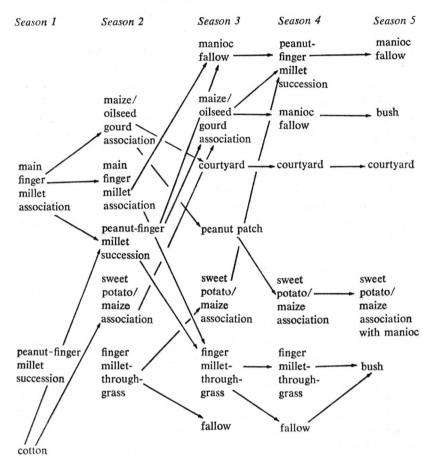

Bambara nuts in or near, fields of the peanut-finger millet succession. The decomposed grass at the border of finger millet field enhances the prospect for a good yield from rice, which is sometimes planted at field borders.[33] Plots in valleys near streams occupy important microclimates which formerly supported maize.

Common hemp (*Cannabis sativa*), or hashish, is prohibited by law; nevertheless it is grown for smoking. In April it is sown densely in a small nursery of good soil, and transplanted during a rainy day in May or June to a well-hidden clearing in the bush. The crop is weeded several times. The leaves are picked, dried, and smoked as desired.

The Azande of the Central African Republic

The Azande of the southern savanna zone extending into the Central African Republic appear to lack one of the two principal field types of the southern Sudan, the peanut-finger millet succession; and the use of the main finger millet association is considerably different.

In place of the peanut-finger millet succession, one finds simply a peanut association which consists of establishment of peanuts interplanted with manioc, oilseed watermelons, and oilseed cucumbers. This association appears often to be allowed to revert to manioc fallow as early as the second year, completing the crop sequence.

The second main crop sequence is the main finger millet association initiated on new land and followed the second season with sesame in part of the field and the maize/oilseed gourds association in the rest. In the third year most of the field is allowed to revert to bush, but a small portion of it is broadcast with finger millet-through-grass.

The Azande of the Congo (Kinshasa)

Garden associations and crop sequences appear to be the same among the Azande of the Congo (Kinshasa) as those of the Azande of the Sudan southern savanna, but field types and crop sequences are considerably different. The main finger millet association has been replaced by cotton interplanted with oilseed watermelons and bananas or maize.

Following the initial cotton crop, the maize/oilseed gourds association or a modified peanut-finger millet succession is usually planted, with some of the cotton field being left fallow. The peanut-finger millet succession is like that of the Sudan, except that, since peanuts are a cash crop, sowing of finger millet is not simultaneous with peanut harvesting but is delayed until the entire peanut crop is pulled and the pods plucked from the vines. This means the soil lies unprotected longer and finger millet gets a later start.

Some maize is grown with the peanuts; the finger millet which follows is interplanted with maize, ratooning sorghum, sesame, and small amounts of hyptis. In some instances a small part of the field will be planted to rice instead of finger millet.

If the maize/oilseed gourds association is planted following cotton, the gourds often fail to cover the field well; in this case finger millet is broadcast after gourds. During the finger millet phase of either the peanut-finger millet succession or the maize-oilseed gourds-finger millet succession, manioc is usually interplanted with finger millet, and the field is allowed to revert in the next season to a fallow in which only manioc and a few of the bananas planted the first season are found. If manioc is not planted with finger millet the second season, the third season crop is a pure stand of sesame.

Although De Schlippe makes no mention of it, the southernmost Congo Azande probably grow relatively small amounts of oilseed crops since they are in the oil palm belt and have alternative sources of oil.

The Congo Azande, like the Sudan Azande, have no cattle, but at least in 1922 they had goats, according to a dictionary published by the Dominican missionaries (*210*, p. 41).[34] It may be that the Sudan Azande also had goats at that time but have since given them up. Pierre de Schlippe does not discuss changes in animal husbandry, but since he does discuss general changes in the Azande way of life, he would appear to have been aware of any changes in animal husbandry.

The Logo

The Logo occupy an area adjacent to the Congo Azande on the east, and employ basically the same field techniques as the Sudan Azande, except that their hoes are larger and used differently.

The population density is about the same as that for the Sudan Azande, averaging from five to fifteen persons per square kilometer in the late 1950's for Faradje territoire, a unit with boundaries which are roughly the same as those of the Logo (*377*, annexe 6). The Logo inhabit mostly open savanna. As with the Congo Azande, who have largely the same vegetation, the southwesternmost part of the Logo country lies within the oil palm belt. The Logo are said to prefer isolated homesteads to villages, although in recent times they have grouped or dispersed according to the changing conditions of security (*108*, p. 16).

Most of the following data on cropping practices were obtained by Pierre de Schlippe in 1946–48, before his intensive study of the Sudan Azande, and come from the area around the Kurukwata experiment station, a post well outside of the oil palm zone. He does not tell how he obtained his data, but the focus of the investigation was on labor requirements, and comments in his later study of the Azande suggest that his study of the Logo was much less detailed. In any event, in what has been published he tells almost nothing about crop associations or sequences.

The Logo are said to have once had cattle, but to have lost them fairly recently; Gustin describes the Logo as cattle keepers as late as 1911 (*168*, p. 468). They still keep goats (*108*, p. 15).

Maize and manioc are the major food crops; sweet potatoes, bananas, sorghum, finger millet, buckwheat, and rice are also mentioned, but appear to be of considerably less importance. Peanuts, pigeon peas, Bambara nuts, beans, cowpeas *(Vigna sinensis)*, and soybeans are grown; in the north at least, sesame and sunflower appeared to be cultivated as sources of oil.[35] Cotton is only a minor crop; the Belgian administration never required the Logo to grow it *(221,* p. 299).

The account of methods of opening land is not complete, but what is given suggests no major deviation from the system of the southern Sudan Azande. Among the Logo the first operation is to to cut the savanna grasses, which may be as tall as a man, with a large hoe on a shaft 1 to 1.3 meters long. The objective is principally to cut the grass; the soil is hardly stirred. Once the grass is on the ground, the trees and shrubs are cut off about a meter up with a hatchet or machete; trunks and branches are partly cut in lengths and piled at the side of the field, partly gathered in piles within the field, and left to dry for two to four weeks. The field is burned, sown the next day, and immediately hoed. A day or two later remaining clods are broken with an L- or T-shaped stick about 65 cm. long, and the field is hand cleaned of unburned refuse.

The field is weeded earlier and more thoroughly than among the Sudan Azande. Immediately after planting, weeding begins, by hand for crops sown broadcast, like finger millet and sesame; by hoe for crops which are planted in holes: maize, rice, sorghum, cowpeas, and peanuts. It appears to be continuous; "from one to three weedings are given, depending on how long each takes" *(107,* p. 366).

Harvesting techniques are the same as for the Sudan Azande — including use of the ring knife for harvesting finger millet. Field types and crop sequences possibly differ considerably from those of the Azande. M. H. Lelong says sesame and finger millet are sown in the first season, followed by sorghum the second, a practice which is unknown among the Azande. Neither Lelong nor De Schlippe describes other sequences.

The Alur

The Congo Alur, who are located around the northern end of Lake Albert, have a population density of over twenty-five persons per square kilometer, one of the highest man-land ratios in the Congo Basin. They are within the humid savanna but outside the oil palm zone.

Manioc and maize are the most important crops. Sorghum, finger millet, sweet potatoes, bananas-plantains, taro, Irish potatoes, beans, sugarcane, and sisal stand out among minor crops. The Alur have large numbers of cattle, as well as sheep and goats. As among the Logo and Azande, the isolated homestead is the center of agricultural activity (*285*, p. 236).

A. Van Parijs, a researcher at the Nioka experiment station, outlines the Alur agricultural calendar (*389*). The agricultural year begins with clearing and burning fields in February. In March beans and early-maturing varieties of maize are planted separately and alone. Two or three weeks after maize comes up, it is interplanted with beans. In late March new manioc fields are started and are interplanted with maize and beans. More maize is sown in April — this time widely spaced; three weeks later it is interplanted with finger millet, amaranth, and sometimes sorghum. In April and May sweet potatoes are planted — always alone — on round, raised beds. In May and June, finger millet, amaranth, and sorghum are sown together, sometimes with one or the other dominant, sometimes with all of approximately equal importance. Early beans are harvested in July and more maize is sown (probably on the same plot and in gardens; we are not told directly, but data given on crop sequences suggest that a maize-beans succession is not practiced in fields). From mid-August to September beans are planted with maize or in pure stand. In September manioc is planted mixed with beans.

Crop sequences in Alur fields are discussed in Chapter 12 on technological change below (pp. 264–65). Information on garden crops applies to marshes, where a maize/beans/gourds association is annually alternated with five or six months of fallow and plots may never be allowed to revert to bush.

M. A. Loeckx's account of agriculture in Djukot chiefdom (*237*) gives some detail on gardens. Plots along streams or in valleys are cleared in December or January. Gourds are planted on mounds, and a month or so later (in January or February) maize is planted between mounds. Other gardens mentioned are small plots behind the hut in which taro, various vegetables, and tobacco are grown. Bananas-plantains, sugarcane, and sometimes Irish potatoes are grown in fertile valleys.

Class 10: Hoe and Cut, Clean, Burn, Plant

A second type of savanna technique involving cleaning is one reported for the Nyangwé area about 1913 by M. Tharin (*339*, p. 202). The natural vegetation of the area is tall grass. Manioc and maize are the principal staples.

In clearing fields, all vegetation is pulled or dug up with a hoe, thrown to one side of the plot, and burned; then the soil is worked to a depth of 8 to 10 cm. A circle 50 to 60 cm. in diameter is made with a stick, and in this furrow rice and maize are planted. Manioc stems are then planted in mounds about 1 meter square and 80 cm. high (it is not clear whether these mounds are between circles containing maize and rice or are made in a separate location).

A second association is maize/peanuts planted in August and succeeded by tobacco, bananas-plantains, sesame, or beans as soon as the maize and peanuts are harvested. In this area weeds are a constant problem and fields are said to be weeded often.

Class 11: Cut, Burn, Clean or Level, Hoe, Plant, Followed by Repeated Hoeings

A refinement of the cut, burn, hoe, plant method employed in savannas is found among the Mandja and probably two of their neighbors, the Banda and Baya. The distinctive feature of this system is that after crops have come up fields are hoed several times (five or six among the Mandja) to eliminate weeds and build up mounds made at planting time.

The Mandja

Much of available data on the Mandja cropping methods comes from an account published in 1911 by Fernand Gaud, onetime commandant of Fort Crampel and the region of Bangui. Gaud estimated the population at about 1.5 persons per square kilometer (*150*, p. 77). The major staple foodstuffs in 1911 were manioc and sorghum.

The principal field, according to Gaud, is a sorghum/maize/manioc association, with sorghum the dominant crop. During the dry season, bushes are felled with a hatchet and smaller vegetation is cut with a knife, probably a machete (*150*, p. 206). The debris is left where it falls until dry, and then burned. The soil is leveled roughly; then, after the first rain, the field is hoed lightly with "small hoes" and mounds are made for manioc. Maize and manioc are planted in holes made with the sharpened end of a hoe handle; then sorghum is planted, four or five grains per hole in holes about 50 cm. apart. No information is given about the planting of other crops.[36]

As soon as plants come up, the field is hoed to eliminate weeds and to pile soil around the base of the plant; this operation is repeated five or six times. Fields are kept free of weeds until heads of grain begin to form. In some areas, but not everywhere, the Mandja thin the stand of young plants while weeding (*150*, p. 207).[37] As sorghum begins to ripen, young boys are sent to the fields to keep birds away.

Sorghum is harvested in December, at the end of the rainy season. Men cut the sorghum heads with a knife, and the women carry them to granaries built in the field. Maize is harvested two to three months after planting, depending on variety, and is stored in the village. Maize ears are tied together into large bundles which are suspended in trees. Manioc is harvested gradually, beginning about a year after it is planted.

Gaud says that maize is rarely grown in pure stand because its high nutrient requirements, and that it is often planted near huts where it can benefit from household refuse. Manioc, also a crop said to demand much from the soil, is usually planted on alluvial soils, often following a crop of sorghum. It is typically weeded only once or twice (*150*, p. 209). Vegetables are planted either with sorghum in the main fields or in plots by themselves; other information on these crops is not given.

A. M. Vergait's account (1937) differs considerably from Gaud's on crop associations. Vergait reports six field types — millet/beans/oilseed gourds, millet, maize/gourds, sesame/oilseed gourds, manioc, and peanuts — but nowhere mentions the sorghum/maize/manioc association described by Gaud.

Only Vergait gives any information on sequences, and he mentions but one: millet/beans/oilseed gourds followed by millet/manioc in the second year and a pure stand of manioc the third year (*397*, p. 117).

The Banda

C. Tisserant provides some information on the agriculture of the Banda in an article published in 1953 based on his field work as a missionary as early as 1928 (*346*). Clearing techniques appear to be the same as for the Mandja. The Banda cultivate at least sixty plants (Table 3-3) and utilize at least fourteen wild plants. The major staple is now manioc but was formerly sorghum. Goats and sheep are about the only livestock kept, and sheep are restricted to the western part of the area.

The Banda have at least sixteen crop associations. Like the Azande they have courtyard plots, gardens near the homesite, small fields (usually near the homesite), and large fields (usually the most distant cultivations

found). In the courtyard one finds an association of taro/sweet pota-
toes/okra with a few plants of several other crops, e.g. *Amaranthus
caudatus, Hibiscus sabdariffa*, and *Solanum aethiopicum*, the leaves of

TABLE 3-3 Banda Crops

Starchy-staples	*Justicia insularis*
Manioc	*Celosia argentea*
Sorghum	*Capsicum annum*
Bulrush millet (*Pennisetum typhoides*)	*C. frutescens*
Finger millet (*Eleusine coracana*)	Fruits
Maize	Papaya
Rice	Pineapple
Plantains	Mango
Yams (*Dioscorea macroura, D. cayen-*	Guava
ensis, and *D. alata*)	Citron (*Citrus medica*)
Taro	Bananas
Sweet potatoes	Sources of sugar
Coleus potatoes (*Coleus dazo, C. lan-*	Sugarcane
gouassiensis, and *C. dysentericus*)	Sweet sorghum (*Andropogon saccha-*
Sources of fats and oils	*ratus*)
Sesame	Sources of salt
Oil palm	*Hygrophilia spinosa*
Peanuts	*Luffa cylindrica*
Castor bean	*Pistia stratiotes*
Bambara nut	*Hydrocharis liberica*
Bottle gourd (*Lagenaria vulgaris*)	*Pennisetum purpureum*
Watermelon (*Citrullus vulgaris*)	*Leonotis Africana*
Cucumeropsis edulis	Tree crops
Cucumis melo	Rubber (*Manihot glazionii*)
Vegetables	Bark cloth tree
Cowpeas (*Vigna sinensis*)	Stimulants
Lablab bean (*Dolichos lalab*)	Tobacco (*Nicotiana tabacum* and *N.*
Lima bean (*Phaseolus lunatus*)	*rusticum*)
Kerstingiella geocarpa	Common hemp (*Cannabis sativa*)
Pumpkin	Fish poisons
Cucumeropsis mannii	*Tephrosia vogelii*
Horned cucumber (*Cucumis metulif-*	*Mundulea sericea* (west)
erus)	*Cassia alta* (north)
Okra	Perfumes
Amaranth (*Amaranthus caudatus*)	*Cyperus articulatus*
Cerathotheca sesamoides	*Cymbopogon densiflorus*
Long-fruited jute (*Corchorus olitorius*)	Fever plant (*Ocimum viride*)
Hibiscus sabdariffa	Tinder
Solanum aethiopicum	*Kamahia consimilis*

Data from C. Tisserant, "L'Agriculture dans les savanes de l'Oubangui," *Bull. de
l'Inst. d'Études Centrafricaines*, N.S., No. 6, (1953), pp. 212–57, and Father Diagre,
"Plantes alimentares du pays Banda," *Bull. de la Société des Recherches Congolaises*,
8 (1927): 125.

which are cooked in stews. Also in or near the courtyard are small plots of tobacco, a few mounds of yams, some bark cloth trees; some *Tephrosia vogelii*, from which a fish poison is derived; *Cyperus articulatus*, used as a perfume; and *Kamakia consimilis*, grown for tinder. Bananas and plantains are often grown in a belt around the village.

Yams, beans, coleus potatoes, pumpkins, and Bambara nuts are found in small fields near the village; and all of these except Bambara nuts are also sometimes grown on the edge of the more distant large fields.

The main fields are planted to a manioc-sorghum-oilseed gourds succession or a sorghum-oilseed gourds-manioc succession; to a manioc/beans/vegetables association; to oilseed gourds with some manioc; to an oilseed gourds-sorghum succession; or to pure stands of either sesame, peanuts, or rice. Hemp plots are concealed in the center of one of the main fields.

Two practices clearly reflect attempts to fertilize crops: debris is piled around growing banana and plantain stalks, and tobacco is planted only on refuse heaps or places where there are ashes from salt making.

The Baya

Information on the Baya comes largely from notes provided by Philip A. Noss in 1964 based on several years of residence in the Baya area during the 1950's and early 1960's. The staple foodstuff is manioc; other crops mentioned are maize, sweet potatoes, plantains, sugarcane, sesame, peanuts, and tobacco. Cattle, sheep, goats, swine, and chickens are kept, but cattle are a fairly recent introduction and most herds are small (277). Animal manures are not used as fertilizers.

The refuse heap behind the hut is planted with squash and gourds; sweet potatoes are grown in gardens near the homesite; maize, sugarcane, plantains, and tobacco are grown along streams and in small valleys; and the main fields are devoted mainly to manioc or a peanut-manioc succession. Data on sequences are not available.

Class 12: Cut, Plant Tree Crops (Forest)

The agricultural system of the Lele, the Kuba, and some of their neighbors deviates from all other methods in the Congo Basin in that tree crops are planted soon after clearing the forest. This reduces the decline of fertility that results from replacing forest with annual crops; the land can be cropped several years longer than would otherwise be possible. The oil and raphia palms planted do not yield a staple food, but their oil, wine, and raphia fiber products are traded to other tribes for foodstuffs. Since the palms are interplanted with staple food crops the first few seasons, the cleared plots still yield a return in food, albeit a reduced one.

The Lele

A sketch of the agriculture of the northwestern portion of the Lele about 1950 is provided by Mary Douglas, who estimated their population density to be about ten persons per square kilometer. The Lele are located on the edge of the forest along the Kasai River; they make their villages in the tall-grass savanna at the forest edge, but most fields are made in the forest. Maize is the primary starchy-staple, with manioc a close second. Cultivation of the raphia palm appears to be the other major agricultural activity. Gardens around the village seem to be limited mainly to peanuts, raphia palm, and bananas (*116*, p. 2). Poultry are commonly found, but cattle, goats, sheep, and swine are not widely kept; the Lele depend on hunting or trade for meat and fish. They do most of their own hunting, but depend on trade with Dinga for some of their fish (*116*, p. 3).[38]

Maize is planted in the forest "by slash and burn methods," usually only one crop of maize being harvested from newly cleared plots (*116*, p. 2). In the second year, and for several subsequent years, raphia palm, manioc, rice, bananas, chilies, or rice and "other crops" are planted. Peanuts and some plots of manioc are grown in the adjacent savanna.

Douglas emphasizes cultivation of the raphia [39] palm (*116*, pp. 2–3):

> The palm takes four or five years to mature, and is very carefully cultivated. All its products are used; its main ribs for hut wall and roof supports, its fibres as strong in hut building and basketry, its smaller ribs as arrow shafts, its outside leaves as thatching for the walls and roofs of huts. The inner cuticle of the young leaf is the material from which they weave their raffia cloths. Finally, one of the most valued products of the palm is the unfermented wine, which forms the second staple article of diet. When the wine is all drawn off and the palm dead, its rotting stem harbours grubs which are a highly prized delicacy. When they have grown fat, and can be heard moving inside the stem, it is chopped open, and made to yield its last product.

The Lele begin harvesting the raphia palm when it is about two years old; the "yellow, closely pleated fronds" are cut, and the cuticle is extracted for weaving. When the palm is four or five years old and about to flower for the first time, the whole crown is cut out and a calabash is attached to the wound.[40] After the sap of the tree is exhausted — in six weeks to four or five months, "depending on season and habitat — the palm is stripped of its ribs and the naked stump is left to rot" (*116*, p. 15).

The fruit of oil palms found in the forest is harvested, but the trees are not cultivated. Apparently forest fields are weeded. Douglas says that women "take on most of the work of keeping the crops clear of weeds" (*116*, p. 2).

An interesting activity that is mentioned but not described is the cultivation of "salt-yielding" plants in the forest.

The Kuba

Most of the data on the Kuba are from unpublished field notes made by Jan Vansina on the Bushoong subgroup between 1953 and 1956. The population density is about three to four persons per square kilometer. Like the Lele, adjacent to the west, the Kuba occupy both forest and savanna. Manioc is the principal food crop, but maize is also of major importance. Goats, sheep, swine, chickens, and dogs are the only domesticated animals.

In savanna areas fields are opened by cutting down all vegetation, burning the debris, hoeing the ash into mounds, and planting. Crop sequences are beans followed by Bambara nuts, then manioc, and finally a fallow of up to twenty years.

Forest area clearing techniques are similar to those of the Lele. In May small trees are cut down and the branches are lopped off the larger ones. In mid-August the debris is burned and the field hoed. Maize is planted the first of September and harvested in January or February. Beans are planted in March and harvested about two months later. In September of the second year peanuts are planted; by January they are harvested; and a month or so later manioc, the last crop of the sequence, is planted. Two years later, when the last of the manioc is harvested, the field is left fallow for about seven years. An alternative forest sequence is maize, manioc, beans, peanuts, manioc, fallow.

All families try always to have both forest and savanna fields in cultivation to maintain an adequate diversity of crops. They also maintain small gardens near the hut for such things as sweet potatoes, tobacco, bananas, and fruit trees. Other special gardens are those found at abandoned village sites.

Like the Lele, the Kuba cultivate the raphia palm as a major activity. Instead of cutting out the entire crown as the Lele do, the Kuba merely make a wound at the base of the large inflorescence.

The Kwilu Area

On the plateaus between the Kwilu and Kasai rivers, palm nuts are broadcast on fields recently fallowed, and the young trees are cultivated until they are large enough to survive among the weeds (*375*, pp. 4–7). Vanderyst reports that according to traditions among the people of this area oil palms were introduced long before European rule; in 1923, he says, cultivation of oil palms was still being spread in some parts of the area (*375*, p. 4).

Henri Nicolaï gives a little information on crop sequences. In forest areas he cites as typical a maize-manioc succession, followed by manioc the second year and fallow the third. In valley savanna areas the sequence is more frequently peanuts followed by either manioc or a manioc/gourds association. Savanna portions of the plateaus are characterized by Bambara nuts, followed by either millet or manioc. Although manioc is frequently the last crop in both forest and savanna, part of the Suku, Tsamba, and Mbala sometimes plant maize among the second year manioc when the latter is almost mature (*276*, pp. 259–61).

4

Ash-Fertilizer-Dependent Long-Fallow Systems

In the dry forest of the southwestern corner of the Congo Basin the central feature of the agricultural systems of the Bemba and some other tribes is production of ashes to supplement the fertility of cleared land (called *chitemene* agriculture by the Bemba).

After plots to be cropped have been cleared, a much larger area is also cleared — from five to twenty times as large as that cultivated, depending on the tribe; the debris from it is piled on the area to be cropped and burned to obtain extra layers of ash.

We have ranked these systems below those which are compost-dependent, judging them to involve less reliance on human effort to replenish soil fertility, because compared with composting they require much more land per capita and, from the fragmentary evidence available, also appear to be characterized by a considerably longer fallow.

The Bemba

Audrey I. Richards' classic study of Bemba diet and agriculture, drawn from fieldwork in 1930–34, provides a fairly complete description of Bemba agricultural methods; C. G. Trapnell's work provides additional material and greater detail on some points. The natural vegetation of the

111

Bemba area is predominantly dry, fairly open forest mixed with savanna. The population density does not exceed 1.5 persons per square kilometer (*305*, p. 18).

The staple food is finger millet; minor starchy-staples are manioc, bulrush millet, sorghum, maize, sweet potatoes, and coleus potatoes. Other crops are peanuts, Bambara nuts, beans, cowpeas, English peas (*Pisum sativum*), pumpkins, edible gourds (*Lagenaria* sp.), cucumbers, chilies, capsicums (*Capsicum annuum* vars.), and solanaceous fruits (*Solanum naumanii*). Little attention is given to keeping livestock. Only in urban areas are cattle kept, and they are not common. Some smaller livestock are raised, but they apparently are not numerous; Richards emphasizes that only "A few Bemba own goats and sheep . . ." (*305*, p. 210). Chickens and pigeons are generally kept, however. Richards makes no reference to beekeeping.

The principal tools for field and garden work are an axe with a wedge-shaped blade that is set at a 45° angle in a shaft about 67 cm. long, and a hoe with a rectangular blade about 50 cm. by 26 cm. attached to a handle 1.3 to 1.6 meters long.

The Bemba live in villages of thirty to fifty huts most of the year, but each family moves to a temporary residence near its fields for a month or so in May or June for millet harvest. Villages are relocated about every five years as soils become exhausted and forest near the village eliminated.

Field Cultivations

From April when the dry and cold season begins to May or June when the family moves to a temporary residence near the millet fields is the usual time for clearing fields, but clearing may be done as late as August or September. Smaller trees are cut down about breast height, while larger trees are only pollarded (*360*, p. 45). Photographs supplied by Richards show tree stumps in fields to be at least five or six times as high as a man.

Cut branches are trimmed enough so that they will lie flat in a pile for burning, and are laid in rows, each man taking care to keep his branches separated from those of his neighbors. Women later carry the branches to the plot to be cultivated and place them radially, with the smallest diameter to the center. At the time of Miss Richards' study, branches were cut from an area up to six times as large as that to be planted. Pieces of wood are piled one on the other until the pile is about

65 cm. high, care being taken to keep the thickness of the pile uniform. The Bemba are said often to single out barren patches of a field as spots where branches were not properly stacked before burning. The last task in piling branches is to outline the edge of the circle with small branches in order to keep the fire from spreading into the bush, and to provide an extra thickness of ashes at the edge for growing cucumbers and gourds.

After the pile is finished, it is left to dry until time for burning. The Bemba attempt to burn just before the first rain of the rainy season in order to get maximum dryness of the branches. When to burn is decided by the chief; commoners delay burning until word is received that the chief's clearing has been fired.

After the plot has been burned, there is no further work on the field itself until the rains begin. A little before the rains or after the first rain, gourds, pumpkins, or peanuts may be planted around the edge of the field. Once the ground is soft from the heavy rains of December and January, millet is sown.[1] If sorghum or maize is to be grown with millet, it will be planted before the main millet crop is sown, when the ground has been well softened by the rains. Either men or women may sow, and enough skill is involved[2] for a specialist often to be engaged to do this task, which is described as follows (*305*, p. 296): "Seeds are carried in a gourd or basket, and the sower first marks out the garden with a stick into strips about a yard wide. This is to ensure that each part of the ground is covered. The sower walks up and down each strip casting the seed broadcast with a flick of the wrist that sends the tiny seeds flying in a fine spray . . . ." A woman follows the sower, spreading a thin layer of soil over the seed with a hoe: "A clod is swung sideways shoulder high on the hoe, and then tossed over with a light movement that scatters the earth evenly over the ground, so that the millet seeds lie with a surface covering of soil." The final operation is the digging of a trench about 33 cm. deep around the perimeter of the field to drain off excess rain.

Once the field is sown, little additional work is done in it until harvest some five or six months later. Burning destroys weeds so effectively that usually no weeding is required. Neither animal manures nor night soil are ever applied to fields, although the Bemba recognize that night soil increases soil fertility. Human excrement deposited by children on plots around the hut is sometimes cited as the reason for good crops in such locations, but the Bemba "have a horror of touching night-soil," and Richards states that adults consider defecating on fields a breach of etiquette and scold children for it (*305*, p. 282). Richards concludes that

"It is not surprising, therefore, that in the few places where cattle are kept, the natives object strongly to the idea of using kraal manure."

Millet fields require little guarding. Birds seem to do scant damage to this crop, although when it is sown with sorghum, the latter must be protected. For this purpose scarecrows made of flapping leaves may be put in fields (*305*, p. 297). In areas where wild animals are a pest, a fence made of stout poles is constructed. A pair of posts about 1.6 meters long and 17 cm. in diameter is placed about every 2 meters, and branches of similar dimensions are stacked between them until the stack is about waist high. Because of termites and decay, fences rarely last more than two years. In some parts of Bemba country a chain of pits with mounds between them is dug around the field to keep out marauders.

Harvesting begins in May. A knife with a handle 5 cm. long and a 10 cm., petal-shaped blade is held in the palm of the hand; the millet head is cut by forcing its stem between the knife blade and the thumb. A small basket held below catches the head as it is cut free. Care is taken to harvest at the right time. If harvesting is too soon, the millet is not fully mature and is of lighter weight than is desirable; if the grain is dampened by rain, the heads hang down and are hard to cut; if grain is too ripe, the field is excessively dusty and seeds shatter easily. The reaper usually harvests with her back to the wind to keep dust out of her eyes.

Peanuts are planted in the second season after clearing. The stalks from the previous millet crop are burned towards the end of the dry season (October or November), and the soil is hoed roughly. Peanuts are usually planted after the first rains (November to December), but can be planted as late as January. One person makes a series of holes about 50 cm. apart with a hoe, and a second person follows, dropping in seeds one at a time and stepping on them.

Since the field is burned only lightly in preparation for the second year, the amount of weed seeds killed by fire and heat may be so small that weeds become a problem. If so, the field may be weeded about February, by means not described. Otherwise, there is no work after planting until the harvest operation in May.

To harvest peanuts, the plant is grasped in one hand and the roots are dug up with a hoe held in the other hand; when the plant is free, it is shaken to remove any soil still attached to the roots.

The third year, finger millet is usually sown again. Planting procedures are not described, except for a note that the millet seeds are sown before the first rains, rather than immediately afterwards as with finger millet grown on newly cleared land.

The fourth year, mounds about 67 cm. high and a little over 2 meters in diameter at the base are made and planted with sorghum, sorghum and peanuts, beans, manioc, or vegetables. If manioc is to be planted, mounds are made larger — about a meter high.

According to the Bemba, the reason for making mounds is to renew the fertility of the soil; they seem generally to believe that the more thoroughly the soil is dug the greater will be the increment of fertility. Richards discusses five terms used to distinguish the thoroughness with which the soil is dug in mound construction, and she implies that there are yet others (*305*, p. 303).

When mounds are made on fields that already contain mounds, any stalks or debris from previous crops are usually piled between the existing mounds, burned, and then covered with soil to form a new mound.

The care of crops after the mounds are made is not discussed; presumably it does not differ from the methods already discussed.

Anthill Cultivation

In one treeless area, near Molema in the flat plain of the Chambesi Valley, Richards found the Bemba relying on sorghum and maize grown on anthills (*305*, p. 281). But methods of cultivation are not given, and no mention is made of anthill cultivation elsewhere among the Bemba.

Garden Cultivation

Mound cultivation is always practiced by the Bemba in the gardens around their villages. When the soil is first cleared, mounds may be made either in the dry season or after the first rains by digging up chunks of turf, piling them in a heap, and covering the heap with a few inches of soil. Early millet, sorghum, sweet potatoes, manioc, maize, beans, and various vegetables are planted in the gardens from September to February. On old gardens where the soil has been loosened by digging when a previous crop was harvested, cucurbits, maize, and various vegetables, with the exception of peas, may be planted before the first rains. At least two crops are grown on each mound: pumpkins or beans may be planted at the base of a mound on which sorghum or maize has been planted; or sweet potato cuttings may be stuck into the side of mounds on which either manioc or sorghum has been planted (*305*, p. 305).

Garden crops, whether grown on village plots or in old millet fields, usually are not weeded even if there is a dense growth of weeds. Threshing and grinding chaff is applied as fertilizer to village gardens near the hut.

Coleus Potato Gardens

Coleus (Livingstone) potatoes are grown only in certain areas,[3] and are given special care. Beginning in May, long grass is pulled and the grass tussocks are broken up with a hoe; next the ground is hoed and clods are broken "by prodding the ground with the apex of the hoe" (*305*, p. 310). Cuttings of chunks of coleus potatoes are planted in June in half the plot. The rest of the plot is planted in September with stalks from potatoes planted in June. All the stalks and leaves of the June crop are removed about September for fear that the potatoes already formed in the soil will begin to sprout again with the rains. Coleus potatoes are harvested at the end of the dry season.

River Gardens

In river gardens, observed only among certain mixed Bemba-Bisa peoples, turf is dug into mounds and left to dry, then mounds are ignited and covered with earth. Except to comment that such gardens are planted "as early as August or September," Richards does not describe them (*305*, p. 311).

Gardens on Old Hutsites

One rainy season after a hut has been abandoned, the rubble of the walls is broken up and dug into the floor; the next season this plot (a rough circle 5 meters or so in diameter) is hoed and planted with maize and pumpkins. This crop association is repeated until the soil is exhausted, when either sweet potatoes or tobacco are planted. Hutsites usually produce exceptionally good yields, because of the lime remaining in the soil from whitewash on hut walls.

Techniques of harvesting garden crops are not described except to say that such crops are harvested over a period of weeks.

Field Crop Sequences

Each year new land is cleared and some land is abandoned. Richards states that the first planting on newly cleared land always includes finger millet grown alone or mixed with manioc or sorghum (Figure 4-1). Peanuts are always grown the second season, either alone or, in fields containing sorghum the year before, with sorghum that comes up without being planted. The third season, finger millet is planted again in fields previously containing only peanuts, and in other fields sorghum is grown with self-propagated peanuts. The fourth season, either sorghum, manioc, beans, or vegetables are grown on fields that have had a millet, peanuts, millet sequence, while sorghum is grown on fields that have had a millet/sorghum, peanuts/sorghum, sorghum/peanuts sequence. The fifth season, the field is often allowed to revert to bush, or sweet potatoes may be planted. Richards does not say what is done the fifth season in the sequence dominated by sorghum (Figure 4-1).

Although Richards gives the above sequences as characteristic of all the Bemba, Trapnell describes other sequences and divides the Bemba into four groups according to the sequences they follow. The four groups have a total of forty-six different sequences as against nine estimated by Richards (Figures 4-1, 4-2, 4-3). Trapnell's and Richards' descriptions have no sequences in common.

The northeastern Bemba have six field crop sequences according to Trapnell. Finger millet and a little sorghum is followed the second year by either finger millet,[4] peanuts, peanuts and manioc, or sorghum, the third year either beans and manioc, manioc alone, finger millet, or sorghum and peanuts occupies the field, followed by fallow, or manioc, which in turn is followed by beans and sweet potatoes before the field is returned to bush (Figure 4-2).

Seven field crop sequences are found among the northwestern Bemba. Finger millet and sorghum are followed by either peanuts or cowpeas the second year, then beans or finger millet. The fourth year bean patches may be planted to finger millet and vice versa, or finger millet fields are planted to cowpeas while beans or finger millet follow beans, or bean fields may be fallowed. Areas planted to finger millet the fourth year are returned to bush the fifth or are planted to beans and then returned to bush the next season. Areas planted to beans the fourth year are either returned to bush or planted to beans or finger millet the fifth season and returned to bush the sixth season. Fields sowed with cowpeas the fourth season are returned to bush the fifth year.

In the southern and western parts of Bemba country, fourteen sequences are noted. Two notable differences compared with northern areas are that cowpeas are not grown, and sorghum may be planted on mounds.

Among the eastern Bemba another eleven sequences are found. Sorghum is usually grown with peanuts or cowpeas the second year; sweet potatoes are sometimes among the final crops, as in the northeastern

FIGURE 4-1 Bemba Crop Sequences, According to Richards

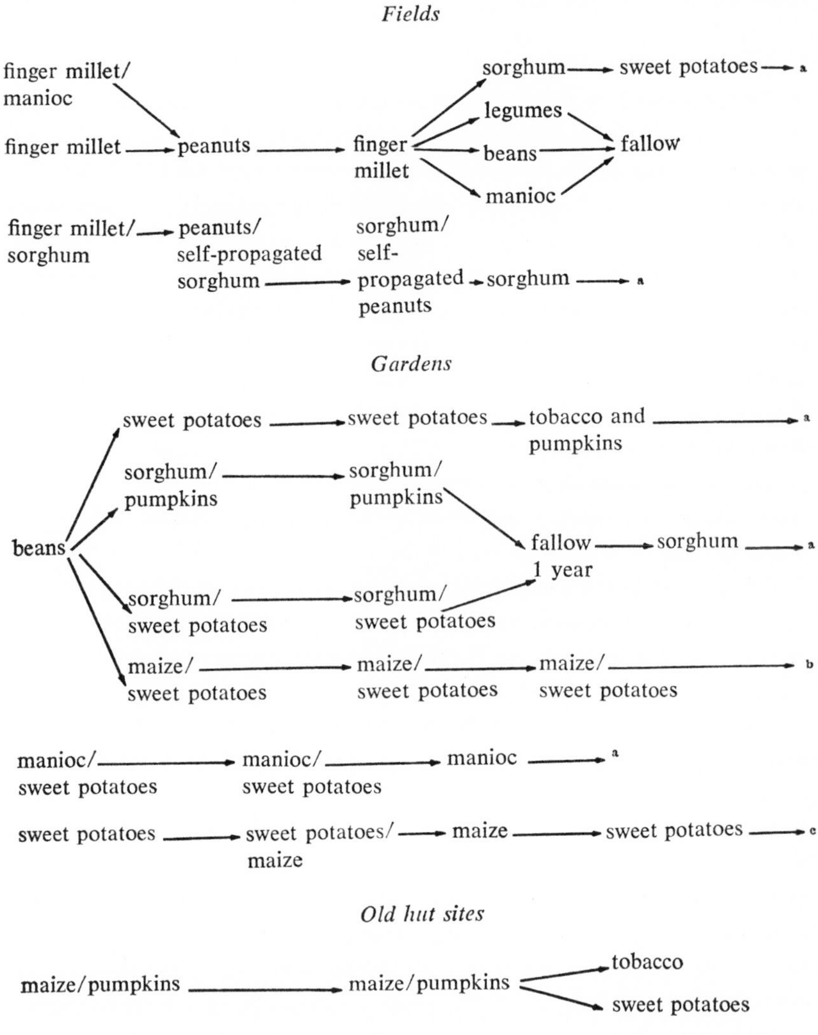

Fields

finger millet/
manioc

finger millet ⟶ peanuts ⟶ finger millet

sorghum ⟶ sweet potatoes ⟶ ᵃ

legumes

beans ⟶ fallow

manioc

finger millet/ ⟶ peanuts/   sorghum/
sorghum   self-propagated self-
                  sorghum ⟶ propagated ⟶ sorghum ⟶ ᵃ
                                   peanuts

Gardens

beans

sweet potatoes ⟶ sweet potatoes ⟶ tobacco and ⟶ ᵃ
                                   pumpkins

sorghum/ ⟶ sorghum/
pumpkins   pumpkins

fallow ⟶ sorghum ⟶ ᵃ
1 year

sorghum/ ⟶ sorghum/
sweet potatoes sweet potatoes

maize/ ⟶ maize/ ⟶ maize/ ⟶ ᵇ
sweet potatoes sweet potatoes sweet potatoes

manioc/ ⟶ manioc/ ⟶ manioc ⟶ ᵃ
sweet potatoes sweet potatoes

sweet potatoes ⟶ sweet potatoes/ ⟶ maize ⟶ sweet potatoes ⟶ ᶜ
                 maize

Old hut sites

maize/pumpkins ⟶ maize/pumpkins

tobacco

sweet potatoes

Based on Richards: *305*, pp. 313–22.
ᵃ No information given on what follows.
ᵇ Maize and sweet potatoes planted year after year until the soil is exhausted, then sweet potatoes alone as the last crop.
ᶜ Maize and pumpkins sown so long as soil is fertile, then tobacco or sweet potatoes.

system. Sorghum is planted in the later part of the sequence, as in the southern areas (Figure 4-2).

Garden Crop Sequences

Trapnell and Richards describe similar garden sequences for plots near the village, but Trapnell describes three general garden sequences and one that is special to the northwestern Bemba that Richards does not mention (Figures 4-1 and 4-3). The principal garden sequence among the northeastern Bemba is maize, finger millet, sorghum, gourds, pulses, pumpkins, cucumbers, and manioc followed by smaller combinations of these crops, with peanuts and Bambara nuts sometimes added, for two or more years. Their general sequences on old millet fields are sorghum or sorghum and cowpeas repeated. Another common garden sequence in some areas is early millet and gourds, castor beans, *tephrosia*,[5] and possibly sorghum, followed by Bambara nuts, beans, cowpeas, or sweet potatoes. The northwestern Bemba plant either peanuts, Bambara nuts, finger millet, or cowpeas the second year, and finger millet, if anything, the third year.

A peanut-finger millet succession much like the one followed by the Azande in the northern Congo Basin is also described by Trapnell. Usually at the time of peanut harvest, or immediately after it (typically in June), millet is broadcast. An early-maturing finger millet may be sown, but Trapnell suggests this is not the usual practice (*360*, p. 52). The millet seeds are covered in the process of digging peanuts, or the ground is swept with tree branches to cover them.

Each five years or so the village is usually moved in order to locate it nearer uncleared land. Former hutsites are planted with a maize/pumpkins association year after year until soils near exhaustion or the distance to be walked has become too long (Figure 4-1). The last season before these plots are abandoned they are planted with either tobacco or sweet potatoes.

Other garden sequences are hard to summarize. They usually involve beans, manioc, or sweet potatoes the first year; manioc, sweet potatoes, pumpkins, sorghum or maize the second and third years, but in different combinations; and the same crops or a one-year fallow the fourth year (Figure 4-1). For four of the sequences information is not given on what is planted the fifth and following years; in two of the sequences sorghum is planted. No information is provided on what is planted the seventh year in any sequence.

FIGURE 4-2 Bemba Field Crop Sequences, According to Trapnell

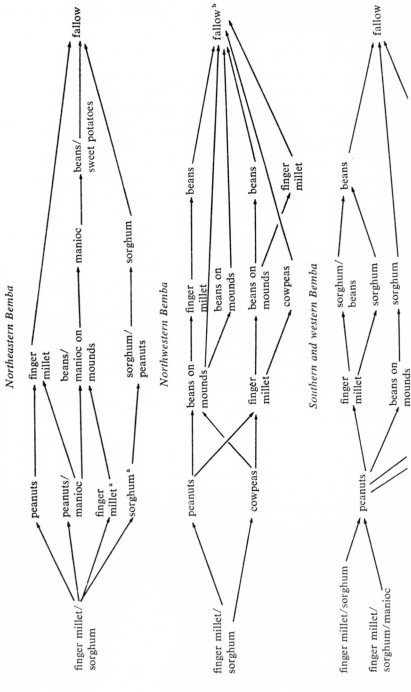

Northeastern Bemba

Northwestern Bemba

Southern and western Bemba

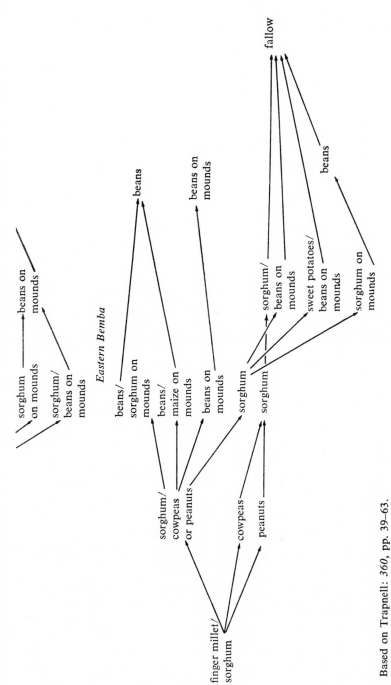

Based on Trapnell: *360*, pp. 39–63.

[a] Rare.

[b] Field may be fallowed two to four years and then beans planted followed by finger millet before long fallow.

FIGURE 4-3   Bemba Garden Crop Sequences, According to Trapnell

Main Gardens, Northeastern Bemba

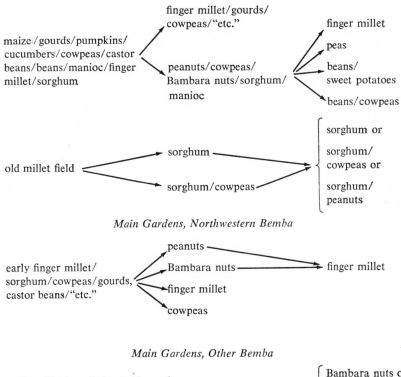

Main Gardens, Northwestern Bemba

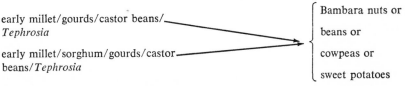

Main Gardens, Other Bemba

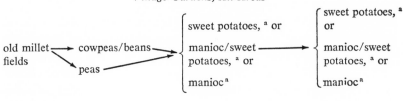

Village Gardens, All Areas

Based on Trapnell: *360*, pp. 39–63.
[a] With a border of sweet potatoes, manioc, maize, beans, gourds, or castor beans.

The Lungu

According to Trapnell, Lungu agricultural methods are "practically identical" to those of the Bemba, except that sorghum is less important and manioc is more so (*360*, pp. 45–46). Trapnell's discussion also suggests that approximately the same crops and livestock are known by both peoples.

Lungu crop sequences resemble those of the northeastern Bemba, but differences are noted. Peanuts planted in the second year are grown on mounds in the Abercorn area, but on the flat elsewhere among the Lungu (*360*, p. 46). The Abercorn Lungu are also exceptional in that they make mounds for peanuts in the main gardens, as well.

Other deviations from Bemba garden methods are the practice of cutting grass rather than hoeing it up[6] and the practice of planting plants on the initial mounds on plots near the village, a technique Trapnell observed in Bemba country only around Kasama (*360*, p. 54).

The Iwa and the Woodland Mambwe

The Iwa — and the woodland portion of that northern group of Iwa called the Mambwe — follow the large circle chitemene technique, but in some areas where few big trees are found most trees are cut down about breast height (*360*, p. 45).

Methods of cultivation are generally like those of the Bemba, and crop sequences are much like those of the northwestern Bemba. A series of fields is made of "diminishing size for millets of different rates of maturing" (*360*, p. 49). Especially among the Mambwe, mounds in fields are spread toward the end of the crop sequence.

Among the Iwa, the finger millet, sorghum, sorghum, sorghum sequence noted as rare among the northeastern Bemba is found. Finger millet and sorghum are sown thickly the first year and are followed by sorghum the next, with sorghum sometimes sparsely interplanted with peanuts the third year. The Mambwe follow a similar sequence, but plant a denser stand of peanuts the last year. Both tribes sometimes plant finger millet the second or third year.

The practice of recultivating a field for two years after two to four years of fallow that is followed by the northwestern Bemba is found among the Mambwe, but the Iwa may grow as many as three or four crops after a short fallow (*360*, p. 50).

Deviations from Bemba garden methods noted are the growing of sesame by the Iwa and greater use of early-maturing millet varieties in the peanuts-finger millet succession.

Gardens in valley bottoms, a type of cultivation "practically unknown among the great majority" of the Bemba according to Trapnell (*360*, p. 53), are common among the Mambwe and Iwa. Several kinds are found, of which Trapnell describes one he thought especially interesting for the techniques employed. In August or September the plot is hoed up and turfs are piled in heaps with the grass pointing inward. In October or November these piles are ignited, then covered at once with topsoil, except for a small vent left at the top (*360*, p. 53): "The fire smouldering within the heap is said to continue to burn for two days and oxidises a great part of the grey dambo clay to a pale orange or buff colour, reducing it to a fine powdery texture suitable for the millet seed-bed."

Livingstone potatoes are common among both the Iwa and Mambwe and are generally grown among the Bemba (as described by Richards) except that they may be grown on pit-mounds. A series of holes is dug, and the potatoes are planted on the soil heaped up between holes.

Among some of the Iwa, early gardens of beans and maize are planted in moist areas near streams in October, and grown several years running.

The Bangweulu-Luapula Area

Several tribes — the Chisinga, Mukulu, eastern Lunda, and portions of the Bisa, Shila, Swahili,[7] and Tabwa — practice a form of chitemene that resembles the southern and western Bemba system more than any other but involves more felling of trees, greater dependence on manioc, and several differences in crop sequences and garden techniques.

The Mukulu and Bisa, adjacent to the Bemba on the west, plant peanuts on the flat the second year, as do the southern and western Bemba; but elsewhere peanuts are usually grown on mounds (*360*, p. 59). Among some of the Tabwa, however, finger millet may be substituted for peanuts the second year.[8]

Rice Fields

Rice is grown by the Bisa near Lake Bangweulu and by the Tabwa, Lungu, and Swahili. In areas with moist soil, branches are lopped off trees and burned; then rice is broadcast in the ashes, as with finger millet. The next year, and possibly for two or three succeeding years, the plot is hoed and again planted to rice without further treatment (*360*, p. 62). Occasionally, but apparently rarely, the plot is opened by hoeing up grass and burning it, then planting rice in holes.

Among the Tabwa and Swahili, mounds may be made near villages or in grassland at the end of the rains and left unplanted; at the beginning of the next rains, they are spread and planted to rice; in each of the next two to four years the plot is hoed over and planted to rice again. After three or four crops such a plot may be fallowed a year or two; it is then sown with rice one additional year (*360*, p. 62). Alternatively, the sequence may be altered by growing manioc on mounds made the first year, or by growing manioc on the flat at the end of a rice, rice, rice sequence.

Garden Cultivation

Manioc is the major crop in village gardens, and is grown on mounds. Peanuts and finger millet are grown on flat beds made by spreading mounds, among the western Bisa and among some of the Chisinga and Tabwa. In other areas garden practices are similar to those of the more southerly Bemba, except that cultivation of old village sites is not general and a greater amount of fruit is grown among the Swahili and neighboring Tabwa (*360*, p. 63).

The Luapula Valley

The Luapula Valley contains a very mixed population composed principally of Chisinga, Lunda, Shila, and Bwile. Trapnell describes it as a "narrow strip of dense population" but he gives no estimate of the population density per square kilometer.

In general there is great diversity of agricultural methods. Manioc is the major crop in much of the area; chitemene finger millet is found in some areas but not everywhere. The methods of growing finger millet vary but are roughly the same as those of the Chisinga.[9] Typically manioc is grown on rectangular or round mounds made by turning turf under, the manurial value of turf being recognized. Mounds are planted with manioc and peanuts or Bambara nuts; with manioc, maize, beans, and cowpeas; or with manioc, maize, cowpeas, and pumpkins or *Mankolobwe* cucumbers.

Garden Cultivation

Three types of gardens are distinguished: early maize and banana gardens, rice gardens, and village gardens. Among the Bwile, gardens are made near streams in September and planted to an early-maturing maize, beans, pumpkins, and a few potato yams and *Gynandropsis*. Bananas are planted along the edge of gardens, or they may be grown on separate plots nearby and interplanted with sugarcane, beans, and pumpkins.

Both the Bwile and Shila near Lake Mweru grow rice on plots near maize fields or near the stream gardens (*360*, p. 72). Grass is hoed down or cut in September or October and burned where it lies; then the plot may be hoed again to mix the ash with the soil. In November maize is planted every 2 or 3 meters and interplanted with beans, and sometimes with pumpkins or *Gynandropsis*. When maize plants are about 6 inches high, rice is planted, three or four seeds being placed in each hole. (Along the lower Lufu, a minor tributary of the Luapula, four or five seeds per hole are usually planted; planting begins before the first rains in October on the wetter plots and may continue through December.) Parts of the field in which planted rice does not germinate are replanted with seedlings; no information is given on where the seedlings come from (*360*, p. 72).

At least in the Lufu Valley, raised shelters are built in rice gardens for watchers who protect the field from birds and hippos (*360*, p. 72). Rice is harvested in April or May.

Everywhere in the Luapula Valley gardens are made near the house. Mounds are constructed and planted to manioc, maize, Asiatic and white yams, beans, pumpkins, two kinds of tobacco — *Nicotiana rustica* and *N. tabacum* — castor beans, roselle, *Tephrosia*, shallots, lima beans, chilies, sesame, *Gynandropsis*, and sometimes Irish potatoes. Bananas may be planted in pits filled with rubbish.

In Bwile villages Livingstone potatoes, mangoes, pineapples, sugarcane, and some guavas, lemons, kapok trees, and physic nuts are also grown. Oil palms have been planted near villages in some areas, particularly in the north between Lake Mweru and Mbereshi about 50 kilometers south of it (*360*, p. 73).

The Southern Tabwa

The Tabwa south and west of the Zambia-Congo border follow the Chisinga type of chitemene already discussed, but the rest of the southern Tabwa — those in thicket areas — practice a special variant.

From April until September rectangular blocks of thicket are cut and the vegetation left to dry where it falls. In October the clearing is burned; finger millet is sown in December, alone or mixed with a little bulrush millet. Seeds are covered by throwing soil over them with a hoe, as described for chitemene agriculture elsewhere. In subsequent years when millet seeds are broadcast in old millet stubble, seeds are "scratched into the stubble with a forked stick" (*360*, p. 64). Cattle melons, edible gourds, cowpeas, and *Mankolobwe* cucumbers are about the only associated crops planted. A little maize may be included, but usually is not, because monkeys would damage it. This finger millet association is repeated until weed growth forces the field to be abandoned, or until yields become unsatisfactory; millet is sometimes grown for four consecutive years (*360*, p. 64).

The field is not weeded. Guards are stationed in stockaded huts in the field at times to keep out game. Trapnell states that because of annual fires little or no regeneration of thicket takes place when the field is abandoned; he predicts that this system is doomed.

Garden Cultivation

Fairly large gardens are made near the villages, and may be enclosed by a trench or fence. Manioc gardens are always protected in this way "because of elephant and other game" (*360*, p. 63). Mounds are made; maize, and possibly cowpeas, are planted on the sides; peanuts or sweet potatoes with pumpkins, edible gourds, or *Mankolobwe* cucumbers are planted on top of the mounds when the maize is about 20 cm. high. Sorghum is also grown on mounds and dolichos or lima beans are grown at the base of stumps.

Manioc is grown on separate mounds which may include a little maize or peanuts. Manioc mounds are "commonly much larger" than those of the maize association, and a great deal of grass is turned under in making them (*360*, p. 64). Manioc mounds may be flattened for millet.

After a year or two of maize and associated crops, some of the mounds are flattened and sown with finger millet, sorghum, or possibly rice. If finger millet is planted, some maize is planted first. The following year mounds may be made again and the maize association repeated. Thus, a maize, millet sequence is followed until the soil is exhausted.

Rice gardens are usually located in valley bottoms, where mounds are made in December and planted to sweet potatoes, sometimes to maize. The next year these mounds are flattened and sown to rice interplanted with maize. Mounds may be made again the third year, but if not, rice is planted for several consecutive years. Sometimes the plot is guarded by a game-watcher who sits in a small shelter supported on poles (*360*, p. 65).

Near huts maize, pumpkins, pineapples, papayas, bananas, prickly pears, castor beans, physic nuts, lemon grass, loofah gourds, and kapok trees may be grown.

A small group of villages on the northwestern side of the Mweru-Wantipa swamps specializes in salt making and has no main fields; food not bought is produced in special gardens. New gardens are started by making large mounds planted with a sweet potatoes/manioc association mixed with some maize. Alternatively, grass may be cut and burned when dry, then the ash patch hoed and sown to finger millet. If finger millet is sown the first year, mounds are made the second year, and the manioc/sweet potato association is planted. When mounds are made the first year, they are spread the second year and finger millet is sown. After millet has been planted twice, manioc and peanuts are usually planted on the flat, and the plot is thereafter abandoned (*360*, p. 65).

MODIFIED ASH-DEPENDENT SYSTEMS

The Lala, Lamba, Ndembu, and part of the Bisa and Kaonde follow a modified chitemene agriculture which involves smaller burned patches than those of the Bemba, combined with mounds made between the burned patches.

The Lala of the Serenje Plateau

A land usage survey from September to December 1945 by D. U. Peters, then an agricultural officer in Northern Rhodesia, and a nutritional survey from 1947 to April 1948 by Betty Preston Tompson provide a fairly detailed outline of the Lala agricultural system. Both surveys describe mainly the Lala on the Serenje Plateau.

The Lala live in small villages of around fifty people which are moved about every five years. Forty-nine moves recorded by Peters averaged 5.5 years, the average distance involved being about 8 kilometers (*289*, p. 51). Population density averages 2.8 persons per square kilometer, according to Peters, but varies from 2.2 to 4.2 persons per square kilometer in individual chieftaincies.

Finger millet is the staple crop, and minor crops appear to be the same as those listed for the Bemba, with the addition of taro. A few cattle are kept in some villages, but cattle are not common (*289*, p. 41). Goats are not numerous, and no sheep are found (*289*, p. 85). Most families have chickens; a few also have ducks or pigeons (*350*, p. 42).

Field Cultivation

The technique of field clearing used by the Lala is called "small circle" chitemene by Peters, Trapnell, and others because a cultivator's clearing comprises several burned circles rather than one large one. Peters found considerable variation in the diameter of circles. Circles in plots of sixteen cultivators chosen at random varied from 3 to 9 meters, but tended to be the same size in any plot. Most of the burned areas were fairly close to true circles, the two diameters measured at right angles differing less than 36 cm. in length; in 57 percent of the circles measured the difference was less than 18 cm. (*289*, p. 88). The number of circles counted in 44 plots varied from 40 to 410 (*289*, p. 87). In some parts of the cultivated plot, rectangular strips rather than circles may be made if the supply of nearby branches is sufficient.

Usually about fourteen times more land was cleared than was planted, in order to obtain the thickness of ash desired. On the average 4.5 hectares of woodland per cultivator were cleared yearly, 97 percent to produce ashes and 3 percent for fencing.[10] Trees are typically cut down at breast height, although occasionally large or hardwood trees are merely trimmed of their branches. The limbs of felled trees are cut off and arranged in a circular stack, often around a stump. Tree trunks are discarded (*360*, p. 40).

Planting and care of finger millet appear to be the same as for the Bemba, except that a smaller portion of the area cultivated is planted to gourds and pumpkins; only a few of the finger millet patches are the borders planted to these crops. The borders of the remaining finger millet circles are apparently left vacant; "Very occasionally a few castor oil seeds are planted" (*289*, p. 8).

A second field type contains sorghum or maize as the dominant crop. Clearing is the same as for finger millet, but burned patches are planted with sorghum, maize, or a mixture of the two. Mounds made between the burned areas are usually planted to sorghum, sometimes mixed with cowpeas, peanuts, or manioc. Some mounds are reserved for sweet potatoes, and others for beans. Later in the season additional mounds may be constructed on the perimeter of the cultivated plot, some of which are planted with seedlings obtained while thinning sorghum. Others are planted with associations of beans and manioc or sweet potatoes and manioc.

Maize fields are cleared and cultivated in the same manner as sorghum fields, but are more frequently located in valley bottoms. Usually more mounds and fewer burned patches are found in maize fields than in sorghum fields because of the shortage of trees in valley bottoms. Maize interplanted with beans and pumpkins or cowpeas is usually grown on the burned patches, and manioc is established on the mounds.

Manioc fields are nearly always found in valley bottoms, where there is little vegetation for ash production; therefore the field is mostly mounds, and burned patches are rare (*289*, p. 10). Each mound is planted with five or six manioc cuttings and perhaps some maize, sorghum, or cowpeas.

Garden Cultivation

Except for small beds of tobacco, there are almost no village gardens, but sorghum fields are located near villages (*360*, p. 45). Gardens made on seepage sites in valleys are planted with maize, beans, and pumpkins. Circles of cultivated ground about 1.6 meters in diameter are made by hoeing grass and turf under in June or July. The turf is burned in August and maize and pumpkins are planted; beans, and sometimes peas, are planted when the maize harvest begins in December. Alternatively, grass and branches from nearby trees may be piled on seepage areas and burned, then maize, beans, and pumpkins are planted (*289*, p. 11).

Special gardens are made in valleys for Livingstone potatoes, with manioc sometimes planted as a border, but no description is given of techniques used (*289*, p. 11).

Peters states that minor crops grown in gardens are gourds, cucumbers, castor beans, and peas; very minor crops are peanuts, potatoes, yams, *Tephrosia*, tobacco, taro, and *Solanum*. No description is given of methods by which any of these crops are grown (*289*, p. 94).

Crop Sequences

Finger millet, sorghum, maize, manioc, beans, and pumpkins may be planted the first year in the sequence (Figure 4-4). On only 7.5 percent of the burned part of the finger millet fields, Bambara nuts, peanuts, or cowpeas were planted the second year (*289*, p. 76); the rest of the field was returned to bush after one year of cultivation. No information is given on what crop follows sorghum in sorghum fields, but usually cultivation continues three or four years. In maize fields, maize and sweet potatoes are grown the second year, but there is no information about later crops. Manioc fields apparently last several years from a single planting, because the plant is left growing when the mature roots are harvested. Peters

FIGURE 4-4 Lala Crop Sequences, 1945

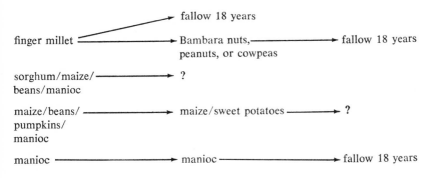

Based on D. U. Peters: *289*, pp. 76–92.

implies that in manioc fields the original planting of manioc occupies the soil until it is returned to bush.

Although Peters was unable to establish the full pattern of crop sequences, he recorded the average length of cultivation of fields and gardens as follows (*289*, p. 92):

Type of cultivation	Number of plots sampled	Average length of cultivation (years)
Sorghum field	32	4
Maize field	32	5
Manioc field	13	3–4
Seepage gardens	23	3

The Bisa

Trapnell describes the Bisa agricultural system as similar in some ways to that of the Bemba, but in other ways more like that of the Lala. Bisa living near the Bemba practice the Bemba system of chitemene; Bisa near the Lala follow the Lala system of small circles (*360*, p. 41). Where small circle chitemene is practiced, however, sorghum fields may be modified. Some Bisa plant the burned circles in the sorghum field to finger millet or peanuts, while intervening areas are made into mounds and sown to sorghum, or to sorghum mixed with sweet potatoes or manioc. Mounds on old sorghum fields (those over three or four years old) located near the village may be spread out and planted to peanuts.

The Bisa have the same garden types as the Lala, and in addition, make village gardens in which they grow such things as vegetables, yams, bananas, sugarcane, pigeon peas, cotton, peanuts, lemon grass, and *Solanum* (*360*, pp. 42–45). In gardens on seepage sites, the Bisa may not hoe off the grass as the Lala do, but instead cut it and place it in coils on the plot. Earth is then hoed up in a circle about a meter in diameter around the coils so that the edges of the grass are covered; then the grass is burned.

The Eastern Kaonde

Among the eastern Kaonde, agriculture generally resembles that of the Lala, but only about twice the area to be cultivated is usually cleared in order to obtain ash. The branches of felled trees are piled in circles or in broad strips. The first year, the ash is "scuffed" with a hoe and maize is planted very sparsely, then sorghum is broadcast throughout and covered with a light hoeing. Small amounts of sesame, cucurbits, and cowpeas are interplanted with sorghum. Mounds are made on the un-burned area between circles and strips that have been fired, and are planted with small amounts of sesame, cowpeas, and cucurbits. Garden methods are described as generally the same as for the western Kaonde, discussed on p. 00.

Crop Sequences

On the main sorghum fields, the plot is hoed the second year, and any readily available partially burned branches or other refuse are burned on the old ash patches. Maize and a little sesame are planted on burned patches, and sorghum is broadcast throughout. The third year little if anything is grown, although fresh mounds are sometimes made and planted with sweet potatoes. The plot is always abandoned by the fourth year (*361*, p. 27).

The Ndembu

E. L. B. Turner and V. W. Turner collected data on Ndembu agriculture in 1951 and 1952 while studying the growth of cash-cropping among the Ndembu in recent years. Manioc is the principal crop; finger millet is grown chiefly for beer making; and maize, rice, sweet potatoes, yams, beans, peanuts, cucurbits, and a number of European vegetables such as tomatoes, cabbage, and Irish potatoes are mentioned; but no basis is provided for judging their relative importance (*363*, pp. 19–20). No cattle are kept, and "only a limited number" of small livestock is raised (*363*, p. 20).

Fields are cleared by a type of chitemene much like that of the eastern Kaonde. Trees are felled and their branches placed in irregular piles which collectively occupy one-fourth to one-eighth of the total area cleared. Finger millet is usually sown in the burned patches, but some burned patches may be hoed into mounds and planted with maize, pumpkins, and "other cucurbits" (*361*, p. 31). Soil between burned patches is made into mounds and planted with manioc sparsely interplanted with sweet potatoes and cowpeas. The second year, manioc planted the first year continues to grow, and remaining patches burned the first year are made into mounds and planted with manioc. At the same time any unburned branches cut the first year are burned between mounds, and cucurbits are planted in the ashes. Manioc harvest begins in the eighteenth month and continues through the thirtieth month after planting; then the field is allowed to revert to natural vegetation for about thirty years (*363*, p. 20).

The Lamba

The Lamba also follow the same agricultural system as the eastern Kaonde, with a few exceptions. Pumpkins and gourds planted on the border of sorghum fields are characteristic of the Lamba, as is the cultivation of old village sites. Except for tobacco, which is grown in the village, principally on anthills (*115*, p. 108), few if any gardens are found in Lamba villages, garden efforts being concentrated on old village sites, on maize gardens in valleys, and on Livingstone potato gardens. (Livingstone potatoes are planted one year and allowed to come up voluntarily the second year, as a new garden is started and the old one is abandoned [*361*, p. 28].)

C. M. Doke, a missionary, describes protection of sorghum fields. About seven weeks before harvest, small shelters are erected on anthills, and watchers — mainly women, children, and the aged — are dispatched to these shelters morning and evening when birds are most active (*115*, p. 112).

5

Compost-Dependent Systems

Various sorts of composting operations are reported as an integral part of preparing fields in some of the southern savannas. After vegetation is cut it is buried in mounds in the field, or perhaps the debris is first burned and the ashes are buried.

The method of composting in the field used by the Tio (Teke) of Congo (Brazzaville), by the Sundi of Niari Valley, and in a sector of Thysville territoire, former Belgian Congo, is unusual because debris is buried in mounds, then ignited. This practice is also described for some parts of the southern Kwango, under the general heading of classic long fallow (Chapter 3, pp. 74–76), and for some secondary plots among part of the ash-dependent systems discussed in Chapter 4, pp. 111–13.

Composting seems to be suited only to savannas.[1] Where both savanna and forest areas are available to a tribe composting is never reported for forest cultivations.

The Grassland Mambwe

Part of Mambwe country is woodland; elsewhere grassland prevails. Woodland areas are cleared by a variant of the ash-dependent system of the Bemba that has been discussed above (p. 111). In grassland areas refuse is buried in mounds. Trapnell speculates that the grassland areas near the

Tanganyika border were originally woodland and that population pressure has eliminated most trees and forced abandonment of ash-dependent methods (*360*, p. 56).

When new fields are opened, in February or March, grass too long to be easily covered in hoeing is cut with a long knife and piled with a hay fork. This grass and any other vegetation is then stacked around stumps and later burned. Top soil is then thrown around the border of these piles, and the rest of the land is hoed up into mounds that may be 2 to 2.6 meters in diameter, "by means of a longish hoe" (*360*, p. 57). Grass that is not too long to be easily covered may be left uncut in the center of the mound to rot.

These mounds are planted mainly to beans, but some manioc, small cowpeas, or sweet potatoes[2] may also be grown on them. Beans are harvested in June; apparently the other crops are harvested later. In November or early December the remaining vines and stalks of harvested crops, and any weeds which have grown on the mounds, are "scraped down from the mounds . . . to rot between them" (*360*, p. 57). In December maize is planted around the sides of the mounds, and "gourds, pumpkins, etc." are planted on burned patches, sometimes with castor beans as a border (Figure 5-1). Around January 1 maize is sown broadcast on the mounds. The mounds are then spread in order to cover the broadcast seed and rotting material between mounds. When the first maize sown has reached about 65 cm. in height (towards February 1), finger millet is broadcast, often with some sorghum. The seeds are covered by throwing soil with a hoe — as described for the Bemba (p. 113). Fields are weeded with a small hoe when the finger millet plants are about 7 cm. high. We are not told whether thinning is practiced, or how many times the field is weeded.

Finger millet is harvested in April. The field is apparently unoccupied except for sorghum until the following December, when mounds are made as before and maize is planted on the sides. When maize is about 20 cm. high, finger millet is sown. An alternative procedure is to plant peanuts on the mounds instead of finger millet. Maize is not sown a second time.

If the maize-millet succession is planted three consecutive years, planting methods the third year are the same as the first; maize is sown twice and mounds are spread to cover it and form the millet bed. If circumstances force delay of millet planting beyond the optimum period in January, beans or peas may be planted the third year and followed by maize-finger millet the next year (Figure 5-1). Millet is generally planted until the growth of grass or weeds forces a fallow of three or more years.

FIGURE 5-1   Grassland Mambwe Crop Sequences

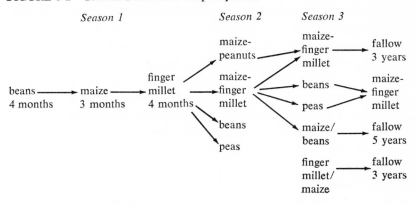

Based on Trapnell: *360*, pp. 56–58.

Special peanut fields are sometimes made on old millet fields that have been fallowed; mounds may be made here but usually are not. Typically, pits are dug around such plots to protect them from wild pigs (*360*, p. 58).

Garden Cultivation

The Mambwe living in grassland areas make special maize gardens in moist places; and old millet fields near the village may be planted to maize, beans, and pumpkins. Small patches of tobacco are sometimes established on old village sites. "The potato yam and a few other minor crops are grown in the village itself and mounded beds of European potatoes are occasionally seen" (*360*, p. 58). Otherwise old village sites are cultivated with the same crops as are grown in the village. Livingstone potatoes are known, but their cultivation is rare.[3]

The Fipa

The agriculture of the portion of the Fipa living near Lake Tanganyika and on the plateau running along its southwestern shore is based on compost mounds like that of the grassland Mambwe. The Fipa near Lake Rukwa do not employ composting. On the plateau the dominant staple is finger millet, but maize, manioc, sweet potatoes, Bambara nuts, and lima beans are also important crops (*424*, p. 23). Minor crops mentioned are spinach, cucurbits, Irish potatoes, tomatoes, onions, chilies, wheat, and coffee. (Crops that are important in the Rukwa Valley but not on the plateau are sorghum, bananas, papayas, oranges, limes, mangoes, and tobacco.) Cattle, sheep, goats, and poultry are raised.

Clearing is usually done in March or April, toward the end of the rainy season. Sod is dug up with a special curved hoe and piled in mounds with grass and weeds turned inward. Mounds are two-thirds of a meter high, 1 to 1.3 meters in diameter at the base, and arranged in rows about 30 cm. apart. In addition to mounds, a special plot is also prepared by making "an oval or circular wall of earth . . . inside which the residue of grass and weeds as well as branches and small bushes are thrown to dry" (*424*, p. 23). The debris is then burned on these special plots, the ash is distributed over the circle, and cucurbits are planted.

Mounds may be left unplanted until the beginning of the rainy season seven or eight months later, or may be planted with a quick crop, such as beans. In October they are weeded and the weeds left on top. In November or December, after the rains have begun, the mounds are broken down and finger millet or maize is sown, sometimes interplanted with manioc.

The following June or July maize and millet are harvested and small mounds are made over stalks, weeds, and other debris. The next January (about a month after rains have begun) these small mounds are broken down and planted with maize or millet, usually the latter. The third wet season — usually the terminal year in the sequence — the field is typically hoed into ridges and planted with maize, beans, and other field crops, excepting millet.

The Pende

The clearing method of the Pende of Kwango resembles that of the Mambwe. Mounds are made, debris being buried in them while much of it is still green (*47*, pp. 63–69). Whether fields are ever burned is not clear, but there is comment that mounds are made before the period of "bush fires," and because of fear of these annual fires the Pende reportedly never let a plot lie fallow more than nine months (*47*, p. 63).

The Koukouya Plateau

Most of the data on the Tio (Teke) come from a 1949 article in which Louis Papy, director of the Institut de Géographie de la Faculté des Lettres de Bordeaux, sketches the agricultural system on the Batéké Plateau of Moyen-Congo, and from a 1960 article by Gilles Sautter.

Almost the entire region is savanna, and all of Papy's description is for savanna areas. The average population density on the Koukouya portion of the Batéké Plateau is estimated at about twenty persons per square kilometer (*314*, p. 12).

Manioc is the dominant staple foodstuff. Yams, sweet potatoes, Irish potatoes, maize, peanuts, tomatoes, eggplant, and tobacco are other crops listed, but their relative importance is not indicated (*283*, pp. 123–25). Small patches of rice are sometimes grown in low places. Bananas-plantains are grown around huts. Goats and poultry are the only domestic animals kept.

Three kinds of soil are identified and named, and each has its characteristic crop associations and sequences. Exhausted, tight soils are called *sissyémé* or *sessyou*; those of medium fertility are *likouba*; and the richest soils, those with the highest natural vegetation, are *boukou*. Old village sites are referred to as *makouba*. The length of fallows varies from short fallows of a single year for good *boukou* to seven or eight years for the worst *sissyémé (314*, p. 16).

The first step in opening a field is to burn it. This is done during the dry season between mid-July and the first of September. Grass is cut, piled, covered with soil, and then ignited (*283*, p. 123). These soil-grass mounds burn slowly and receive no further attention until the beginning of the rainy season, when crops are planted on them.[4] As the rains begin in October, the fields are hoed again, mounds are remade, and manioc, yams, or sweet potatoes are planted on them, the last two being planted much less frequently than manioc. Maize, tobacco, tomatoes, and eggplant are also planted in the manioc field. Tobacco may be grown alone in a special field. There is no mention of whether crops are mounded, or of what planting distances or planting techniques are.

Peanuts are often planted in separate fields, but may be grown with manioc. Two crops of peanuts can be grown per season, the first being planted in October and harvested in February, the second planted in February and harvested in June. Peanut fields are usually hoed three times — once to remove vegetation, once to level the ground, and a third time as the crop is planted (*314*, p. 17).

Crop Sequence

Roger Prevost gives the following sequences as typical (*297*, p. 16): (a) peanuts four months, manioc three years, and fallow two to four years; (b) beans four months, fallow eight months, tobacco, and fallow two years; and (c) tobacco four months, tobacco four months, and fallow two years.

According to Sautter boukou land is planted with peanuts, two crops a year, followed by a manioc/maize/gourds association, to which tobacco, Irish potatoes, or beans are sometimes added. Likouba may be planted with peanuts followed by a manioc/gourds/maize association; alternatively it may be planted with tobacco or a tobacco/manioc association (*314*, pp. 14–15).

The Mbé Plateau

Data on the Mbé portion of the Batéké Plateau, about 125 kilometers northeast of Brazzaville, come from unpublished 1963–64 field notes kindly provided by Jan Vansina. The area is sparsely populated (only 0.3 to 0.5 persons per square kilometer). Manioc is the dominant staple, but at least thirty other crops are grown, largely the same ones as on the Koukouya Plateau. The only livestock are goats, dogs, chickens, and a few ducks. Clearing techniques are similar to those on the Koukouya Plateau except that compost in mounds is not burned.

In savanna areas a field is opened by hoeing a square block into a raised bed (or sometimes hiring it plowed by tractor first). Peanuts are planted in the center and manioc on the edges of this bed. When the peanuts are harvested mounds are made around the remaining manioc (three or four stalks per mound), and the peanut vines are dug into other mounds made in the middle of the original squares. Such crops as yams, eggplant, cabbage, tobacco, and onions are then planted on the mounds in the center of the squares.

Trial plots where young girls exhibit their skill as cultivators are a second type of savanna field. Located near the village (around holes for soaking manioc), these are planted to peanuts, Bambara nuts, squash, gourds, bananas, or pineapples.

In forest areas trees and undergrowth are cut, the debris burned, and a tobacco/maize association or sugarcane is planted. Tobacco is typically followed by a maize/manioc association, then fallowed seven or eight years (until trees are as thick as a man's arm).

Other types of cultivation are fenced gardens near the hut where bananas, kola nut trees, and cabbage are carefully planted. Kola trees are often planted in small pits filled with a mixture of rich soil and straw. Such plots may also contain *safou* (*Pachylobus edulis*) and oil palm trees, but there are no longer planted although they were in the first decade or two of this century.

The Kamba of the Niari Valley

Sautter, in a 1955 article, describes the agricultural methods of the Kamba group of the Sundi that occupies the Niari Valley. Two clearing techniques are employed: the cut, burn, hoe, plant method and that of burning debris within mounds. There is no clear indication as to which method is more important; hence we have arbitrarily classified the Kamba under the least widely reported of the two methods.

Field Cultivation

If the field is burned before mounding, grass is cut with a hoe toward either the beginning or the end of the dry season; it is burned just before the rains start. After the fire dies the incompletely burned grass roots are collected in piles and reignited; the field is then hoed (*313*, pp. 81–82).

When debris is buried in mounds and burned, vegetation of the field is cut as before, but is placed in rectangular piles 2 or 3 meters long, over which earth is pulled with a hoe. These piles are then ignited and allowed to smolder. (In the western part of the area the mounds are circular.) Weeds and other debris taken from the field after crops have been planted are collected in piles at the edge of the field, covered with earth, burned, and planted to crops demanding especially fertile beds.

Crop Associations and Sequences

Angole or pigeon peas (*Cajanus indicus*) and sugarcane are the only crops grown alone; they are planted about a month and a half before the end of the rains; harvest is toward the end of the dry season. The principal crop association, yams/maize/gourds, is initiated with the planting of yams on mounds at the beginning of the rains; these are then interplanted with maize and gourds.[5] The field is weeded only once. Maize is harvested two to two and a half months after planting (in January or early February), and a little later the gourds mature. At the harvest of maize and gourds the field is again weeded and pigeon peas or beans are planted among the growing yams. Weeds removed are piled in rectangular heaps along the side of the field; earth is hoed over them; and they are burned, as described earlier; maize and beans are planted here later.

In March, about a month after the gourds are harvested, maize again is planted among the yams, and bananas-plantains are planted to replace the gourds. Occasionally bananas-plantains are planted initially instead of gourds. When bananas-plantains are associated with yams, peanuts and maize are typically planted among the banana-plantain plants after the yams are harvested. Sugarcane may be planted with bananas-plantains, but it is often grown alone in valley bottoms. Pineapples or tobacco are usually planted on some of the mounds of the yam/maize/gourd field. Beans are planted on mounds in separate fields at the beginning of the rains and are also interplanted with maize and manioc. Peanuts are interplanted with either manioc or bananas-plantains. Manioc fields are interplanted with maize, peanuts, or pigeon peas.

Crop sequences vary considerably within the Niari Valley, but six sequences are found fairly widely. The most common is peanuts, manioc repeated several times. Three other crop sequences begin with pulses, and two sequences start with the yams/maize/gourds association (Figure 5-2).

FIGURE 5-2   Kamba Crop Sequences, 1955

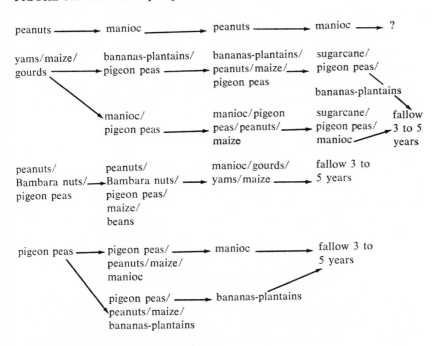

Based on Sautter: *313*, pp. 81–101.

All sequences terminate with bananas-plantains or manioc or an association which includes one or the other. Fallows are only three to five years, an unusually short period for the Congo Basin, which Sautter attributes to the quality of the soil and the fact that a large portion of the crops grown is legumes (*313*, p. 101).

Garden Cultivation

Bananas and probably other crops are grown in gardens near the house. Old village sites are cultivated, but again the only crop specifically mentioned is bananas-plantains (*313*, pp. 93–94). Gardens are also made in alluvial soils and planted to vegetables.

Dunga-Lukanga Sector, Thysville Territoire

In Dunga-Lukanga sector, Thysville territoire, former Belgian Congo, mounds are made and burned in the same manner as on the Koukouya Plateau; but crop sequences are different. Dunga-Lukanga sequences reported in 1955 are either maize/manioc/beans, then manioc two or three years, followed by fallow three to five years, or peanuts/beans/manioc/pigeon peas, then manioc two or three years, followed by two to four years of fallow (*47*, p. 78).

Luozi and Matadi Territoires

In savanna zones, clearing is the same as in the Dunga-Lukanga area;[6] but in the forest areas vegetation is cut, burned, and the soil hoed. Savanna crop sequences are peanuts, maize, manioc, then manioc, then yams, and finally either two years of fallow or a peanut-maize succession (peanuts planted in October; maize planted the following February), followed by two years of fallow (*47*, p. 84). For forest areas maize/manioc or maize, bananas-plantains, then manioc or bananas-plantains, followed by five or six years of fallow is reported (*47*, p. 83). In addition to these sequences, "the common sequences of Bas-Congo" are said to be employed (*47*, p. 83).

The Boko Area

In the Boko area of Congo (Brazzaville), adjacent to Luozi territoire on its eastern border, the same clearing techniques (both forest and savanna) are found, but a third field type — sugarcane plots and vegetable gardens in moist depressions — is also mentioned in a study by Sautter. Sequences reported are less complex than those of the Luozi area. In the Boko forest belt no sequence is indicated; and in the savanna it is simply manioc, peanuts or the same crops in the reverse order (*312*, p. 68).

6

Short-Fallow Systems

Greatly reduced dependence on fallows is the outstanding feature of the agricultural systems of a cluster of predominantly temperate, high altitude areas on the eastern rim of the Congo Basin: Rwanda, Burundi; some adjacent areas, the Beni-Lubero region near Lake Edward, and the area occupied by the Lugbara north of Lake Albert.

Use of animal manures as fertilizer on some main fields and, in some areas, terracing and irrigation are suggestive of permanent field agriculture; but accounts available indicate that dependence on shifting cultivation in some main fields continues, although fallow periods typically are not nearly so long relative to the cropping period as in the classic long-fallow system.[1]

This type of agriculture resembles the infield-outfield system in that permanent field agriculture, made possible by use of animal manures and composts, is found near the homestead, while shifting cultivation prevails on the more distant outfields. However, not all outfields are necessarily characterized by shifting cultivation. Riverine areas, and, in some places, parts of the upland outfields may be unfallowed and permanent.[2]

The Bututsi Region

Short-fallow agriculture is described by De Schlippe (*107*) as characteristic of the Bututsi agricultural region in southern Burundi,[3] but less

143

thorough accounts of other areas suggest that it may be found throughout Rwanda-Burundi (*99*).

Most of Rwanda-Burundi is a high plateau 1,500 to 2,500 meters above sea level. The vegetation is almost entirely tall-grass savanna, except along the western edge of the region, where at the higher altitudes a thin strip of forest is found, most of it uncultivated reserve.

The population density was estimated at 88 persons per square kilometer in 1960 (*45*, p. 9). In 1949 it varied from 27 persons in Kibumpu territoire in southeastern Ruanda to 147 in Kitega territoire in central Urundi. The median density by territoire was 84 persons per square kilometer (*45*, p. 9). Areas of greatest population concentration are along the shore of Lake Kivu and in the north-central and south-central sections of the country (*45*, Map 2).

Homesteads are established, and fields near them are regularly fertilized with manure collected in a large pile behind the hut, or with compost.[4] Cattle, sheep, goats, and poultry are kept everywhere. Major field types seem generally to be groves of bananas-plantains, fields of annual crops near the hut, and special marsh gardens. Some irrigation is usually practiced, ditches and even wood ducts being used to divert water from streams to fields.

Sixteen different tools are described (Figure 6-1). A hatchet and an adze are sometimes used in clearing fields; two long-handled hoes — one with a rectangular blade and one with an elliptical blade — are used to clear fields, make mounds, and destroy weeds; two types of spearheads are used to harvest millet and sorghum and to peel roots; and five types of long-handled hook knives are employed in cutting grass or maize, sorghum, or banana stems.

By acreage, maize is the most important single crop in the Bututsi zone, with an estimated 27 percent of staple crop acreage; beans are second with 20 percent; and sweet potatoes, sorghum, and peas are third, fourth, and fifth, respectively, with from 10 to 11 percent of staple crop average each. Wheat, manioc, Irish potatoes, and coleus potatoes each account for less than two percent of staple crop acreage (*45*, p. 355).

In each of the three field types, finger millet is the first crop after fallow. When a new homestead is established because of growth of the family — homesteads are not moved once established — a hilltop is cleared, a hut is built, and finger millet is planted around the hut. In subsequent years a grove of bananas-plantains will be established in part of this field, and the rest will support the other crops mentioned, plus some taro and gourds. Both the banana-plantain grove and the adjacent homestead plots are kept in continuous cultivation by use of fertilizers. Some distance from the homestead, on the hillside or perhaps adjacent to it, other fields are cleared each year and planted with finger millet. The size

FIGURE 6-1   Agricultural Tools of the Rundi

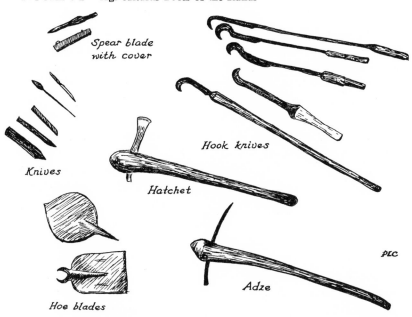

Spear blade with cover

Knives

Hook knives

Hatchet

Adze

PLC

Hoe blades

Based on Pierre de Schlippe, "Enquête préliminaire du système agricole des Barundi de la région Bututsi," *Bull. Agri. du Congo Belge,* Aug., 1957, p. 830. Figure: Food Research Institute.

of these unfertilized fields relative to homestead plots depends largely on the size of the farmer's manure pile, which is placed near the hut in a conspicuous spot and is a matter of pride, since it reflects the size of the farmer's herd. The final field type consists of cultivations in marshes, where finger millet and sweet potatoes alternate year after year.

New land is cleared by hoeing it roughly — enough to turn the turf over at the end of the rainy season or the beginning of the dry season (mid-May to mid-July) — then hoeing it again to break up the turf and clods of earth. At the same time, grass and roots are gathered and placed in small piles in the field to be burned in August just before the rains begin (*109*, p. 842).

On the day of the burning, or the next day, ash piles are spread out with a hoe. Nothing more is done until the rains come. After two or three rains have fallen, finger millet is broadcast and the field is hoed lightly to cover the seed and kill any noxious plants that have begun to grow. Any grass remaining after this hoeing is pulled by hand. The next weeding is two or three months later, a little before harvesting.

When finger millet is grown after another crop, the land is prepared from December to January with a single hoeing, a lighter one than is given new fields. In this operation small vertical blows that do not displace the earth are used, and maize is immediately planted in widely spaced holes.[5] There is no burning or leveling of the soil. When the maize is 30 to 40 cm. tall, finger millet is sown broadcast, and the field is hoed to cover the seed and kill weeds; the subsequent operations are the same as for finger millet on new land.

For beans, a crop never planted on newly cleared land, the first planting operation is spreading fertilizer on the field in early October or late September. Immediately afterward, the field is hoed lightly to remove grass. Two weeks later a deeper hoeing is given, mounds are made, and beans plus maize or peas are planted in the holes which are made in the mounds.[6] About a month after sowing, the field is weeded by hand.

Other fields are prepared in the same fashion, but are planted with a mixture of maize and gourds, or sweet potatoes. When sorghum is to be planted, maize is sown alone as soon as the soil is prepared; about a month later, when the grass is 30 to 40 cm. high and nearly as tall as the maize, the field is hoed again, and sorghum and gourds are sown broadcast (*109*, p. 850). As with finger millet, the day after the sowing the field is hand-weeded to eliminate any remaining weeds or grass that might compete with the sorghum. A little later, when the sorghum is 10 to 15 cm. tall, the field is weeded with a hoe.

Crops that may follow unfertilized finger millet on the hillsides are sweet potatoes and coleus potatoes. Any time between November and March sweet potatoes are planted in mounds made to follow the contours of the hill; potatoes grown this way are never weeded.

For coleus potatoes, the land is apparently not mounded but is hoed lightly — or if weeds are thick, perhaps more thoroughly — at the beginning of the rainy season. Once the soil is prepared the tubers are planted close together. About two months later the field is given the only weeding it gets.

In marshes, grass is pulled in September and burned, then the ashes are spread, and a week or two later finger millet is broadcast. The field is hoed and hand-weeded immediately thereafter, just as on the hillside finger millet fields. About two months after planting (in late December or early January), the crop is weeded; it is harvested in March. During April mounds are made and sweet potatoes are planted on them. As soon as rains cease, in June, these are weeded once with a hoe. They are harvested in July when water begins to rise in the marsh.

Small plots of tobacco are established near the hut, or in places where debris has collected. Tobacco seedlings are not transplanted (*258*, p. 79). Tobacco patches are fertilized, irrigated, mulched, and weeded once or twice (*109*, p. 854; *258*, p. 79).[7]

Groves of bananas-plantains are permanent plantations, with new shoots growing each year from the old rootstock (*258*, p. 75).

Crops are guarded from March to June by children who are sent to the sorghum and millet fields between 7 and 9 A.M. and 3 and 5 P.M. to make fires for scaring away birds.

At harvest, finger millet heads are cut or pulled off. Sorghum stocks are cut with a crooked knife and shocked; later, when dry, the heads are cut from the stem and stored (*109*, p. 851). Sweet and coleus potatoes are unearthed with a hoe.

Some thirty crop sequences are reported (Figure 6-2). The following are the main principles used in sequences by the farmers in this area: early beans (harvested in February or March) are usually followed by late beans (planted the following December); sweet or coleus potatoes tend to be followed by sorghum or finger millet; sorghum (when grown alone) is usually followed by early beans. Grains are never grown three consecutive years; and early beans never follow late beans.

The Busoni Subsector

A brief description of agriculture in the Busoni subsector of Bugesera agricultural zone, Ruanda-Urundi, was published in 1960 by M. Nannan, the agronomist of the territoire (*273*). The principal staple crops are beans, which represent 25 percent, and sorghum, which accounts for 24.9 percent, of estimated staple crop acreage. Secondary crops are manioc, sweet

FIGURE 6-2 Bututsi Crop Sequences

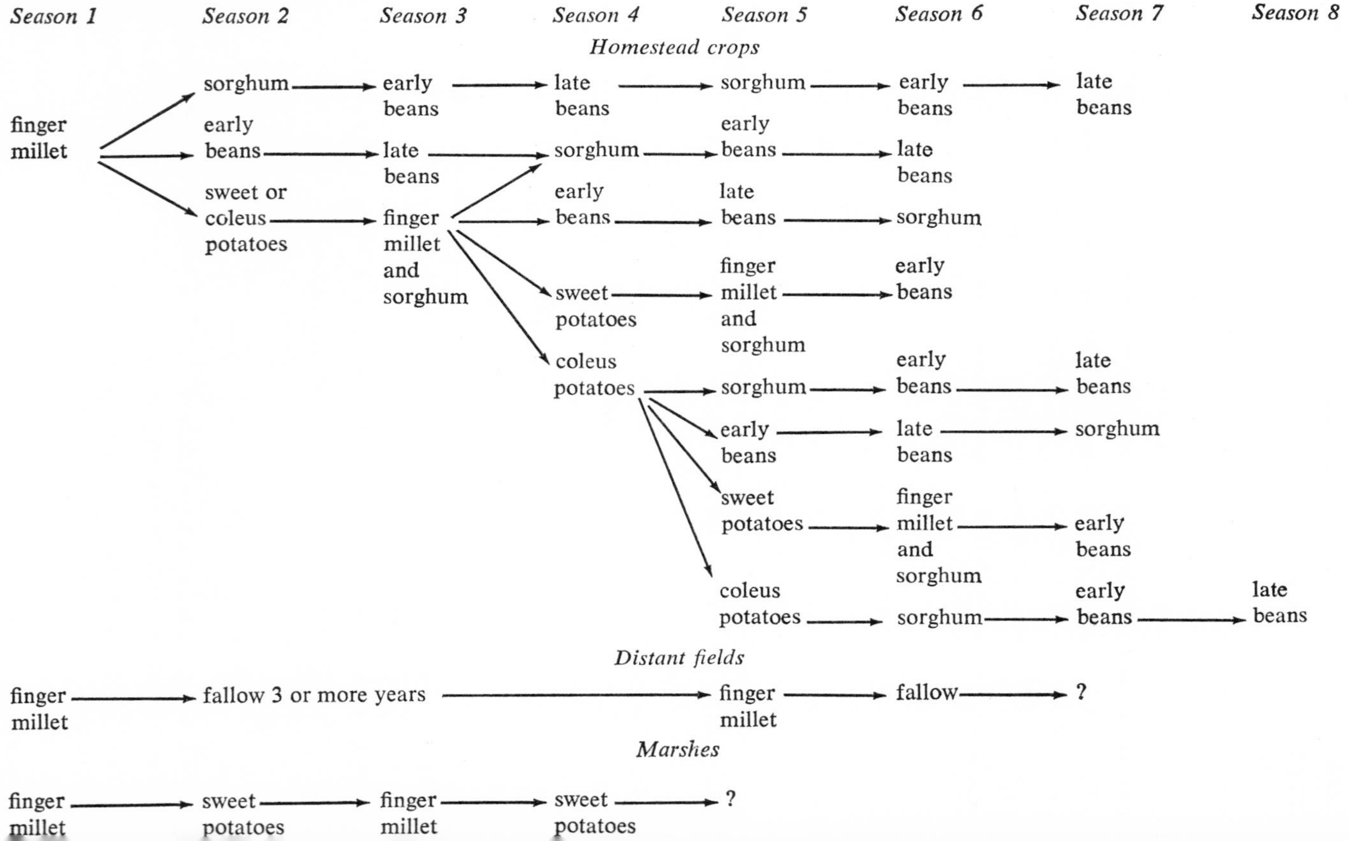

Season 1   Season 2   Season 3   Season 4   Season 5   Season 6   Season 7   Season 8

Homestead crops

finger millet → sorghum → early beans → late beans → sorghum → early beans → late beans

finger millet → early beans → late beans → sorghum → early beans → late beans

sweet or coleus potatoes → finger millet and sorghum → early beans → late beans → early beans → late beans

sweet potatoes → finger millet and sorghum → early beans → sorghum

coleus potatoes → sorghum → early beans → late beans

→ early beans → late sorghum

→ sweet potatoes → finger millet and sorghum → early beans → late beans

coleus potatoes → sorghum → early beans → late beans

Distant fields

finger millet → fallow 3 or more years → finger millet → fallow → ?

Marshes

finger millet → sweet potatoes → finger millet → sweet potatoes → ?

potatoes, and bananas-plantains, with 16.6, 16.5, and 8.7 percent of staple crop acreage respectively. Small amounts of maize, peas, peanuts, and finger millet are grown (*273*, p. 292):

Crop	Percentage of estimated staple crop acreage
Beans	25.0
Sorghum	24.9
Manioc	16.6
Sweet potatoes	16.5
Bananas-plantains	8.7
Maize	3.7
Peanuts	2.2
Peas	1.0
Finger millet	0.9
	99.5 [a]

[a] Does not add to 100 because of rounding.

Nannan identifies three kinds of fields: those near the hut, which are fertilized; fields adjacent to these; and distant fields. The crops and techniques characteristic of these field types are not given except in the statement that bananas-plantains, gourds, taro, sweet potatoes, manioc, and tobacco are grown in the fields near the hut, and that maize is always grown with either sorghum or beans.

Nannan says that one of the reasons for the popularity of sorghum is that the stems make a second growth after harvest in the middle of the dry season, thereby providing much-needed pasture for the cattle (*273*, p. 291).

The crop sequence on fields adjacent to the hut fields is sorghum following sorghum for five years, then a year of beans or peanuts, and two or three years of fallow. On distant fields the sequence is sweet potatoes, sorghum or beans, manioc, followed by two or three years of fallow (*273*, p. 294).

Other Areas of Rwanda-Burundi

M. Mortehan (1921) states that the elliptical hoe and the crooked long-handled knife were generally characteristic of southern Ruanda and northern Urundi in 1921 (*270*, p. 462). He reports that at that time most hoes came from the Belgian Congo, and were obtained through barter, goats or goat skins being exchanged for hoe blades. Meyer's account

(1917) is the same on these points; he adds that the long-handled hoes (i.e. with handles about 1.25 meters long) predominated in northern Ruanda and around Lake Kivu about 1916 (*258*, p. 73). Czekanowski (1924) found digging sticks — with or without an iron tip — in some areas at about the same time (*90*, p. 21).

Some information on crop associations and sequences is given by Mortehan in a report of a tour he made across much of Ruanda and some of northern Urundi in 1921. He found that sorghum and beans were often grown with bananas-plantains and that an association of sweet potatoes/manioc/peanuts/gourds/sorghum was often grown (*270*, p. 466). The following are the sequences he found to be characteristic of the Rwanamukale and the Kissaka areas of southern Ruanda (*270*, p. 466):

Area		*Sequences*
Rwanamukale	1	Sweet potatoes, sorghum or beans
	2	Sweet potatoes, fallow, sorghum or beans
	3	Sweet potatoes, fallow, sorghum, beans
Kissaka	1	Beans, beans, fallow
	2	Sweet potatoes, sorghum or beans, fallow
	3	Peanuts, beans, fallow

Possibly the use of sweet potatoes as the initial crop is found more generally, for F. Fallon, in an account published in 1930, states that sweet potatoes do well on newly cleared land (*134*, p. 884). Czekanowski states that in Ruanda beans and peas are the initial crop on new land (*90*, p. 19).

None of the authors includes bark cloth trees in his discussion of cultivated crops, but a comment by Meyer that this tree is "really planted and cared for" suggests it should be mentioned (*258*, p. 80).

Meyer's summary of the use of fertilizers in Ruanda-Urundi gives information not mentioned in any of the studies of particular areas (*258*, p. 82): "As fertilizer, they use either animal manure (*ikiragiriro*) from cattle, goats, sheep, and chickens, or the ashes of burnt plants (*amase*) from the hearth and from the roots of grass or papyrus which they have dug up, or green fertilizer (chopped pieces of banana trunk, sorghum stalks), or kitchen refuse, sweepings, etc." Czekanowski says that in areas of Bugoyi, where the soil is very rich, fertilizer is not used for fear the growth of millet would be too rapid and the stalks weak. Farmers are said sometimes to bind the stalks together in an attempt to avert this (*90*, p. 19).

Meyer suggests that greater use of terracing is the only major difference between agricultural techniques of Ruanda and Urundi (*258*, p. 81):

The location and arrangement of the *fields* (*umurima*) in Urundi does not differ much from Ruanda. One thing that soon strikes the observer is that in Urundi, with the exception of the western mountain areas, terraced fields are much more rare in Ruanda, where they cover entire mountain slopes and constitute the characteristic appearance of the cultivated areas. In Urundi the fields extend predominately over level either on the broad ridges or plateaus or at the bottom of the valleys. . . . If the land is cleared on a hill slope, the fields are laid out in long narrow strips which follow the contour horizontally. These are made as level as possible by removing the soil from farther up the hill and heaping it farther down. Thus, if there are several strips of land on a hillside situated one above the other, they are arranged in terraces. Each field is separated from the one below by a narrow grass-covered ridge in the same manner as in Ruanda.

According to Czekanowski, terraces are often "two to three meters high" (*90*, p. 19).

Mortehan describes two types of irrigation. Dams may be built across hillside streams to divert water from them onto a slope, or small plots about 8 meters wide and 15 meters long, circumscribed by a ditch, may be established near streams. Apparently water diverted into the ditch is gradually diffused into all parts of the field (*270*, p. 465).[8]

Meyer states that irrigation is found in both Rwanda and Burundi and suggests that irrigation systems are extensive (*258*, p. 83):

In the valley plains and on the river bottoms, water is channeled from the main stream through a whole network of larger and smaller canals and ditches distributed over the area. . . . In order to irrigate the fields on the hillsides as well, the upper course of the stream is damned up with earth and lattice-work so as to form a pool. From there the water is led along the mountain slopes in a ditch, which is often several kilometers long, until the desired destination is reached. Small channels lead off from this main artery at various intervals and irrigate numerous fields on the hillsides. . . . It is amazing with what understanding of the velocity and pressure of the water the ditches have been leveled, damned up, and conducted along the valley slopes. . . . If the slope is interrupted by a gulley that also interrupts the course of the irrigation ditch, a long tree trunk, often brought from a long distance, is placed horizontally across the gulley. The upper side is hollowed out to form a groove through which the water may flow. There are tree viaducts of this type 30 or 40 meters long. . . . The construction of such an irrigation network is the joint enterprise of the men. Each is entitled to his share of the water.

Crops are guarded by various methods: Caterpillars, beetles, and snails are picked off plants and killed; birds are frightened away with scarecrows such as "gallows-shaped sorghum stalks tied one upon the other with dry, rattling fruit suspended from them" (*258*, p. 84). Fences are sometimes constructed if wild pigs are a problem, and guards are stationed in fields against baboons (*258*, p. 84).

The Ha

Farming methods of the Ha, adjacent to the Burundi on the south and east, appear to be similar to those of the Rwanda and Burundi. The starchy-staples are sorghum, manioc, sweet potatoes, plantains, maize, and beans. Pigeon peas, peanuts, Bambara nuts, tomatoes, and leaves of vegetables (e.g. amaranth and pumpkins) are the major secondary food-stuffs. As in Rwanda and Burundi, the raising of cattle is a major economic activity. Both manuring and irrigation are practiced.

A major crop association is a beans–maize–sorghum succession. Beans are planted first and harvested when maize is about 60 cm. high; then sorghum, and sometimes pigeon peas as well, are planted. Such fields are carefully manured with cow dung and household refuse (*218*, p. 301), and may not be fallowed. Each farmer also has fields that receive no fertilizers; crop sequences and fallows are the sole means of replenishing their soil fertility (*316*, p. 185).

The Bashi

The agriculture of the Bashi, a tribe found to the west of Lake Kivu in country ranging in elevation from 1,500 to 2,500 meters, is sketched in several articles by Belgian agronomists and veterinaries published in the late 1940's or early 1950's (*125, 174, 175, 204,* and *205*).

High grass is the prevailing natural cover in much of the Bashi area; the population density is over twenty-five persons per square kilometer in most areas, and in no territoire inhabited by the Bashi does it average less than fifteen persons (*377*, Annexe 6).

The principal crops are bananas, sorghum, sweet potatoes, beans, manioc, and in some areas, coffee. Large herds of cattle and small livestock are kept.

In 1957 bananas were the dominant food crop in terms of acreage, but manioc, beans, sweet potatoes, and sorghum each accounted for from 15 to 22.5 percent of acreage in staple crops in Kabare territoire, the administrative division in which the Bashi are predominant (*175*, p. 5):

Crops	Percentage of staple crop acreage
Bananas	23.6
Manioc	22.5
Beans	19.7
Sweet potatoes	18.7
Sorghum	15.0
Maize	0.5
	100.0

The arrangement of the fields and gardens is the same as among the Bututsi of Burundi (*174*, p. 9). Clearing is accomplished by cutting grass and herbs, then burning them in piles, and hoeing the field to a depth of 5 to 10 cm. At the same time all roots and debris found are pulled up and later burned. In a second hoeing mounds are made.

Sorghum is usually sown twice. The main crop is sown on the flat in September, but in some areas a second crop follows in February (*204*, p. 970). Sorghum is broadcast and is often grown with beans. It may also be sown in marshes in April or May (*205*, p. 1252). Sweet potatoes are planted any time during the rainy season, and may be replanted at harvest (*204*, p. 971). Manioc is not grown at the higher altitudes. Where grown, it is usually planted in October or November and harvested ten to twelve months later. In at least some areas it is grown in mounds (*216*, p. 81). Forty varieties of beans are grown in some areas, and are sown broadcast in September or October and again in April and May; often several varieties are grown together. Beans, like sorghum, may be grown in marshes; harvest is three and a half to four and a half months after sowing.

Crop associations are not described except for the observation that beans are often grown with sorghum or manioc. Crop sequences mentioned are sweet potatoes followed by an association of sorghum/maize/beans/cucurbits or beans followed by sorghum/maize/beans/cucurbits (*176*, p. 390). Eeckhout suggests that to regenerate soil fertility, some fields are planted with bananas for ten years in place of fallow: "A banana grove regenerates the field . . . at the same time producing" (*125*, p. 2201).

Although bananas grown for beer are a major crop, they are mainly planted near the village, where they can be fertilized with refuse. Plantains are not grown (*216*, p. 78). Near the banana grove a plot of tobacco is usually grown; it too is fertilized. Tobacco is sown twice yearly and is thinned and topped (*204*, p. 973).

According to Hendrickx, neither irrigation nor terracing is found (*176*, pp. 391–92).

The Beni-Lubero Area

The agricultural system of a high plateau zone — the Beni-Lubero area north of Rwanda-Burundi — is based on similar crops and may be characterized by short fallow, although use of animal manure is not mentioned.

E. Van Daele, chief of the Ndihira experiment center, describes agriculture in these two former Belgian Congo territoires adjacent to Lake Edward and the Ruwenzori Mountains, in an article published in 1955. Three vegetation zones are distinguished according to altitude. In the extreme east is an area over 2,100 meters in elevation that is characterized mainly by ferns and short grasses; the middle zone ranges from 1,600 to 2,100 meters and is dominated by tall grasses and bushes; still farther west is the area below 1,600 meters, which is forest in parts and savanna elsewhere (*365*, p. 236).

The Konjo are the principal tribe in the area. The population density of the two territoires is relatively high: five to fifteen persons per square kilometer in Beni.

Beans and peas are the dominant staple foodstuff in terms of area planted, accounting for 35.7 percent of total crop acreage (*365*, pp. 238–47). Either sweet potatoes or bananas-plantains — not separated in the data given — may have the second largest acreage. In 1937 banana-plantain acreage was estimated at 4,786 hectares (*28*, p. 503). If most of the rest of the 12,578 hectares in "other crops" is sweet potatoes — and Van Daele says "they are grown on a large scale" in the middle zone (*365*, p. 242) — this would make sweet potatoes the second most important crop. The probable ranking of staple crops by acreage, then, is beans and peas, sweet potatoes or plantains, wheat, maize, Irish potatoes, and rice or barley.

Whether cattle are kept is not clear. Sir Harry Johnston listed small livestock — but no cattle — for the Beni area around the turn of the century; and so did J. Czekanowski a quarter-century later. However, Gaston Derkinderen, in 1955, showed both Beni and Lubero well within the zone where cattle are raised (*104*, p. 106; *192*, p. 557; *90*, pp. 444–50; *347*, p. 131). Small livestock are clearly kept.

In the high altitude zone the major crops are beans, peas, Irish potatoes, wheat, and taro. Plantains for beer are grown on slopes well exposed to the sun. Marshes and valley are reserved for pasturing small livestock (*365*, p. 233). Some taro may be irrigated; J. Claessens reported irrigated taro in the area near Kayumba in 1926 (*77*, p. 25).

Irish potatoes are planted the year around to assure a continuous harvest, and appear to be at the head of the crop sequence. Wheat is planted after Irish potatoes and is followed by beans or peas (*365*, p. 238). In some areas the bean, wheat sequence goes through several cycles before the field is fallowed. Peas are often the last crop in the sequence because "they do not wear out the soil" (*365*, p. 244). Peas may be grown in place of fallow for several years; if so, they are not weeded: tall grass and ferns are let grow to serve as supports in place of the stakes usually provided.

At middle altitude, beans, sweet potatoes, and plantains are the major crops; barley, oats, finger millet, manioc, maize, yams, peanuts, and purple arrowroot (*Canna edulis*) are minor crops.

In the low altitude zone manioc is the principal crop, but plantains, maize, rice, peanuts, and beans are important. In forest areas beans are usually the first crop in the sequence, and manioc is often the last one. Until that terminal crop, peanuts usually follow manioc, and maize is typically grown in association with beans or peanuts. In savanna areas peanuts are usually the first crop planted after clearing.

In all three zones gardens are usually made near the hut and planted with bananas, yams, vegetables; in middle altitudes but not elsewhere, purple arrowroot is included.

Animal husbandry is not discussed.

The Lugbara

Information on the Lugbara, located in the northeastern corner of the Congo Basin, comes mainly from field work by John Middleton from 1949 to 1953. The area they inhabit is a savanna plateau ranging from 1,300 to 2,000 meters above sea level. The population density varies from 20 to 250 but averages 150 people per square mile. Finger millet is the dominant starchy-staple. Secondary crops are maize, sorghum, manioc, bananas, plantains, sweet potatoes, sesame, peanuts, pigeon peas, "various peas and beans," pumpkins, gourds, sugarcane, tobacco, and "many other plants" (*260*, pp. 7, 11; *259*, pp. 562–63). Cattle, goats, sheep, and poultry are kept in most areas.

The Lugbara recognize three types of fields: infields or home fields, near the homesite, that receive manure and ashes as fertilizer; outfields that receive no fertilizer and are unirrigated; and unfertilized, irrigated outfields. In addition, there are special types of gardens, such as those made on rubbish heaps near the hut, and old hutsites (not possessed by all farmers).

Infields are planted with "the more demanding crops, especially white sorghums used in beer brewing"; and are fallowed, but so infrequently that Middleton sometimes refers to them as permanent fields (*260*, p. 11). Finger millet, sorghum, sesame, and pigeon peas are mentioned as the crops found in unirrigated outfields. Such fields may be cropped two or three years before being fallowed, but then are rested a minimum of three, and sometimes as many as fifteen, years (*261*, p. 452). While in fallow, fields are used as pasture. Riverine outfields are irrigated by channels dug from streams and are planted with such things as sweet potatoes, maize, sugarcane, and bananas. They are usually naturally fertile and are given "very short" fallows (*260*, p. 11).

There is mention that each of the three types of fields has its own crop sequence, but no details are provided.

7

The Rationale of
Traditional Cropping Methods

Lack of data prevents comparison of the amount of labor expended per hectare or of the relative yields per hectare in the various agricultural systems of the Congo Basin. But other data suggest that practices followed are reasonable, considering the environment and the tools and power available.

Soil Selection

Methods of selecting locations for new fields, when declining soil fertility or other factors prompt abandonment of those in cultivation, cannot be described in any detail at this juncture, but evidence at hand suggests that there is generally a body of knowledge linking the suitability of soil for certain crop associations and sequences with the natural cover. The detailed accounts of agricultural practices by Trapnell, De Schlippe, Richards, Van Moesieke, Tisserant, and Wilmet all clearly indicate careful selection of areas to be cleared; and several other writers imply that this is the case, although they do not explicitly discuss the matter.

Trapnell, speaking of most of the Zambian section of the Congo Basin, states that (*360*, p. 12) "The use of vegetation as an index of fertility is widely found in Native agriculture. Various tall grasses of the genus *Hyparrhenia*, for example, are commonly used as indicators of good land, while *Trichopteryx superba* and *T. simplex* are preferably avoided. The nature and height of grass is especially helpful but the indications given by trees and other plants are also used. Certain species of *Acacia* are well known as growing on the most fertile soils while an abundance of *Uapaca* spp. denotes a poor soil and not infrequently one with an impermeable ironstone pan."

Richards lists fifteen soil fertility indicators she was given by one Bemba informant or another, and concludes that most Bemba know a few such indicators (*305*, p. 287). De Schlippe lists six indicators of declining soil fertility recognized by Azande and spends several pages discussing the rules governing where and when each crop association can be planted (*108*, ch. 9 and p. 213). His description of Bututsi agriculture also suggests a sizable body of knowledge about where to plant each crop association. Van Moesieke says of the Mongo that the African farmer in selecting land to be cleared is "always guided by the fertility of the soil, which he estimates by the abundance of certain plants" (*383*, p. 421).

When clearing new sorghum and manioc fields, the Banda look for land supporting various species of *Hyparrhenia*, of which the most common is *H. rufa*. Moreover, they prefer land with the thickest vegetation, as one might expect since it is the land that will yield the thickest layer of ash when cleared (*346*, p. 212). Tisserant states that other indicators of soil fertility are used for other types of fields, but does not provide details (*346*, p. 212).

J. Wilmet, in discussion of agriculture between Jadotville and Lumbumbashi (formerly Elisabethville) in Katanga, reports the following trees and shrubs used by African farmers as indicators of soil fertility: *Acacia macrothyrsa*; *Pterocarpus polyanthus, Strychnos pungas*; *Aframomum Saquineum; Beckeropsis uniseta*; and *Hyparrhenia cymbaria* (*426*, p. 25).

Scattered suggestions of the use of soil or vegetation indicators are statements that the Banza "never plant in natural clearings" (*193*, 1: 269); that in the Ubangi area maize is always grown on forest soil or soil rested four or five years (*255*, p. 884); and that around Nyangwé hilltops are never planted with rice (*339*, p. 202).

Clearing Techniques

Differences in clearing techniques in the Congo Basin are difficult to interpret because many of the data are incomplete or for different time periods; the differences nevertheless appear to be fairly well explained by variations in ecological conditions. The simplest and least intensive techniques are all found among tribes in the heart of the humid forest belt; the number of operations and amount of labor required tend to increase for areas in the edge of the forest zone, and are greater yet in savanna areas, where the soil must be tilled much more to establish crops and control weeds. Moreover, peoples who have access to both forest and savanna areas employ different techniques on them and tend to use techniques that are more complex and labor-intensive in their savanna fields.

Diversification of Production

The practice of growing a variety of crops, rather than specializing in a few, cannot be explained entirely by lack of markets, but probably relates also to labor bottlenecks, storage considerations, and advantages of growing several crops together.

When several crops, each with different peak labor requirements, are grown, available labor can be spread more evenly throughout the year and each crop given more nearly the attention it needs. (Charts 7-1 and 7-2 show the difference of labor requirements for crops in the only two areas for which quantitative data on this are available.) In a like manner, diversification can extend the harvest period — as discussed more fully on pp. 192–93 — and thereby reduce the amount of storage required, an important consideration not only because dishes from fresh produce may be tastier but also because storage losses and labor expended in building granaries are reduced or eliminated.

Agronomic factors may also strongly contribute to decisions to grow several crops. Although some crops are grown in pure culture in some areas for reasons not clear, planting of two or more crops together is usual. Perhaps a major reason for this is that through trial and error farmers have discovered that soil loses its fertility more rapidly if it is left bare under the climatic conditions of the Congo Basin. Therefore crops with different planting times are grown together so that all cleared land will be partially protected at all times. (In most areas it is impossible to stagger the clearing of land — by clearing for early crops and planting them, then turning to later crops — because fields must be cleared during the dry season so that the felled vegetation will burn; where rainfall is light enough for felled vegetation to be burned after rains begin, the rainy

CHART 7-1 **Banda Agriculture: Distribution of Labor Requirements in Field and Garden Operations**

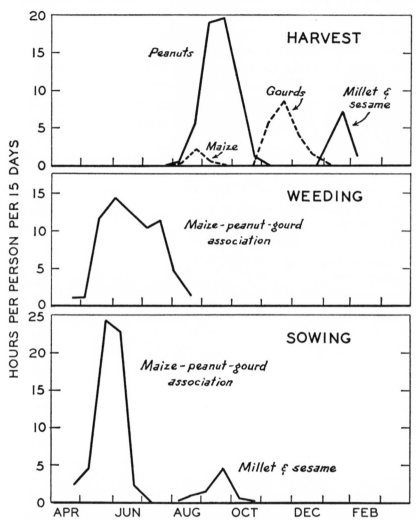

Data from Central African Republic, Mission Socio-Économique, Centre Oubangui, *L'Emploi du temps du paysans dans une zone de L'Oubangui Central 1959-60* (Paris, Nov. 1961), p. 83. Cotton, one of the major crops, is omitted here because it is grown under supervision. Minor fields — manioc and "diverse crops" — are not shown here because labor in them is not broken down by operation. However, total labor spent on them is relatively well distributed (*ibid.*, p. 82).

season tends to be too short for most crops planted much after rains begin to have the moisture they require.)

Mixed cropping may also be motivated by desire to control weeds, especially the second and all following seasons after clearing. In the Ubangi area the reason given for growing cucurbits with maize is that the companion crops will choke out weeds and will help to conserve moisture (*256*, p. 884). Several crops, such as maize, millets-sorghums, and rice, do not develop enough foliage ever to control weeds effectively; and some other crops which develop enough foliage by maturity to suppress most

CHART 7-2 **Azande Agriculture: Distribution of Labor Requirements in Field and Garden Operations**

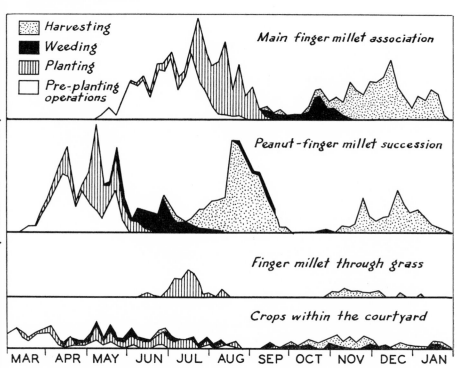

Data derived from Pierre de Schlippe, *Shifting Cultivation in Africa* (London: Routledge, Kegan Paul, 1956), Figure 21. Cotton, one of the major crops, is omitted here because it is grown under supervision. Four minor field types are not shown here because they require relatively little labor, and that devoted to them is fairly well distributed over the year. See De Schlipp's chart for a breakdown of operations according to crop.

ᵃ Presumably hours per week; De Schlippe does not give the time unit.

noxious plants may need a companion crop to aid weed control when first planted.

Another reason for interplanting crops is that certain areas within a field — termite mounds, soil around stumps, and borders, for example — may well have special ecological characteristics that make them suitable for a crop or crops other than those planted generally throughout the field. Moreover, certain crops may be aided by the presence of other crops; for instance, maize and sorghum stalks provide support for climbing crops.

Mounding and Ridging

Whether crops are grown on mounds or ridges varies considerably from area to area (see Map 7-1). The reasons for the uneven distribution of mounding and ridging in the Congo Basin are not entirely clear. Mounds and ridges are more commonly made in savanna than in forest areas, partly because soils must be hoed to remove grass roots in savannas, but often need not be hoed at all in the forest zone. But there are areas within the savanna zone where neither mounding nor ridging is practiced.

There is no explanation of mounding and ridging in the literature, but work in experiment stations in Nigeria and Tanzania shows that in some ecological zones of Africa mounds or ridges strikingly increase yields. Mounding experiments in Nigeria show surprisingly large increases and for all crops. In both Nigeria and Tanzania mounding and ridging were positively correlated with the size of mounds, up to a point; in some instances increases of 600 percent or more were recorded (*135*, pp. 177–78). But in both countries, as in the Congo Basin, areas can be found where neither mounds nor ridges are made despite the striking advantages of these practices under conditions like those at the experiment stations.

Making mounds or ridges increases the amount of top soil within the reach of crop roots; makes the harvesting of roots and tubers easier; and perhaps improves drainage or reduces loss of moisture through runoff. It may also produce a better soil condition for some crops. African informants in the Ivory Coast tell us that if mounds are not made for yams the tubers will not have room to develop and yields will be lowered.

Weeding

In a number of areas several — and in a few areas all — of the major crops grown on newly cleared land need not be weeded; either incineration

MAP 7-1

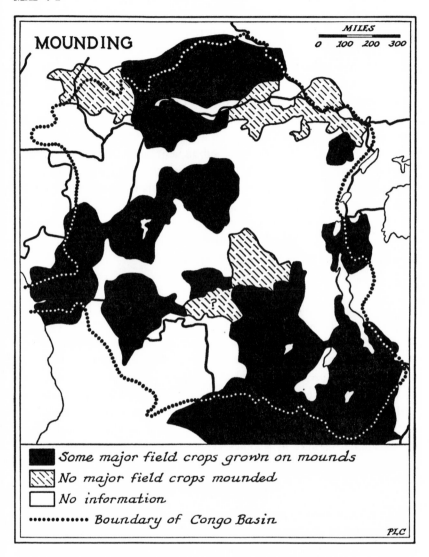

MOUNDING

MILES
0   100   200   300

Some major field crops grown on mounds
No major field crops mounded
No information
•••••••••••• Boundary of Congo Basin

PLC

of the field or the density of crops planted retards weed growth sufficiently. There is some tendency for more weeding to be required in grassland than in forest, and for some crops to be weeded more than others.

Almost everywhere weeding appears to be a major operation in rice production. With some crops the amount of weeding depends on the position of the crop in the crop sequence followed. When manioc is the terminal crop in the sequence it may be weeded little because there is always the possibility that it will not be harvested; i.e., since manioc is easy to plant and can be harvested over a long period, it is sometimes grown at the end of the sequence, where no other crop would give much of a yield without care, and is harvested only if other crops yield poorly. For most crops other than manioc, the amount of weeding is lowest at the beginning of the sequence and greatest at the end. The season after the initial clearing of a field, the fire that can be built is much weaker than it was the first season of cultivation: relatively little debris is available to be burned, the proportion of weed and grass roots and seed destroyed is greatly reduced, and weeding of subsequent crops is usually required whether or not the preceding crops were weeded. (Thus peoples with long crop sequences can be expected to spend relatively more time on weeding. And, since clearing operations can be spread over a long period whereas weeding usually must be done over a relatively short period to be effective, labor bottlenecks are much more likely to be an important restraint on yields where long crop sequences are followed.)

Use of Fertilizers

Nearly all of the tribal agricultural systems of the Congo Basin for which we have data employ household wastes to enrich special gardens. In several instances some use of animal fertilizers for special crops is also mentioned. Yet use of night soil is not reported and there is indication that animal manures are not as completely collected as they might be. Although use of cattle manure as fertilizer is found among four of the cattle-keeping peoples for whom we have data, there is no mention of use of animal manure by peoples keeping only small livestock, and no hint as to why.

Crop Predators

Agricultural systems may depend to a considerable extent on the kinds and densities of domestic and wild animal populations found, although the evidence is thin. The problem of crop predators is frequently mentioned in the literature but rarely related to the agricultural system. References to fence building in some areas but not in others may reflect differences not only in the amount of small domestic livestock but in the importance of wild predators as well. There is also evidence that reduction in the labor available to guard maize, millet, and sorghum has led to considerable changes in the composition of crop associations and sequences, suggesting that crop predators can be a major factor in determining the type of agricultural system found.

Crop Sequences

Data for the Congo Basin abundantly verify Pierre de Schlippe's argument that in systems of shifting cultivation in Africa the pattern of crops over time on a single field is better described as a sequence than as a rotation; the regularity that the word rotation suggests is not found (*108*, pp. 207–10). In all instances where the cropping pattern over time has been described in any detail, African farmers are found to have certain principles such as usually sowing certain crops on newly cleared land, or never following crop A with crop B, but in most cases any one of several crops or crop associations may be grown at a particular point in the cultivation cycle, depending on such things as the timing of rains and the availability of labor. The result is that variation in observed crop sequences is extreme: for no two tribes in the Congo Basin are the same sequences reported, and it is hard to find any two that are even similar in length or composition.

Few generalizations can be made about common features of crop sequences, except that bananas-plantains are most frequently the initial crop in forest areas, by a good margin; and that manioc — a crop with considerable tolerance for poor soils and one which can be left with little or no deterioration for as much as a year after it is first ready to harvest — tends to be the terminal crop in both forest and savanna areas (Table 7-1).

TABLE 7-1 Initial and Terminal Crops and Crop Associations in Congo Basin Crop Sequences[a]

Crop or crop association	Initial position		Terminal position	
	Forest	*Savanna*	*Forest*	*Savanna*
	(*Percent of observations*)			
Bananas-plantains	44.1	0.0	16.7	2.7
Millets-sorghums	0.0	16.7	0.0	7.7
Maize	11.8	3.8	8.3	0.0
Manioc	8.4	3.2	41.7	36.2
Peanuts	0.0	14.3	0.0	5.0
Beans or peas	0.0	10.0	0.0	14.5
Sugarcane	5.9	0.0	0.0	0.0
Yams	5.9	0.0	8.3	1.9
Sweet potatoes	0.0	7.4	0.0	5.0

Crop or crop association	Initial position Forest	Initial position Savanna	Terminal position Forest	Terminal position Savanna
Irish potatoes	0.0	0.6	0.0	0.3
Rice	0.0	0.6	0.0	0.0
Urena	0.0	0.6	0.0	0.3
Cotton	0.0	1.2	0.0	0.0
Tobacco	0.0	0.0	0.0	1.0
Bambara nuts	0.0	0.0	0.0	1.0
Pigeon peas	0.0	1.2	0.0	0.0
"Legumes"	0.0	0.0	0.0	0.8
Manioc/bananas-plantains	0.0	0.0	8.3	0.0
Maize/bananas-plantains	3.0	0.0	0.0	0.0
Peanuts/bananas-plantains	0.0	0.4	0.0	0.0
Beans/bananas-plantains	0.0	0.4	0.0	0.0
Irish potatoes/bananas-plantains	0.0	0.4	0.0	0.0
Manioc/bananas-plantains/beans/maize	0.0	0.6	0.0	0.0
Maize/gourds/bananas-plantains	0.0	0.6	0.0	0.0
Beans/maize/bananas-plantains	0.0	0.8	0.0	0.0
Bananas-plantains/maize/yams/tobacco	3.0	0.0	0.0	0.0
Manioc/maize/beans/bananas-plantains	3.0	0.0	0.0	0.0
Peanuts/maize/yams/bananas-plantains/manioc	0.0	0.0	0.0	0.3
Beans/maize/yams/bananas-plantains/manioc	0.0	0.0	0.0	0.3
Sugarcane/pigeon peas/bananas-plantains	0.0	0.0	0.0	0.8
Manioc/maize	0.0	1.9	16.7	2.3
Manioc/beans	0.0	0.4	0.0	0.3
Manioc/peanuts	0.0	4.2	0.0	0.7
Manioc/millets-sorghums	0.0	1.2	0.0	0.0
Manioc/pigeon peas	0.0	0.0	0.0	0.4
Tobacco/manioc	0.0	1.0	0.0	0.0
Manioc/gourds	0.0	0.0	0.0	1.9
Manioc/beans/maize	3.0	0.4	0.0	0.0
Manioc/beans/peanuts	0.0	0.0	0.0	0.4
Sesame/peanuts/manioc	0.0	0.0	0.0	0.8
Sugarcane/pigeon peas/manioc	0.0	0.0	0.0	0.8
Manioc/peanuts/"vegetables"	0.0	0.4	0.0	0.0
Sweet potatoes/maize/manioc	0.0	0.0	0.0	0.8
Manioc/peanuts/yams	0.0	0.4	0.0	0.0
Maize/manioc/beans	0.0	1.9	0.0	0.0
Maize/peanuts/manioc	0.0	0.8	0.0	1.5
Gourds/maize/manioc	0.0	0.4	0.0	3.8
Gourds/maize/manioc/yams	0.0	0.0	0.0	0.8
Peanuts/beans/manioc/pigeon peas	0.0	1.9	0.0	0.0
Millets-sorghums/maize/beans/manioc	0.0	1.0	0.0	0.0
Peanuts/manioc/beans/tomatoes/gourds	0.0	0.4	0.0	0.0
Maize/beans/pumpkins/manioc	0.0	1.0	0.0	0.0
Peanuts/manioc/beans/Bambara nuts/ pigeon peas	0.0	0.6	0.0	0.0

Crop or crop association	Initial position		Terminal position	
	Forest	Savanna	Forest	Savanna
Maize/peanuts	3.0	0.4	0.0	0.0
Maize/millets-sorghums	0.0	0.0	0.0	1.5
Maize/beans	0.3	0.6	0.0	0.8
Gourds/maize	0.0	0.4	0.0	0.0
Maize/sweet potatoes	3.0	0.0	0.0	0.0
Tobacco/maize	3.0	0.0	0.0	0.0
Maize/millets-sorghums/beans/"cucurbits"	0.0	0.0	0.0	3.8
Peanuts/beans/maize/tobacco	0.0	0.4	0.0	0.0
Yams/maize/gourds	0.0	1.2	0.0	0.0
Maize/pumpkins/"cucurbits"	0.0	1.9	0.0	0.0
Peanuts/Bambara nuts	0.0	0.6	0.0	0.0
Peanuts/beans	3.0	5.4	0.0	0.0
Peanuts/millets-sorghums	0.0	1.2	0.0	0.8
Peanuts/millets-sorghums/pigeon peas	0.0	1.2	0.0	0.0
Peanuts/Bambara nuts/pigeon peas	0.0	1.2	0.0	0.0
Sweet potatoes/peanuts/beans/Bambara nuts/ pigeon peas	0.0	0.6	0.0	0.0
Millets-sorghums/sweet potatoes	0.0	1.0	0.0	0.0
Millets-sorghums/beans/oilseed gourds	0.0	3.8	0.0	0.0
Beans/yams/"vegetables"	0.0	0.0	0.0	0.8
	100.4[b]	100.6[b]	100.0	100.0
Number of tribes	17	26	6	32

[a] To give tribes equal weighting the total number of initial and terminal crops and crop associations for each tribe has been weighted as one; thus if a given crop is reported as the initial crop in three of one tribe's crop sequences, the value of 0.3 is recorded for that crop. Sequences in gardens and other plots outside main fields have not been included; and when successions rather than crop associations are grown, only the first crop in the succession has been counted.

Richards' account of Bemba sequences has been followed rather than Trapnell's. The sequences reported by Sautter have been used for the Koukouya Plateau.

[b] Does not add to 100 because of rounding.

In forest areas, bananas-plantains were the initial crop in 44.1 percent of sequences on which we have observations, and associations containing bananas-plantains accounted for another 9 percent; 11.8 percent of sequences started with maize, but another 21.3 percent began with an association containing maize. The third most common initial crop was manioc, reported in 8.4 percent of sequences.

In savanna areas, no single crop was found as the first crop in sequences in more than 17 percent of the sequences observed, and 47 different crops or crop associations were reported. Millets and sorghums were the initial crop in 16.7 percent of sequences; peanuts in 14.3 percent; and beans or peas in 10 percent.

Manioc was the terminal crop in 41.7 percent of forest sequences, and associations containing manioc accounted for another 25 percent; bananas-plantains were second, with 16.7 percent.

Although manioc was also the most frequently reported terminal crop in savannas, the margin was considerably smaller (36.2 percent of observations, with another 15.1 percent of terminal associations containing manioc). Beans or peas were the second most frequent terminal crop, (14.5 percent of observations), but were reported mainly in high areas on the eastern rim of the Congo Basin. A total of 32 different terminal crops or crop associations was reported.

In both forest and savanna zones farmers clearly have considerably more choice of crops at the beginning of the sequence than at the end. In both vegetation zones the number of terminal crops or crop associations is far less than initial crops and crop associations. This is what might be expected since crops grown at the end of sequences need a relatively high tolerance for poor soils, weeds, and grass.

The enormous diversity of crop sequences observed probably reflects to a considerable extent the thoroughness of observations made by those writing about tribal agricultural systems; but the instances in which the same author has reported on more than one tribe — Trapnell's work, for example — also show a great variation in crop sequences. Differences in environment and in crops and crop varieties known are undoubtedly of major importance in explaining such variations, for evidence of changes in crop sequences over time (see Chapter 12) suggests that not only differences in crops available but also differences in the varieties of major crops known can cause striking distortions of crop sequences.

Geographical differences in crop sequences may also reflect differences in dietary preferences, which in themselves vary widely. In much of the Congo Basin one can choose among at least three starchy-staples that can be grown. There is a common tendency to plant valued or particularly demanding crops on newly cleared land because the soil has more nutrients the first season it is cropped than at any other time in the cultivation cycle, and frequently the level of soil fertility falls rapidly once land is cleared.

8

Shifting Cultivation of the
Congo Basin in Perspective

The notion that shifting cultivation is simple and varies little from area to area and continent to continent runs through much of the literature. H. H. Bartlett, for example, writes: "Wherever there are sparse populations of primitive man within the tropics there is also a peculiar type of shifting agriculture which exhibits only minor variations around the world" (*39*, p. 693). Pierre Gourou, who through his widely read book, *The Tropical World*, has strongly influenced thinking about the agricultural potential of the tropics, gives elsewhere a somewhat longer and more detailed description of shifting cultivation, but he too indicates that it is much the same throughout the world (*159*, p. 338): "In Africa, America, and New Guinea shifting cultivation (*landang*) is the primary source of vegetal foods; agriculturalists clear a portion of forest or savanna, burn the dried vegetation, make holes with a stick and put in various grains, weed or do not weed, protect the cultivated plants from wild animals, and reap. The cleared field may be abandoned after a single harvest or after two or three." P. H. Nye and D. J. Greenland have provided the best-documented study yet on the effect of shifting cultivation on soils, and point out distinct differences between forest and savanna belts in the effect on soils of various operations found in shifting cultivation — such as clearing, burning, and fallowing; but otherwise they imply that within the

169

same vegetation zone shifting cultivation is much the same the world over (*278*). They provide a single description of it (based on Ghana) as typical of all western tropical Africa.

As our Chapters 3 to 6 indicate, the Congo Basin is a large and striking exception to such generalizations, with cultivation methods ranging from the simple slash, burn, plant technique to more intensive systems involving hoeing, and still more intensive ones characterized by use of specially produced ash fertilizers, composting, application of animal manures, irrigation, or terracing, some of which are very close to permanent field agriculture. But even within the less intensive types of cultivation, in which there is no attempt to alter the decline of soil fertility through human effort — the classic long-fallow systems — cultivation methods vary greatly in intensity even within a single vegetation zone. Indeed, diversity appears to be the outstanding characteristic of shifting cultivation in the Congo Basin. In addition to variations in methods of working the soil in main fields, there is extreme diversity in the combination of agricultural enterprises found; in the number, types, and importance of fields or gardens other than main fields; and in crop associations and sequences followed.

Comparison with Other Parts of Africa

How representative the systems of shifting cultivation in the Congo Basin are of tropical Africa cannot be clearly determined until we have better data. However, information now available clearly suggests that in most other areas of Africa characterized by shifting cultivation one or more of the cultivation methods of the classic long-fallow system prevails.

Classic Long-Fallow Systems

Among a number of tribes in areas of the Sudan where the natural vegetation is predominantly a thick, tall grass, a type of savanna cultivation not observed anywhere in the Congo Basin is followed. Called *Harīq*[1] cultivation in the Sudan, it is a special form of fire farming. Its distinctive features are that 1) plots are protected from uncontrolled fires and are left fallow until the grass has developed into a dense, matted cover (two to four years of growth uninterrupted by uncontrolled fires)[2]; and 2) burning of fields is done not in the dry season, as is typical of most savanna methods of shifting cultivation, but long enough after the first rains for the green shoots of the new growth to have appeared. Because of the thick accumulation of dead grass, heat generated by burning may be sufficient to kill the new grass and no weeding will be required (*62*, p. 292).

Although reduction of the weeding effort seems to be the underlying motivation for this technique, it also results in greater restoration of soil fertility during the fallow period and a larger stock of nutrients deposited on the field as ash during the clearing process — provided fields are sucessfully protected from uncontrolled fires. Thus, compared with other methods of opening fields in savannas, we should expect it to be characterized by higher productivity per acre as well as higher productivity per laborer.

The ecological condition needed for *harīq* cultivation may not be widely found. The system requires a thick growth of grass and works well only with certain species of grass. Tufted grasses, for example, are said to be unsuitable.

Ash-Dependent Systems

The only ash-dependent systems reported outside the Congo Basin are for parts of Zambia (*361* and *360*), although a somewhat similar technique has been observed in parts of the Sudan. Among the Dinka of southern Sudan a larger area is cleared than is to be planted, and the extra wood is piled on the plot to be cultivated, as in ash-dependent systems; but instead of the pile being burned it is left for termites to work on. Within four months they reduce it to dust, in which crops can be planted (*62*, p. 294). This method is apparently known among some of the other tribes of the Sudan, but its importance is not clear. J. R. Burnett, who describes this technique among the Dinka, reports that "Many other tribes follow the same practice, but on a smaller scale, and probably confine the spreading of branches to material cleared off the ground actually to be cultivated" (*62*, p. 294).

Composting

Composting is reported on the edges of the Congo Basin, but rarely elsewhere in Africa. Among the Ganda of Uganda a central feature of traditional agricultural techniques is use of composts in maintaining the fertility of banana-plantain groves, a technique much like that reported for one area between the Congo and Ubangi rivers. The Ganda collected dead leaves for compost; they chop up old stems that have been cut down in the harvesting process; and they also make compost out of old thatch from their huts and from household refuse (*247*, p. 88). By careful use of composts they are said to have been able sometimes to keep banana-plantain groves bearing thirty to fifty years without resting the land (*133*, p. 38).

S. G. Wilson describes a system of digging refuse into mounds among the Ngoni and Tumbuka of northern Malawi that is much like the system of the Pende in the Congo Basin (*427*, pp. 91–92). A. S. Stenhouse reports a composing method in the Matengo Highlands of Tanzania that employs pits rather than mounds, but otherwise is similar. Small pits are made throughout the field and crops planted between them. As crops are weeded, and at harvest, all debris collected is deposited in the pits; then the soil is spread; crops are planted, and new pits dug where crops were the preceding season (*334*, pp. 22–23).

A composting technique involving incineration of composts within mounds, similar to the method used on the Koukouya Plateau of the Congo Basin, is said to be found among the Bamiléké and in the Bamenda Highlands of southwestern Cameroun; it is also reported for the Kipsigis of Kenya and for parts of Ethiopia (*136*, pp. 180–82, cited in *283*; *201*, p. 58; *280*, p. 93; and *146*, pp. 141–42).

In the Bamenda Highlands this method is employed only when maize is to be grown. Piles of dry grass are covered with soil and left four to six weeks, then ignited and left to smolder. The process turns the soil light vermilion and makes it "rather puffy." Soil given this treatment reportedly "yields an excellent crop the first year . . . followed by a much poorer one in the second season" (*201*, p. 58). Benefits claimed for the technique are that it concentrates the relatively fertile topsoil within the reach of crop roots and in certain ways enriches it; it destroys pests such as wire-worm; and it possibly reduces soil acidity. As the same time there are negative effects through burning of humus (*35*, App. 3, cited in *201*, p. 58).

The Kipsigis, who are found in the western highlands of Kenya, clear fields in such a way that the turf comes off in large thin slabs, which are dried and stacked in piles. Once the whole field has been cleared and the last slabs are dry, hot coals are inserted into the stacks and the piles are left to smoulder two or three days. When the burning is finished the mounds are scattered evenly over the entire field (*280*, p. 93, and *288*, p. 134).

A similar practice is reported for areas of plow culture in north and northeastern Shoa Province of Ethiopia. Fields are first "scratched" in several directions with a wooden plow to dislodge the turf, which is then heaped into piles about a meter in diameter. A small pile of cow dung is placed on the windward side of each pile and set afire. The turf is gradually pulled over the fire until all debris is burned. The ash and burned soil are spread evenly over the field, and the area is plowed twice. The burning process is estimated to make the soil considerably less acid in reaction, sometimes raising the pH as much as 0.2 or 0.3 (*146*, pp. 141–42).

Use of Animal Manures

The use of animal manures, found in the Congo Basin only in the short-fallow systems of the Lugbara, and among the peoples of Rwanda, Burundi, and some neighboring areas, is reported here and there in widely scattered areas of tropical Africa.

The Hill Pagans of Dikwa Emirate, northern Nigeria, and three groups in eastern Africa — the Kara, found on Ukara Island in Lake Victoria; the Chagga on Mount Kilimanjaro and some of their neighbors; and the Konso of southwestern Ethiopia — all have developed permanent field agriculture based largely on stall feeding of cattle and use of animal manures, although shifting cultivation prevails among surrounding peoples (*309*, pp. 3–4; *272*, p. 343; *419*, p. 132; and *206*, p. 415). A number of peoples in the savanna belt of western tropical Africa use animal manures as fertilizers, although shifting cultivation still continues (*60*, pp. 107 and 112; *311*, p. 53; *337*, p. 49; *223*, pp. 21 and 76).[3]

The most common method of utilizing animal manures in western tropical Africa is to shift corrals from time to time and plant old corral sites with crops. Sometimes cultivators who do not own cattle obtain manure by providing corrals for nomadic cattle peoples and in some areas even paying the nomads to use them (*167*, p. 35; *149*, p. 34; and *147*, p. 25). In some instances the nomads use corral sites of their own for crops but they do little or none of the actual cultivation, depending on laborers from neighboring tribes without cattle, who exchange their labor for milk and sometimes other commodities or money wages (*7*, pp. 250–51, and *180*, pp. 29–30).

Among a portion of the Dinka — the western Dinka of Aweil District, Sudan — fields are manured by a system of tethering. Toward the end of the dry season herds are brought in from distant grazing areas and tethered at night 6 to 8 feet apart on fields to be cultivated. After three nights in one spot stakes are moved, until the entire field has received manure (*62*, pp. 294–95). Similar tethering is reported for the Wolof of Senegal and Gambia (*149*, pp. 31–32).

The Birom of northern Nigera, the Kirdi of northern Cameroun, the Kuku on the northern Uganda border, the Tetia of Kenya, and the Nubas of Kordofan Province (south-central Sudan) may also manure some of their main fields, but manuring methods are not discussed (*62*, p. 295; *183*, p. 44; *299*, p. 426; *298*, p. 108; *166*, p. 79; and *122*, p. 86).

North of the Gambaga scarp in Ghana, among the Jerawa of northern Nigeria, and in the savanna zone near the border in the southwestern corner of Chad one finds a system of manured infields and unmanured outfields much like those of Rwanda, Burundi, and some other areas on the eastern edge of the Congo Basin (*243*, p. 17; *166*, p. 23; and *122*, pp. 65–68). A similar practice is suggested for much of central Sudan. Many tribes there are said to manure secondary fields of tobacco, vegetables, or sorghum near the homesite (*62*, p. 295).

Irrigation

Irrigation, of major importance within the Congo Basin only in Rwanda, Burundi, and possibly among the Lugbara is practiced extensively in parts of eastern Africa. It is found along the Nile in northern Sudan; in Ethiopia; along streams and rivers throughout Somalia; in much of the Malagasy Republic; on the island of Zanzibar; and in some mountainous areas of Kenya and Tanzania — among the Suk, Keyo, Endo, Marakuet, and Teita of Kenya; among the Sonjo and Chagga of Tanzania (*146*, pp. 149–51; *143*, (1961), pp. 7–9; *182*, pp. 81, 82, and 91; *298*, pp. 107–8; *161*, pp. 472 and 478–79; and *292*, pp. 95–96).

Little irrigation is reported in western tropical Africa, except in the Cape Verde Islands or for special fields elsewhere planted with such things as onions (*75*, p. 844, and *60*, pp. 114–15). In most of Nigeria, at least, use of wells for irrigation is said to be limited by lack of wells that yield enough water to justify bullock lifts or motorized pumps (*60*, pp. 114–15).

Terracing

Terracing, found only in Rwanda and Burundi in the Congo Basin, is reported in several scattered areas elsewhere in tropical Africa. Terracing without irrigation is a central feature of the agriculture of the Pagan peoples of the southern fringes of the Jos Plateau, among the Birom, and in the northeastern corner of Nigeria (Dikwa Emirate); in northern Cameroun; and on Ukara Island in Lake Victoria (*166*, p. 79; *60*, pp. 109–10; *223*, p. 21; and *309*, p. 5). In Ethiopia elaborate systems of terracing that may be irrigated are found in Tigre and Shoa provinces, in the Chercher Highlands, and among the Konso (*146*, pp. 145–49). Terracing is also found, but not well described, in parts of the hill areas of northern Cameroun and western Sudan, among the Iraq of Tanzania, and in central Madagascar (*122*, p. 86; *137*, p. 34; *182*, p. 129; and *328*, p. 230).

9

Animal and Insect Husbandry

Much less information is available on animal husbandry than on crop production, although most tribes, with the possible exception of fishing tribes, keep domestic animals and make special provisions for their care.

Animal Husbandry

Where cattle are kept they are typically attended at all times by a cowherd; when pastures become too coarse they are usually burned to make grazing easier; animals are given salt regularly; calves get supplementary feed. Quite a number of treatments for animal maladies are known and practiced. Sterilization of animals is not common, although the practice is widely known. Animals kept for breeding purposes may be carefully chosen.

In several areas where they are kept, swine are penned part of the time and given some feed. Goats, sheep, chickens, and dogs are often given access to the owner's hut at night, or are provided with special shelters.

The most detailed information about animal husbandry is available for the Bashi of Kivu and for Rwanda-Burundi.

The Bashi

A detailed description of animal husbandry among the Bashi by F. Carlier was published in 1912 (69); supplementary information is given by P. Colle (*84*). According to Carlier's account, use of cattle is more common than ownership.[1] The chief owns cattle and lends them to selected subjects, with the agreement that most of the male calves and the milk will go to the borrower, while all female offspring, and occasionally a male calf, will go to the chief (*69*, p. 783). The borrowers then hire herders, who are paid with two or three male calves annually and possibly with part of the milk — Carlier states merely that herders have "some use of the herd."[2] A. J. Van Gheluwe, writing of the Mumosho area about 1952, says that a number of other arrangements also exist, involving (a) exchange of cattle and small livestock between equals and (b) loan of the use of cows between equals in exchange for interest in the form of small livestock and poultry (*381*, pp. 114–16).

Care of Cattle. The Bashi have three kinds of cattle, classified by horn size and shape: cattle with long horns, 70 to 110 cm. long; cattle with medium horns, something like half as long, and hornless animals (*69*, p. 776).[3] The last two types are preferred because especially wide doorways must be built in the farmer's hut if long-horned cattle are to be sheltered in it, and also because the long-horned animals do not fatten easily and are poor milkers.

The herd is taken to pasture daily and lodged in the keeper's hut at night during the rainy season.[4] In the dry season (June to September) the quality of pastures declines sharply, and animals must be taken a long distance — usually to higher elevations where rainfall is heavier — to find enough grass. During this period cattle spend the night in the pasture. The bulls are staked at night, the other animals are driven near them, and then a ring of small fires is built around the herd to discourage predators. The herder builds a temporary shelter on the perimeter of the circle which he and weaker calves occupy.

Animals are always watered in streams because of the belief that stagnant water is a source of intestinal parasites (*69*, p. 786). In some areas cattle are taken to salty marshes at the change of seasons for salt, but in areas lacking access to natural salt, locally produced salt is bought in the market and fed to the herd. According to M. Jussiant, forage is sometimes given the herd when it is brought in from pasture (*200*, p. 431).

Bulls run with the cows. Usually the ratio is one bull for forty or fifty cows, and breeding takes place any time of year. A bull is judged by his ability to fatten, the percentage of cows he can impregnate, his readiness to service them, the quality of his offspring, the percentage of them which are females, and the quality of his ancestors (*69*, p. 781). A good bull is not used for breeding until he is three or four years old, and heifers "are never bred before three years of age" (*69*, p. 782). Persons desiring to breed a cow with a bull of another herd usually give a pot or two of banana beer or palm wine, or something of similar value, in exchange.

Old or sterile cows are sold or slaughtered. Most cows bear seven to eight calves. Cows are judged by the ease with which they become pregnant, the amount of milk they give, and the percentage of the offspring which is females. Usually a cow is sold or slaughtered if her first four or five calves are all males (*69*, p. 782).

Cows are not penned at calving time. Animals having difficulty calving may be assisted, but are also sometimes slaughtered. The newborn calves are kept in the herder's hut the first three or four months. If the mother refuses to let her calf nurse, she is baited with a little salt sprinkled on the newborn. If this fails, the cow is usually hobbled and an attempt is made to force her to let the calf suck. Should this also fail, a nurse cow is sought; as an alternative, the calf is slaughtered, for the herder never attempts to hand-feed it (*69*, p. 788). The purgative power of colostrum is well recognized, and care is taken to prevent a calf from drinking too much of its mother's milk at first. Calves are allowed to nurse twice daily, at milking time, and are permitted to take as much milk as they need. If the cow gives little milk, the calf may be given all of it.

Cows are milked on a spot previously sprinkled with "white salt" and water to keep flies away (*84*, p. 678). They are not fed at milking, but are merely immobilized by a cord tied around the hocks. The milker washes his hands and the containers for milk before milking (*84*, p. 678). The milk vessel is washed with hot water (*69*, p. 792), not cow's urine as in Rwanda. The milker squats on his heels or sit on a stool and milks into a wooden pot, whistling as he works in order to help tranquilize the cow (*69*, p. 790). To induce the cow to release her milk, the calf is allowed to nurse a little — even after weaning — before she is milked, or she may be given a lick of salt, or "a suppository made from banana peels and warmed over a fire" may be inserted (*84*, p. 682).

As the calf develops, it is gradually fed tender grass. When it has reached three or four months of age, it is allowed to roam near the hut from about 9:00 A.M. until 4:00 P.M. being watched by small boys, while the herd is away in pasture. Calves may also be staked in a nearby fallow (*169*, p. 113). They are weaned when about four months old; after they are a year old, they are allowed to run with the herd.

Ticks are removed when found, and cattle are generally kept clean.

Manure is carefully removed from the area around the hut where animals are apt to lie down, and is stacked in a pile. (Manure is not only used to fertilize bananas-plantains and tobacco plots; in areas short of fuel it may also be burned. Mixed with clay, it is used as a plaster for granary walls, baskets, or as the final layer on the hut floor [*69*, p. 793].)

The Bashi have several remedies for cattle illnesses. Piroplasma,[5] a disorder the Africans recognize as contagious, is treated by isolating the stricken animal — but taking care not to move it; then providing it with a cold cover, and giving it an enema or a purgative made from wild cucumber, papyrus leaves, or leaves of a bush called *mugenge* which have been cooked about twelve hours (*69*, p. 681). If the beast does not recover in three days, it is killed and the meat eaten (*69*, p. 794).

Pneumonia is treated by applying an irritant to the forequarters of the diseased beast, or by cauterizing that area with a red-hot iron (*69*, p. 795).

Pleurisy is mentioned, but its treatment is not described.

A disease locally called *ruika*, which Carlier says is a nutritional disease characterized by an edema, is treated by bleeding the ill animal.

Vundja is the Bashi name for a disease which causes slobbering and sores in the animal's mouth. Treatment is by sprinking the infected areas with potash made from marsh herbs, mixed with ground leaves from indigo and a bush called *mutuzo* (*84*, p. 681).

Three treatments are known for sunstroke: a cold pack applied to the animal's head; red pepper rubbed in its eyes; and cauterization of its head.

"Staggers" is treated by placing a leather blindfold over the eyes of the animal (*84*, p. 682).

Inflammation of the throat or shoulder is treated by cauterizing it and applying a plaster of cow dung (*84*, p. 681). Calves with swollen throats may be forced to consume a drink made from centipedes and the leaves of the "false cork-oak" (*84*, p. 682).

Cattle with diarrhea are given a dose of a mixture obtained by kneading the leaves of *lukalaju* or *mukuzonyana* in sour whey (*84*, p. 681).

Abscesses are cauterized and bathed with herbal medicines not described.

Rutandara, characterized by general trembling, is treated by cauterizing the animal's flanks (*84*, p. 682).

Swelling about the hooves, accompanied by intense lameness, is treated by lacerating the swollen areas and bathing them with running water (*69*, p. 797).

Eczema is treated by applying "oil" to the udder. For runny eyes, an ointment made from monkey dung mixed with butter is applied.

The Africans know no cure for two maladies Carlier calls hygroma of the knee and "udder disorder" (69, p. 797).

Small Livestock. Both long-haired and short-haired goats are common to the region. Carlier gives the impression that goats are owned by even the poorest households (69, p. 750).

Goats are allowed to roam the village, and they may follow the cattle to pasture. At night they occupy their owner's hut. Kids are kept in the owner's hut day and night until they reach an age of two or three months.

Sheep are kept and apparently are treated as goats are. Swine are not kept.

Small livestock suffering from diarrhea may be fed salt mixed with soil from a termite mound and given an enema. Often sheep are killed as soon as they show symptoms of diarrhea, so that the carcasses may be obtained before they lose weight (69, p. 795).

When either sheep or goats contract an eczema, they are killed immediately to prevent the disease from spreading (69, p. 796).

Poultry. Chickens are common and Barbary ducks are found in some areas. Except for a statement that they are found in their owner's hut, information is not provided on the care of poultry.

Rwanda-Burundi

Several accounts of cattle care in Rwanda-Burundi are available, but none is as detailed as Carlier's study of cattle among the Bashi. Except for a few points, practices in Rwanda-Burundi appear to be roughly the same as those he describes.

Grassland is burned annually, and in some parts of Rwanda-Burundi pastures are irrigated (91, p. 28). Usually cattle are herded by day, and kept at night in a corral built of wood, or hedge of euphorbia or fig if wood is scarce. Contrary to the Bashi practice, it is apparently uncommon for animals to sleep in the herder's hut, although young calves may be housed with the herder or in a special hut (245, p. 630; 82, p. 246; 99, p. 54).

Because adult animals are not usually sheltered in huts, there is no reason for concern about their ability to pass through hut doorways. In Rwanda-Burundi, breeds with long horns predominate; horn growth is even encouraged by irritating the horn buds on calves, then rubbing the irritated area with butter.[6]

Cattle are not corralled everywhere. The Hima, a nomadic group located in the northern part of Rwanda, have no permanent corrals. They "follow their herds and in the evening bunch them around a fire; sometimes a rudimentary corral is made of branches from thorns to protect the herd from wild animals . . . they move on the next day in search of new pasture" (*245*, pp. 629–30).

Meyer's account of Rwanda-Burundi, like Carlier's of the Bashi, stresses the great amount of care given large livestock (*258*, p. 63):

The animals are conscientiously cared for every day. Every night fresh litter is provided in the pens for the herds returning from pasture. The animals are scrubbed clean with straw whisks and searched for ticks and other parasites which may have attached themselves to the animals. The udders are washed each time after milking. While cattle are standing in the kraals or drinking from the troughs, they are bothered by stinging flies; . . . . For this reason fires are kept burning in the kraals and near the watering places, the smoke driving away the flies. . . . From time to time the animals are given saliferous ashes to lick. Even in the pastures the herdsman is constantly occupied with his herd. He is able to give it all kinds of orders by shrill whistling. As a result of good treatment, the animals are in most cases very good-natured; they do not kick, and they keep still when something is being done to them. In the latter case one of the herdsmen usually uses his stick or reed to stroke the animal gently between the upper part of the hind legs. Despite their long horns, the animals also cause much less damage among themselves than one might expect. Even if they are crowded together when driven to or from the pasture, a constant muffled rattling and clanking of the colliding horns can be heard — the characteristic sound of a moving Urundi herd — but it is extremely seldom that animals injure each other. In case an animal is seriously injured or becomes sick and the owner himself is unable to help which, however, he is usually able to do — a Mutussi or Muhutu who is skilled in medicine is called to act as a veterinarian. For this help he is paid very well. . . .

In some areas "every sixth or eighth" animal wears a metal or wooden bell; in other areas no bells are worn (*258*, p. 61).

Sacred cattle, a selected group of animals with long upright horns, are kept in separate herds from other cattle and are never bred with other types (*82*, p. 240). Within each sacred herd, care is taken to introduce bulls from other long-horned herds in order to prevent degeneration of type (*258*, p. 64).

Evidence on general practices to control the fertility of cattle is contradictory. Colback and Mortehan say castration is not practiced, and the latter adds that it was forbidden under penalty of death (*82*, p. 240; *270*, p. 476). Meyer states that castration is known and that there is a term for it — *kuschahura* — but that most bulls are not castrated (*258*, p. 64). Similar discrepancies are found in discussions of sterilization of cows.

Marchi says that cows are neither sold nor killed because of sterility (*245*, p. 631). De Greef states that sterile cows are valued because they fatten more readily, and says that attempts may be made to sear a cow's reproductive organs and thereby induce sterility (*99*, p. 56). Czekanowski seems to be referring to this practice in Ruanda when he says "it is rumored that cows one is forced to return are cauterized in revenge" (*91*, p. 29). Meyer states that "there are a great many sterile cows in both Urundi and Ruanda," but he says nothing about how they became sterile (*258*, p. 65).

The ratio of bulls to cows in the herd is kept within desired limits by regular slaughter of bull calves, as among the Bashi.

No attempt is made to regulate the time of calving, but according to Mathieu, chief of the Luvironza livestock research station, the availability of pasture brings about a natural cycle of fertility in the cows which causes most conceptions to occur in February or March, i.e. four or five months after the rains begin, a time when animals have regained strength lost during the dry season. Thus calves are usually born in November and December, at the beginning of the rainy season (*249*, p. 899). When a calf is born it is rubbed with butter (*258*, p. 65).

A number of exceptions to Bashi milking practices are noted. Meyer suggests that only unruly cows are hobbled at milking; otherwise they are not held at all (*258*, p. 65). The milk vessel is rinsed daily with cow's urine [7] and smoked. Other milking practices mentioned are ones for which only Rwanda-Burundi data are available; it is not possible to determine whether they represent deviation from Bashi methods. If a cow refuses her calf, salt water may be rubbed on both her udder and the calf, "whereupon the cow will lick the calf and will also allow it to lick and suck her udder" (*258*, p. 65). When a calf dies, or is slaughtered, the calf's skin is stuffed with straw and presented to the cow at each milking for a while to induce her to release her milk (*258*, p. 65; *91*, p. 26; *270*, p. 477).[8] When a calf is to be weaned, its mother's teats are smeared with cow dung to keep the calf from sucking (*258*, p. 65).

Small Livestock.   Care of goats and sheep is little discussed. Czekanowski states that goats are frequently castrated, even though cattle rarely are (*91*, p. 29). Neither goats nor sheep are eaten; they are raised for their hides and for use as sacrifices or oracles (*258*, p. 69).

The Alur, Bira, Lugbara, and Lendu

M. Turco, veterinary for the Société des Mines d'Or de Kilo-Moto, gives a very brief general description of animal husbandry among the tribes in the Ituri area of the northeastern Congo Basin in an article published in 1934 (*362*) and singles out the Alur and Lugbara as especially important. He notes that livestock products, "meat, butter, milk, skins, etc., are objects of a rather important trade" in this area, and points out that animals are eaten when they die of natural causes but are only rarely slaughtered (*362*, p. 577). Hides are used as body wraps and bindings.

M. A. Loeckx states that animals are not penned, although cattle are picketed near the hut at night (*237*). Other writers, however, credit at least the Bira, Lugbara, and Lendu with use of corrals for enclosing animals at night (*335*, p. 358; *378*, p. 54; *43*, pp. 120–21). According to Loeckx, cattle and goats are herded in fallow fields near the hut. Traps, lances, and bows and arrows are employed in protecting the herd from marauders (*362*, p. 578). Turco indicates that selective breeding is practiced. Pastures are given a supervised burning in October to bring a growth of new grass (*422*, pp. 13–14).

The Northern Tabwa

The Marungu Plateau — rising from 1,800 to 2,300 meters above sea level — comprises the central part of the zone occupied by the northern Tabwa on the southwestern edge of Lake Tanganyika. Off the plateau the average elevation about 1,000 meters. Everywhere the vegetation is woodland or grassland; no forest is found. In 1956 the population density was estimated at 4.1 persons per square kilometer. The staple crop appears to be manioc; but maize, finger millet, sorghum, wheat, barley, sweet potatoes, Irish potatoes, coleus potatoes, taro, possibly yams, bananas-plantains, shallots, and sesame are of some importance (*73*, pp. 38–55). In 1956 goats, sheep, cattle, and a few swine were counted in the census of African livestock in Baudouinville territoire, but no ducks, pigeons, or turkeys were reported (*73*, p. 97):

Category	Number
Cattle	585
Goats	9,468
Sheep	4,772
Swine	37
Chickens	39,445

Cattle are not widely owned; the 585 head belonged to 13 individuals.

V. Roelens, an early missionary in the Baudouinville area, states in an article published in 1911 that goats and sheep are penned together at night in either a communal hut built to house the village animals, small houses built behind the huts of the persons owning them, or the owners' huts (*307*, pp. 328, 330). Huts built for goats and sheep are usually placed on high ground, and a mound may be constructed if no natural mound is available. Litter of maize or manioc stalks is placed inside such shelters, and a thorn fence is built around the goat huts. When goat shelters are no longer serviceable, they are burned and another is built. Whether old goat shelter sites are cultivated is not stated.

If a village has a large goat and sheep population, gardens are usually not attempted in the village; if the herd is small, animals are usually tethered. Large herds may be herded by adolescents (*232*, p. 216).

To prevent gastric disorders goats and sheep are not let out of their huts in the morning until after the dew dries.

Bangu Area, Bas-Congo

Some farmers keep swine in the Manilonde area, but elsewhere there is little swine production (*121*, p. 826). Where swine are raised, pig pens are built in the village, and pigs are penned during the day but allowed to roam at night. Swine are fed wastes and some "manioc, maize, etc." to supplement what they find while foraging at night. Sheep and goats are given neither shelter nor feed.

Chickens and ducks are found in all villages except Congo-Botongo, "where for some unknown reason there are only a few chickens and no ducks at all" (*121*, p. 827). No feed is given poultry, but they are sometimes locked in the kitchen at night, where they eat scraps and processing offal lying about. Some farmers keep pigeons, which they house in specially constructed coops and feed maize and peanuts.

Inkisi Area, Bas-Congo

Animal husbandry seems to be the same as in Bangu sector, except that swine are let out of their pens "after the hot hours of the day" at Inkisi, rather than at night. Swine are fed manioc, maize, and oil palm fruit (*121*, p. 827).

The Luvale

The Luvale feed manioc and kitchen wastes to their swine, but other care is not described (*418*).

The Ngandu

The Ngandu construct small shelters for goats, the largest livestock they raise. Otherwise little information is available on their techniques of animal husbandry, except a note that castration is practiced and animals may be fattened for slaughter (*106*, p. 223).

The Luba

Goats and sheep are kept in special small raised huts at night; swine are never penned. Care of chickens is not described, but there is discussion of pigeon shelters. Pigeon lofts are made by building on a wattle platform cylindrical wattle and mud coops with a conical grass roof (*83*, p. 216).

The Southern Songe

Cattle are not herded and are half wild. Neither cattle, goats, nor sheep are milked. Goats and sheep are penned at night. Swine are penned during the rainy season, when crops are grown near the village. Villages with a large population of small livestock grow few if any crops near the village. Small livestock are generally fed refuse from the kitchens of their owners.

Small livestock are often castrated (*400*, p. 26).

Mange is treated with the sap of a bush called *panda-nganga* which is boiled and applied to the irritated skin (*400*, p. 27). Diarrhea is treated by feeding the ill animals manioc peelings, grain, balls of flour, or kitchen scraps.

Dogs are kept both for their meat and for hunting; hence Vermeesch lists them among livestock (*400*, p. 24).

Chickens roost in the kitchen hut or in a small hut specially constructed for them.

The Northern Songe

Care of cattle, goats, and sheep is not discussed. Chickens roost in their owner's hut at night, resting on special baskets fixed for them about 1.5 meters off the ground in corners of the hut (*387*, p. 217). Pigeons are kept in special houses built for them.

The Sundi

The Sundi have no cattle, and efforts by missionaries to introduce them have been unsuccessful; but small livestock are of some importance and are given special attention (*213*, p. 7). Goats, sheep, and swine are cared for by paid specialists who live apart in special villages located a considerable distance from fields. Pigs are penned at night to protect them from leopards.

Dogs are cared for by their owners and have special shelters; pups are fed on sweet potatoes (*213*, p. 119). Cats are also considered valuable animals, but their care is not described.

The Mbé Tio (Teke)

The Tio of the Mbé Plateau lend goats under an arrangement by which the borrower gets half of the offspring. The only care reported is the practice of penning goats in a sturdy log goat house at night. Chickens are also penned in special shelters at night. Dogs, valued for hunting, are fed manioc and are kept in the owner's dwelling at night (*394*).

The Holo

The Holo say they have had no cattle since about the turn of the century, when their herds were reportedly destroyed by disease epidemics. Little is reported on their care of cattle then except that all village animals were herded by a chief herder assisted by two small boys, and that for his services he received every eighth calf (*103*, p. 25).

The Lulua

The Lulua and some neighboring Luba keep not only goats, sheep, swine, chickens, ducks, and pigeons but also some rabbits and guinea pigs, according to a study of the Kamuandu and Bakwanga areas by H. Beguin in the late 1950's (*44*, p. 88). Rabbits and guinea pigs are penned day and night, and are fed kitchen and tables wastes; other small livestock, except swine, are locked in the owner's hut at night. Special huts are built for swine.

During some seasons, goats and sheep are tethered to keep them out of fields; otherwise they roam about the village freely, and fields are protected by their distance from the village, or by fences (*44*, p. 89).

Other Tribes

Among the Kongo of former French Equatorial Africa, goats and sheep suffering from *pelade* (*Aloepcia*) are treated with "pounded leaves of *mbaka* (*Tephrosia* sp. or *Strychnos* sp.?)" that are mixed with palm oil (*331*, p. 44). Animals with "gangrenous head colds" are made to drink a mixture of chilies and ashes.

The only remedy that the Huana, a group of the Mbala, on the Kwilu River try when livestock are ill is bleeding. The usual procedure is to cut off a portion of the animal's ear to start the flow of blood (*355*, p. 280).

Castration of animals being fattened, particularly swine, is reported to be common among the Kongo. Both goats and swine are castrated by the Ha and Mbala; among the latter this is the work of specialists, and salt is rubbed in the wound.[9] There is also report of castration of swine by the Luchazi and possibly the Luvale (*361*, p. 26). The Banza, in the northern part of the Congo Basin, are noted for the practice of castrating goats; and the practice is also reported for the Logo (*193*, 1:362; *221*, p. 308).

For the Azande and Kela a little information is available on chicken care, although data on care of animals are not given. Among the Azande "chicken-pens are built against the walls of the hut, either on ground level, rather like dog kennels, or raised from the ground like a dove cote" (*43*, p. 46). The Kela provide "little houses" for chickens, "a luxury to which most Congo fowls are unaccustomed" (*179*, p. 181).

Beekeeping

Along the eastern edge of the Congo Basin and in a few areas in the south, hives are made for bees; in a number of other areas bees are robbed, but no effort is made to assist them in producing honey.

A valuable source of information about beekeeping in the Belgian Congo proper is provided by the inquiry undertaken in 1911 by the Congo government in which agricultural officers in various parts of the basin reported on conditions in their districts (*12*).

Rwanda-Burundi

Shantz states that in Burundi bees are kept in cylindrical hives 1.3 to 1.6 meters long and about 50 cm. in diameter that are made from tree trunks, papyrus, or palm fiber. Usually hives are placed in trees or bushes. Swarms in the air are made to settle by loud cries and by throwing water on them (*326*, p. 348).

Hans Meyer, in a treatise just published in 1916, gives the following account (*258*, p. 57):

Agriculture is most widespread in the outer provinces of Ujogoma and Usige which still contain most of the forest and tree steppe. For the Barundi honey is of the greatest importance since they do not have any other sweetening. . . .

The *beehives* (*umusingo*) are shaped like short, thick tubes about one and a half meters in length and half a meter in diameter, and they are made either from a hollowed-out tree trunk or, in areas where there are only a few trees, from papyrus and sorghum stalks tied or twisted together. . . . The two openings of the tube are closed by discs made of wood or of plaited straw with a hole for the bees to fly out. There is also a flight board in front of the hole. As soon as a new swarm flies out with its queen, it is sprinkled with dust and water so it will not fly afield or will drop to the ground. The swarm of bees with its queen is then carefully swept into the tubes which are brought to it, the opening is closed, and the hive is suspended from a tree or a pole . . . the "beekeepers" know quite well how to protect themselves by covering the whole body with barkcloth.

Gathering honey from the beehives later is a much simpler procedure. At night, when the bees are not flying, the back of the hive is opened, and a glowing wisp of straw which is smoking strongly is introduced, causing the bees to crowd together in the opposite corner. The honeycombs are cut out and then preserved in a pot. . . . There are many different uses of the *wax* in the Barundi household. . . . Since a demand for it has developed in the markets, bee keeping has noticeably increased in the border regions accessible to trade.

Czekanowski says hives are daubed with clay and are placed in trees or on "special frames that have crossed legs . . . [and] are placed on the ground near the huts. . . . Special long-handled knives (*ulukezo*) with short, wide blades are used to cut out the combs" (*91*, p. 34).

The Bashi

Cylindrical grass and wattle beehives are made, and in some areas people specialize in beekeeping. Kevers states that in Kabare territoire some farmers have as many as a hundred hives (*204*, p. 974). Bees are robbed once a year, usually after the rainy season. In the dry season, the period when pastures are burned, hives are transferred to marshy areas or to higher altitudes. Honey is eaten alone or mixed with flour (*12*, p. 473).

The neighboring Hunde are said to place beehives near the village or in sorghum fields; honey is harvested every three months and is "consumed with fermented milk and banana wine" (*13*, p. 704).

The Beni-Lubero Area

Long cylindrical hives are made of grass and wattle in the Beni-Lubero area and are placed either in trees or on forked stakes about a meter off the ground (*77*, pp. 42–44).

The Logo, Kakwa, and Lugbara

Among the Logo beekeeping was possibly more important in the traditional economy than in any other area of the northern Congo Basin. In a note published in 1911 comparing beekeeping practices of the northern Congo Basin, Gustin says of the Logo and Modo, "not only are they cultivators and cattlekeepers but they practice bee culture" (*168*, p. 469). For most other tribes he gives only data on how honey is used. That the importance of beekeeping is exceptional among the Logo is also suggested by the fact that the most detailed account of beekeeping in the northern Congo Basin is one given by R. Bélot of an area occupied by the Logo, Kakwa, a group of the Fajulu, Lugbara, and Mundu.

Bélot says that at the end of the dry season (March or April) cylindrical hives 25 cm. in diameter and 50 cm. long are fashioned out of coarse grass and plastered with cow dung. The ribs of the frame are made of small tree branches formed into hoops with crosspieces placed in the same plane as the hoop to support wax and honey. Care is taken to use a wood which will not easily rot. When straw and cow dung have been applied to the frame, a hole is made in each end, and a conical roof, made of straw, is attached over one end to keep out rain. In March or April, after hives placed the previous year have been robbed, new hives are placed near the village in low trees of any species.

Robbing is accomplished about 7 P.M.; the robbers protect themselves by wearing calabashes in which an opening made for vision is screened with straw. Grass torches are used to drive the bees away and provide light. Once emptied, the old hive is destroyed, often burned, to prevent the bees from attempting to find shelter in its fragments (*48*, p. 456).[10]

The honeycomb collected is heated in jars, and when the wax has melted and floats on top, it is skimmed off. Honey is stored in pots and eaten as it is, diluted with hot water, or mixed with milk. Unlike some other tribes in the northern Congo Basin, neither the Logo, Lugbara, nor Kakwa use honey in making beer (*48*, p. 456). No use is made of the wax.

The Mandja

The Mandja carefully search for beehives in the dry season, assisted by a bird, the honey guide (*Indicator sparmanis*), which by its cries leads men and animals to hives hoping to get bee larvae and honeycomb once the hive is robbed.[11] The Mandja do not always provide hives for bees, but if they do it is a long cylindrical straw hive that is placed in a tree. Unidentified leaves are chewed and spit into the hive to attract the swarm (*397*, p. 133).

The Ndembu, Luvale, and Chokwe

Information given to the editors of the *Bulletin Agricole du Congo Belge* in 1912 by one Arbulot (*33*) suggests that beekeeping may be of considerable importance among the Ndembu, Luvale, and Chokwe. To construct a hive, a log of "large diameter" is cut into lengths of 1 to 1.5

meters and hollowed out,[12] then sticks are placed in the interior to support the honeycomb. The two extremities are sealed, except for a hole in the center of each, and the hive is placed in a tree, 3 to 5 meters off the ground. Hives may be located either near the village or in nearby woodland (*33*, p. 937). Honey is used to flavor foods and to make a fermented drink.

Other Tribes

Emin Pasha, who traveled among the Azande and other tribes of the northeastern Congo Basin in the 1880's, says of that area: "The natives hang baskets on the top of isolated trees. . . . The bees avail themselves of the dwellings thus provided for them, and complete the business. If the natives, upon inspection, find the baskets full, they expel the bees with smoke and gather the honey. . . ." (*70*, p. 261).

According to a report by Engles, published in 1911, the Mongo place beehives in dead trees (*128*, p. 471). M. Soret states that beekeeping is unknown among the eastern Kongo but that the western Kongo, particularly the Bembe group, give bees care (*331*, p. 43). Nemery provides a few notes on beekeeping in the southern part of Tetela country about 1912. There hives are placed in trees; honey is harvested by felling the tree, forcing smoke around the hive, and, when the bees are calm, removing the honeycomb (*16*, p. 934). The Luwa make cylindrical hives out of bark and place them in trees bearing flowers sought by bees (*47*, pp. 72–73).

The Lungu, located at the southern tip of Lake Tanganyika, apparently do not provide hives for bees, but rely on the honey guide bird to help them locate hives. Holes are cut in the tree trunk below the hive; smoke and fire are applied to expel the bees; and the honey and comb are removed (*336*, p. 226).

Caterpillar Husbandry

The Holo practice an interesting form of insect husbandry that partly supports an active commerce with Kinshasa (formerly Leopoldville) in dried and smoked caterpillars. Early in the dry season a carefully selected parcel of savanna is burned. Female butterflies are attracted to the burned patches in which grass is greener than in the surrounding savanna, and lay their eggs. As the eggs hatch the young caterpillars begin to feed on the pasture created for them. When they start to crawl out of the pasture a band is burned around, and the process is repeated until they are grown (*103*, p. 24). They are then killed, dried, smoked, and are ready for market. Denis underscores the importance of caterpillars as a cash earner (*103*,

p. 24): "In season, during the month of September, the Portuguese of Leopoldville come and buy them by the truckload in south Kwango and resell them at a large profit on the markets of the capital [Kinshasa]. The consumers who fancy this delicacy do not hesitate to pay five francs for a cup of caterpillars. These Lepidoptera larvae are the delicacies of connoisseurs, the equal of caviar, snails, or truffles among the European gourmets."

10

Storage and Processing Techniques

Methods of storage and processing are less frequently discussed in the literature than methods of cultivation and animal husbandry, but enough data are available to suggest a wide range of techniques. Everywhere in the Congo Basin storage and processing methods reflect heavy substitution of labor for capital, as can be expected where capital is extremely scarce. Both storage and processing operations tend to be small scale and decentralized. Foodstuffs appear to be stored largely on the farm, and many of them are rarely transported more than a few miles once they are processed. Like cultivation techniques, storage and processing are often strikingly different in forest and savanna areas.

Storage

Only outside the forest zone are large quantities of foodstuffs stored, and the amount of storage probably increases with the length of the dry season. Many of the crops grown in forest areas, such as bananas-plantains, manioc, yams, taro, can be harvested over an extended period of time; furthermore, because the dry season is short, planting of most crops can be staggered over a considerable period, to extend the harvest season. Moreover, a larger variety of crops can be grown, giving scope for extending the planting period within the agricultural calendar.

An additional factor is the importance in forest areas of manioc, a crop that grows well in all the vegetation zones of the Congo Basin, except in relatively small areas with elevations above 2,000 meters. People who rely on manioc have a reduced need for storage because this crop can be left in the ground without deterioration for as much as a year after it is mature.

Crops may be stored in four principal ways: in the farmer's hut; in granaries; in hermetically sealed pots kept either in the farmer's hut or in a granary; and in packages suspended in trees (Map 10-1).

When foodstuffs are stored in the farmer's hut, they are usually put on a shelf placed on supports over the hearth or suspended from the roof. This keeps their moisture content low, and the regular application of smoke reduces weevil damage. Evidence available on maize strongly suggests that storage losses incurred with grain stored in this fashion are often less than 5 percent in the Congo Basin — and not 20 to 30 percent as has often been asserted — because of the beneficial effect of the smoke and heat (*264*, pp. 241–43).

Granaries are cylindrical or rectangular structures raised off the ground so that air can circulate under the floor and small fires can be built under them from time to time. They are usually filled and emptied by raising one corner of the thatched roof, or by removing it if the granary is small. Various materials — mud and wattle, bamboo, and perhaps cow dung — are used in granary construction. At least two groups — the peoples of the Congo's Ubangi District and the Azande — build their granaries with supports tall enough so that the space beneath can be used as a kitchen, thus combining the advantages of storing over the hearth with those of granary storage.

Across most of the savanna zone of the northern Congo Basin, in Rwanda-Burundi, and in some parts of the southern savanna, foodstuffs may be wrapped in packets after harvest and suspended in trees until needed, a technique I have also seen in the savanna zone of western tropical Africa — in the Ivory Coast and Cameroun. In the northern savanna of the Congo Basin maize ears are often tied into large bundles and placed in trees (*221*, p. 301; *108*, pp. 278–85; *256*, p. 886), and among the Rega, maize is stored in fields on racks (*102*, p. 87).

The Pende in the southern savanna place peanuts and other foodstuffs that are especially vulnerable to rodents in conical basket-like structures, each of which is suspended from the top of a tall pole (*351*, p. 212).

Among the Holoholo on the edge of Lake Tanganyika, sorghum, the

MAP 10-1

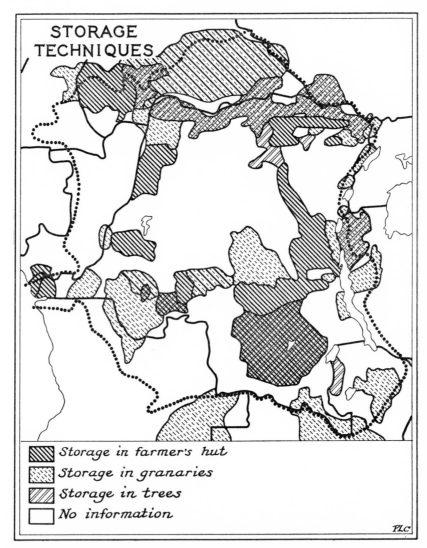

Data from sources cited in text and from J. Annaert, *Contribution a l'étude geographique de l'habit et de l'habitation indigènes en milieu rural dans les provinces orientale et du Kivu*, Mémoire de l'Académie Royale de Sciences d'Outre-Mer, N.S., Vol. X, fasc. 3 (Brussels, 1960). Map: Food Research Institute.

staple crop, may either be placed in granaries or be wrapped in packets 50 cm. long and 20 cm. in diameter, using wide leaves for wrapping material (*317*, p. 67). These packets are kept in the farmer's hut, and no granary is built. If the harvest is large, granaries are made out of bark. Such structures are about a meter high and 60 to 75 cm. in diameter, and are closed on the bottom with a disk of bark. All holes and cracks are sealed with mud, and the cylinder is placed on a platform where it is given a conical grass roof.

Maize and beans are put in packages like those described for sorghum and are stored in the hut. Peanuts are thought to dry out too rapidly if stored in the hut, so they are wrapped in grass packets which are placed in the fork of a tree near the hut.

The Bemba employ egg-shaped grass containers about 65 cm. in diameter for storage of legumes and peanuts, but appear always to keep these bundles in granaries. Richards tells how they construct their grass containers (*305*, pp. 86–87): "A round or oblong hole about 18 inches across and a foot deep is dug in soft ground. Strands of bark[1] are laid crisscross over the hole, sometimes with short sticks beneath to strengthen them. A bundle of grass is then spread out on top of the bark fibres and groundnuts or beans poured into the lined hole. More grass is then laid on top of the pile and the bark strands beneath pulled up and knotted firmly on top of the bundle, the projecting ends of grass being cut off smooth." The Bemba store other crops in small baskets or in leaf or gourd containers that are placed in the millet granary. Often "precious seeds or dried legumes" are put into a clay water pot or a gourd, and the mouth of the container is sealed with a layer of clay.

Processing

The amount of processing required by staple foodstuffs grown in the Congo Basin varies greatly. Sweet potatoes, immature maize, and sweet varieties of manioc (i.e. varieties with a low enough concentration of prussic acid for them to be safely consumed raw) may be merely boiled or roasted over coals. Fresh plantain, taro roots, and yams require only peeling and cooking. Millets, sorghum, mature maize, and rice must be threshed and ground or pounded into flour. Bitter varieties of manioc must have their prussic acid content reduced before they are cooked or made into flour.

These are minimum amounts of processing; in fact, most of the staple

dishes prepared in the Congo Basin are derived by somewhat more complicated techniques. Plantains, yams, sweet potatoes, and manioc are
often sliced and dried before flour is made; and most manioc roots are
soaked before being dried. Much of the maize that is eaten is mature
grain, and the more complicated techniques must be used on it, also. To
obtain the colors, textures, and flavors that African peoples desire in
their foods often requires a good deal more than the minimum processing.

Few observers have described foodstuff processing in African tribal
economies in any detail, but relatively more information is available on
production of flour and *chickwangue*, a manioc product, and on methods
of producing alcoholic beverages and oil. The following account is restricted to these products.

The major method of producing flour is to pound grains or dried chunks
of roots or tubers in a fairly large wooden mortar[2] with a pestle made of
heavy wood. In some areas grain is first soaked to soften it, and it may be
pounded more than once in order to produce a finer flour. In the woodlands and grasslands in the north, east, and south, grain is also ground
between two stones among such tribes as the Sanga (*59*, p. 12), northern
Mandja (*150*, p. 234), Banda (*113*, p. 125), Bemba (*305*, p. 92), Lamba
(*115*, p. 116), northern Luba (*400*, p. 338), and the Bunda (*276*, p. 237).
Sometimes coarse flour from the mortar is refined on the grindstone.
Whether grindstones are employed in forest areas cannot be determined
until better data are available,[3] but information at hand clearly suggests
that they are not common; this is what one would expect, considering that
the principal foodstuffs of the forest zone are relatively easy to process
in a mortar. (Obtaining flour from grain is more difficult with a mortar
than with a grindstone, but little flour is made from grain in the forest
areas. Maize is largely consumed immature, rice is boiled whole, and
other grains are little grown.) Thus it is reasonable to suppose that grindstones are employed most often in areas where a considerable portion of
the flour comes from grain.

Methods of processing bitter manioc differ considerably. Manioc roots
are soaked in running water in some areas, but in stagnant water elsewhere.
On the Batéké Plateau, an area where water is scarce, manioc is soaked
in specially made mud holes. Holes are dug and enough water added to
produce mud. Manioc roots are then added and the hole is covered for
three days (*394*). Some tribes peel the roots before soaking; some peel
afterward (Table 10-1). The length of soaking varies greatly from area
to area. It may be as long as two and a half weeks or as short as six hours.

After soaking, the pulp from the root may be boiled at once, or first dried, then pounded into flour and boiled.

Among the Teke group of the Kuba, manioc roots are typically peeled, soaked, and dried over a fire; but sometimes the procedure is to cut them into thin slices after peeling, boil the slices "a considerable length of time,"

TABLE 10-1 Techniques of Making Flour from Bitter Manioc, Selected Tribes, Congo Basin

Tribe or area	Days 1–6	soaked 7–17	Soaking water Stagnant	Running	Peeled before soaking	after soaking	Soaked roots Fire-dried	Sun-dried
Tetela	X			X	X		X	X
Kaka and Baya	X			?		X	?	?
Sakata		X	X		?			
Kasai–Lake Leopold II area	X			?	Xᵃ	Xᵃ		
Mongo		X	X		X			
Ngala	X			?		X		
Bira		X	X		X		?	?
Kuba	X						X	
Yombe		X	X		?			
Brazzaville area		X		X	X			
Kinshasa area	X			?	?			
Kindu area	X			?	X		X	X
Bakusu	X			X	X			
Kwango area	X		X			X		X
Luapula Valley		?		?	X			X
Luvale		?		?		X	X	
Luba	X		X		?			X
Songe	X			X	?			X
Southern Buye	X			?	?			X
Bemba	X			X	X			X
Moyen-Congo area	X					X		
Southern Kongo	X			X		X		X
Yanzi	X					X		X
Dzing	X			?		X		
Holo	?			?		X		X
Tio (Teke)	X		X			X		X
Suku	X		X			X		X
Banda	X		X					X
Mandja	X		X			X		X
Baya	X		X			X		X

ᵃNorthern Songo-Meno peel, then soak roots; southern Songo-Meno soak roots, then peel them. Information is not available on other tribes of the area.

then soak the cooked slices in running water five days (*41*, pp. 70–78). A third method is practiced by the Portuguese in Angola: manioc roots are peeled and "rasped down into a kind of coarse flour" which is then dried on heated stones. The Teke call this preparation by a variant of its Portuguese name: *farinha de mandioca* (*41*, p. 72).

In parts of the western Congo Basin the pulp may be carefully kneaded, defibered, wrapped in leaves, and cooked by various methods, or first cooked before being wapped in leaves. Manioc paste wrapped in leaves is usually called chickwangue, but a more precise term would be simply "wrapped manioc paste," for products called chickwangue are produced by vastly different processes, only one phase of which, the wrapping, is common to them all (Map 10-2).

The Sakata make wrapped paste by soaking manioc roots in stagnant water for two to two and a half weeks, then removing the skin and core fiber. Next, the root is cut into thin slices with a knife which has a double blade 50 to 65 cm. long. The fibers are removed and the slices are rolled with a wooden or stone roller that is about 8 cm. in diameter and 18 cm. long. A fraction of the mass thus produced — considerably less than half — is wrapped in leaves, often banana leaves, and boiled 20 minutes or until glutenous. Actual cooking time depends on the kind of fires and utensils used. Then the cooked part of the mass is mixed with the uncooked remainder, and the mixture is wrapped in a large leaf and cooked 20 to 30 minutes (*274*).

In the area east of the Sakata occupied by the Ekonda, Kutshu, and Songo-Meno, bitter manioc is soaked for five to eight days, peeled, and partially dried in the sun. In the western part of this region (among the Bale and Lese, and all tribes west of them to the Tio) the next step is to chop the peeled manioc before pounding it into flour. In the central part of the area (among the Ipanga, Titu, Yaelima, and Bokala) the roots are not cut up, but are kneaded before they are placed in the mortar[4] (*241*, p. 119). If the roots are chopped, the resulting flour is sifted to remove fiber and impurities; if kneading is practiced, impurities are picked out by hand. Once a fine flour is obtained, wrapped manioc paste is made as described earlier for the Sakata, except that the rolls of paste are stacked in a pot containing water and steamed several hours (*241*, p. 121).

In the Kwango area, ends of manioc roots are cut off to aid removal of toxin, and the roots are soaked in stagnant water three or four days (*4*, p. 487). Usually after three days the roots are peeled and returned to the pool for an additional day of soaking.

Methods of drying the leached roots vary from village to village and may differ within villages (*4*, p. 487). The simplest technique is merely to sun-dry the roots; but the central fiber may be removed and the leached flesh of the root molded into balls before drying. The Mkano, Mbeko, and Sonde defiber the roots, knead the paste in a large wooden mortar, partially dry the mass in the sun, and then make balls of it before it is dried completely (*4*, p. 478). To make wrapped paste the dry manioc ball is pounded into flour; water is then added to make a paste; finally this paste

MAP 10-2

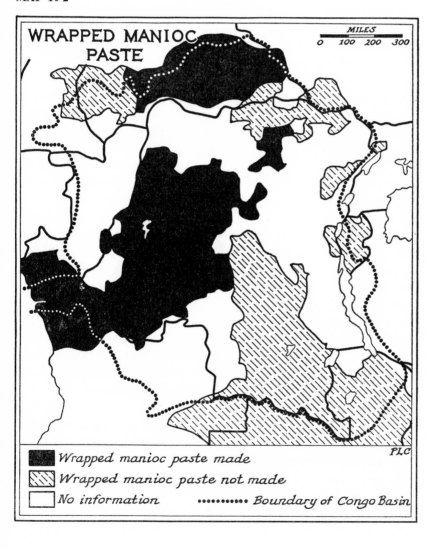

WRAPPED MANIOC PASTE

MILES
0   100   200   300

P.L.C

■ *Wrapped manioc paste made*
▨ *Wrapped manioc paste not made*
□ *No information*   •••••••••• *Boundary of Congo Basin*

is wrapped in leaves and steamed: "Chickwangue is, in sum, only well laminated paste of manioc rolled in leaves and heated a rather long time in as little water as possible" (*4*, p. 478). Adriaens states clearly that "The paste used is made from flour." Except for the Yanzi, this is the only area in the Congo Basin where so far as we know wrapped paste is made from flour (*357*, p. 138).

Among the Ngala the product is wrapped after the steaming. There is great variation in the cooking process, too. William O. Jones reports that in some areas wrapped paste is not cooked, the pounded paste being eaten raw (*195*, p. 104). Where wrapped paste is cooked, it may be either steamed or boiled. The Sakata boil their wrapped pastes about an hour, the Yombe boil it "several hours"; but some of the neighbors of the Sakata, as well as peoples of the Kwango area, and the Ngala, steam paste several hours instead of boiling it.

In the portion of the Congo Basin formerly administered by the French, aromatic herbs are added to the manioc paste before it is cooked (*195*, p. 104); no reference has been found to this practice elsewhere.

Relishes

Relishes are usually prepared by boiling the ingredients together. Some greens and herbs may be dried first, but usually it is only oils, meats, fish, and insects that are processed.

Fish from nearby lakes or streams are not processed, but those from distant sources are either packed in ice or preserved. If preserved they are usually cleaned and gutted as soon as caught, then are dried, smoked over simple wood fires, or salted before being sent to market.[5]

Likewise caterpillars may be cooked fresh, or dried first. In either case the initial operation is to "gut" them by opening the mouthpart with a stick and squeezing them between the thumb and finger. If cooked fresh, they are washed, then boiled an hour or so. Caterpillars that are to be dried are roasted over a fire for several hours after being gutted, then are spread out on a mat and placed in the sun for three or four days.

Termites are usually roasted on a sheet of metal or in a pot. Bee larvae may be boiled; the honeycomb is broken into small pieces and squeezed to extract the honey, then is boiled half an hour or so to cook the larvae.

Salt and potash production continues to be of some importance in isolated and relatively poor areas, although everywhere it is much less significant than it once was. Production of salt in the tribal economies typically involves burning certain plants and filtering water through the ashes obtained, although mineral salts are also obtained in some areas (*53*, pp. 89–99).

Beverage Production

Drinks made from starchy-staples, sugarcane, tree sap, pineapples, or honey are found throughout the Congo Basin. Most drinks are fermented, but their alcoholic content varies from 1 or 2 percent for sweet maize beer and fresh palm wine to 4 or 5 percent for regular grain beer, 15 to 20 percent for old palm wine, and perhaps 50 percent or more for distilled drinks (*52*, pp. 33–40).

Wines are made from palm and bamboo sap, sugarcane, bananas-plantains, and pineapples. Beers are made from maize, millet, sorghum, and manioc. In some areas where mead is made the process resembles beer production; in other areas the process is more like wine making.

In the forest areas and the more humid low altitude grasslands and woodlands where oil and raphia plams grow, the major beverages are wines from the sap of these trees, from sugarcane, or from bananas-plantains, and beers made from maize, millets-sorghums, or manioc. In the drier savanna, where neither palms, sugarcane, nor bananas-plantains are abundant, beers made from maize, millet, or sorghum predominate.

Most of the work in making wine from the sap of the palm tree is obtaining the sap, which unaided begins to ferment immediately and produces a weak wine within twenty-four hours or less in most of the Congo Basin. Fermentation will continue several days, but palm wine is usually consumed before it reaches its full strength.

The most common method of obtaining palm sap is to tap the tree, but in much of the western Congo Basin the tree is felled, and in some of the eastern areas only the felling technique is employed (Map 10-3). When trees are tapped, the wound is usually made near, or at, the top of the trunk.

Short palms can be climbed by stepping on the stubs of previously cut fronds. Tall palms are usually climbed with the aid of a section of vine or a rattan belt that is placed loosely around the tree trunk and then tied behind the tapper's back. The tapper climbs by flipping the portion of the vine support that is in front of him as high on the tree trunk as it will reach, then bracing against the portion of the vine behind him while climbing with his feet.

Usually the incision is made at the base of the male inflorescence, and a gourd is tied below it to catch the sap. As noted earlier, the Lele cut the

whole crown out of raphia palms to obtain a flow of sap, and kill the tree
in so doing. The neighboring Kuba merely make a gash at the base of the
large inflorescence, a method which does not kill the tree (*118*, p. 15). The
Holo of Kwango and northern Angola use both methods (*103*, p. 23). In
parts of the Kwango area, and among the Kuba, a hole is made in the

MAP 10-3

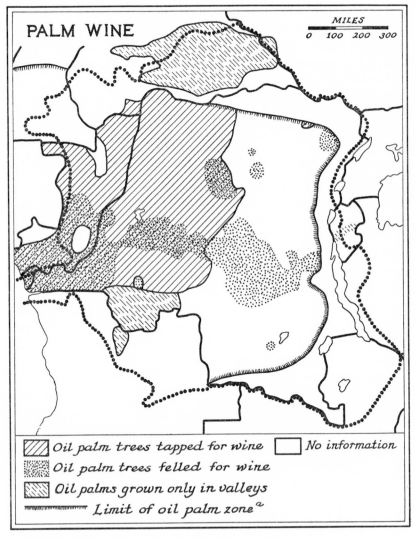

PALM WINE

MILES
0   100   200   300

Oil palm trees tapped for wine   No information
Oil palm trees felled for wine
Oil palms grown only in valleys
Limit of oil palm zone[a]

[a] Some oil palms are found outside this limit in special environments such as along
streams or in small valleys. Map: Food Research Institute.

trunk of oil palm trees to drain sap; and among the Mbala, in the northern part of the Kwango area, sap is also extracted from the roots of oil palms (*4*, p. 508).

When the felling method is employed, the tree is cut down or toppled by cutting its roots on all sides and digging around the base of the trunk. A hole is usually made in the terminal bud, and a receptacle is placed under it. The Mamvu dig a pit under the felled trunk and place receptacles in this, then make multiple wounds in the tree trunk. This method is said to exhaust the trunk of its sap in a day or so (*70*, p. 100), while with the technique of making a single wound in the bud, saps flow considerably longer. Among the southern Buye, for example, felled trees yield two or three liters a day for thirty to fifty days (*233*, p. 555).

Whether trees are tapped or felled, receptacles are replaced daily and a fresh incision is made at the same time, until the sap is exhausted or needs are filled. Relative yields under the two methods cannot be estimated from data available.

Among the Sundi and Kunyi, "certain bark" is crushed and added to the palm sap in order to improve the drink (*331*, p. 54).

It is possible that raphia palms are always tapped; no reference to felling them has been found.

The Banda make a palm wine from the sap of the wild date (*Phoenix spinosa*), but no information is available on tapping techniques (*113*, p. 134). A number of peoples from the lower Kasai River to the mouth of the Congo are said to tap the Borassus palm (*Borassus flabellifer*) for wine (*124*, p. 219, and *250*, p. 71).

Wine from bamboo sap is also found in some areas (*52*, p. 35), but the only discussion of methods employed is data kindly provided by Igor Kopytoff for the Suku and Sande of Kwango. The leaves of the plant are cut off when the bamboo stalk is about 2 meters high, and an incision is made at the top to start the flow of sap; each new incision is made about 2 cm. below the last one (*207*).

Sugarcane wine is widely made in the western portion of the Congo Basin (Map 10-4). Among the Sakata, sugarcane stalks are peeled with a knife and placed in a vat shaped like a dugout canoe.[6] The stalks are then beaten with a baton 1.0 to 1.3 meters long. The crushed stalks go from the vat to a cylindrical basket press made out of vines that is a meter or so in length and about 35 cm. in diameter. By twisting a stick extending through the bottom of this cocoon-like basket, the press is contracted, and the sugarcane stalks in it are squeezed of any remaining juice.

Juice from the vat and basket press is mixed and placed in a bottle gourd. Bark and leaves from an unidentified species of tree are added, and the juice is left to set six hours, or until foam ceases to exude from the neck of the gourd. The last step is straining the wine through a sieve constructed by placing sugarcane fibers left from the crushing in a calabash with a hole in its bottom.

The Ngala employ a similar process in making sugarcane wine, except

MAP 10-4

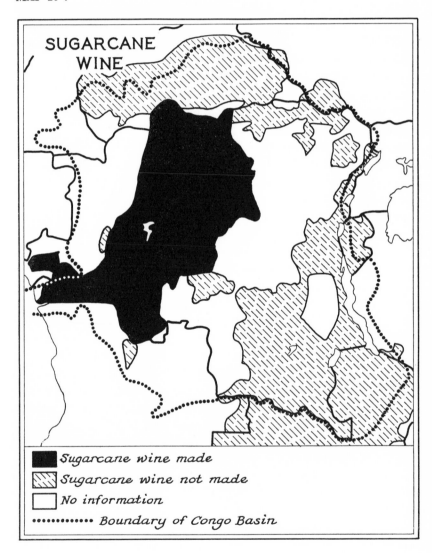

SUGARCANE WINE

■ Sugarcane wine made
▨ Sugarcane wine not made
☐ No information
•••••••••• Boundary of Congo Basin

that they add a little palm wine or sugarcane wine to the newly crushed sugarcane juice to aid fermentation (*411*, p. 101; *385*, p. 115). The practice of adding palm wine dregs is also followed by the Sundi and Kunyi (*331*, p. 54).

The most complete description of banana wine production is for Rwanda-Burundi. A hole is dug in the ground and partially filled with dry banana bark. Then almost ripe bananas are placed in the hole, the debris is ignited, and the hole is covered with soil to make the burning debris smolder. (The slow fire is thought to hasten ripening.) When the fruit is ripe, it is removed, peeled, and placed in a canoe-like vat. Water is added, and an emulsion is made by squeezing the fruit, with the aid of coarse grass held in the hands, until most of the banana pulp is well broken up. Sorghum gruel is added, and the mixture is set to ferment for two or three days, then consumed (*281*, p. 117; *99*, p. 14).

R. Roy gives a similar description of banana wine production among the Bashi, but according to him, the mixture of sorghum gruel and banana paste is filtered through grass before it is set to ferment (*310*, p. 330).

According to M. Gorju, in Urundi bananas are put in a hole to ripen only if enough ripe bananas are not available. Gorju also mentions another type of banana wine in Urundi to which no sorghum gruel is added. His account suggests it is more important than the variant containing sorghum gruel (*154*, p. 202).

Conflicting descriptions of banana wine production among the northern Bira are given by the Reverend Constance-Marie and P. E. Joset. The date of Constance-Marie's observations is not established, hence the possibility that the differences in techniques reported may be due to secular changes in processing methods cannot be checked.

Constance-Marie states that bananas are buried in the ground three days, then removed, placed on a cowhide, and either squeezed by hand or covered with herbs and trampled with the feet to extract the juice (*86*, pp. 75–76; *378*, p. 65). The juice is then put in jars, a mixture of flour ground from germinated finger millet and sorghum is added, and the liquid is set to ferment two or three days.

The method described by Joset is a good deal simpler: bananas are peeled, cut up, and placed in an earthen jar, where they are crushed and left two days to ferment (*197*, p. 48; *378*, p. 65).

The Mbagani also make banana wine, but the process is not described (*425*, p. 333).

Pineapple wine is made in Kwango region and in Moyen-Congo, former

French Equatorial Africa (*331*, p. 43), and perhaps elsewhere. In Kwango
the fruit is crushed and a little pineapple wine or "aromatic herbs or roots
of mango, for example," are added to the juice extracted; the mixture is
then set aside to ferment (*52*, p. 35). Among the Sundi and Kunyi "certain
bark" or dregs of palm wine are added to aid fermentation (*331*, p. 54).

Very weak alcoholic drinks are reported for at least seven of these
tribes, and are possibly widely found. The Lala make a drink that is called
munkoyo after a plant used in its preparation. Betty Thompson describes
it (*350*, p. 46): "Sweet beer or *munkoyo* is a slightly fermented drink
usually made in small quantities just for the family. Millet flour or the
coarse fractions left over after sifting kaffir corn [sorghum] or maize may
be used. A thick porridge is prepared and allowed to cool slightly. Crushed
roots from the *munkoyo* shrub (*Eminia Holubii*) are added and the mixture stirred. After a short time it becomes greenish in colour and much
thinner. It is then strained and left to stand overnight before drinking."

In Katanga munkoyo is made from a variety of carbohydrates — maize,
finger millet, sorghum, manioc, and sweet potatoes — and the wild roots
used are often *E. polyadenia* (but sometimes any of three other unidentified roots) rather than *E. Holubii* used by the Lala. G. Bernier and
A. Lambrechts give the following exceptionally detailed account of maize
munkoyo production in Katanga (*50*, p. 12). Maize is pounded with a
little sand to break the pericarp, soaked two to three days and pounded
again, then sun-dried, pounded a third time, and sifted. Next, about 15
kilograms of maize flour are mixed with a little cold water to obtain a
dough ball, which is heated, but not cooked, to form a paste. This paste is
removed from the fire, mixed with 3.5 kilograms of crushed munkoyo
roots, and left six to seven hours, after which the roots are removed. The
liquid is then sieved and is ready for consumption as sweet munkoyo. If let
sit two to four days it becomes fermented, or strong, munkoyo.

The Banza make a weak mead "by steeping small, very acidulated
green leaves in honey and water"; it is said to be "As good to taste as it is
refreshing" (*193*, 1:362).

Beer is made from a number of raw materials and by diverse methods
(Map 10-5). Germination of grain and the use of boiling water to arrest
fermentation are about the only features common to all processes.

Finger Millet Beer. Among the Bemba finger millet beer is made by
immersing baskets of millet grain in a stream until the grain begins to
sprout (from twelve to twenty-four hours), then drying the sprouted
grain for one day and grinding a portion of it the third day to make yeast.

The portion of the grain ground into flour at this stage is placed in the bottom of a large pot, boiling water is poured on it, and the mixture is set aside to ferment until it begins to "froth and bubble and finally to rise over the top of the pot" (*305*, p. 97). How long this takes depends on the temperature of the air; two days were required in the brewing Richards observed. When the yeast has risen to the top of the pot, a second pot of boiling water is heated, the yeast is added to it and cooked about three

MAP 10-5

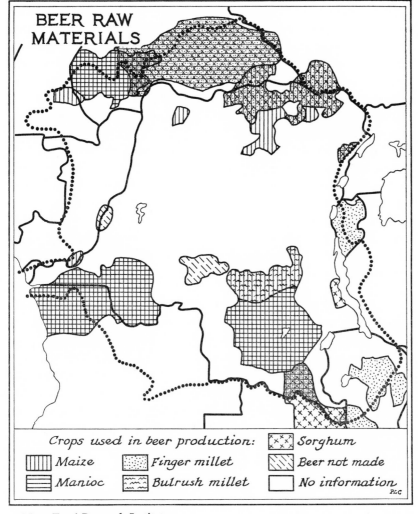

BEER RAW MATERIALS

Crops used in beer production:

Maize	Finger millet	Sorghum
Manioc	Bulrush millet	Beer not made
		No information

Map: Food Research Institute.

hours, then left to cool. Meanwhile the rest of the sprouted grain — the portion not used for yeast — has been made into flour. Next, this flour is made into paste and is spread on winnowing baskets; then yeast is dipped out of the yeast pot with a gourd and is mixed with the paste until a "thick brown sludge results." This sludge is poured into gourds and allowed to set for twenty-four to forty-eight hours; it is now beer paste — which is diluted with hot water before being consumed. The total brewing process takes five to nine days, depending on weather conditions.

The Lala make finger millet beer by a rather different process according to Betty Thompson (*350*, p. 45): "Millet grain is germinated by soaking in water for twenty-four hours and then drying in the sun. Meanwhile flour is prepared from unsprouted grain and a thin porridge is made by mixing the flour with cold water in a large calabash kept for the purpose and then adding boiling water to the paste. After three days the light porridge is transferred to another pot to be boiled and then put back into the calabash. The next day half the flour made from germinated grain is made into porridge and added to the calabash, and the following day the other half. It is left overnight and is then ready for drinking."

The Sudan Azande sprout finger millet, then sun-dry and grind it. Finally the malt flour is filtered through leaves, boiled a second time, and set to ferment (*108*, p. 147). Among the Mangbetu the same process is followed except that the second boiling is omitted (*221*, p. 127).

In Rwanda-Burundi, mash is made of flour from germinated finger millet and is boiled, then cooled and diluted with cold water. Finally, a little stout banana wine is added and the mixture is set to ferment (*258*, p. 91).

Among the Mandja, millet is soaked three days, then drained and covered with leaves until it sprouts. The sprouted grain is pounded, and the paste is left to ferment two days. The third day balls are made from the paste and are thrown in boiling water, cooked, mixed with pounded germinated grain, and a little wood of Guinea peach (*Sarcocephalus esculentus*) is added to give extra flavor. The mixture is then left to ferment. If the weather is cool a fire may be built near it to keep it warm during the fermentation process. When fermentation is finished the brew is filtered and is ready to drink (*397*, pp. 95–97).

Sorghum Beer. The northern Bira make sorghum beer without the aid of any other foodstuff (*378*, p. 65). Sorghum grain is threshed, winnowed, placed in a hole in the ground, covered with water, and left overnight. The second day ashes are mixed with the grain and water is again added. The third day the grain is washed, placed before the hut, covered with reeds or banana leaves, and left about two weeks to germinate. When it has begun to sprout, the cover is removed and it is left in the sun a day to dry. Then it is removed to the interior of the hut for about two days, after which it is sun-dried again and winnowed. The sprouted kernels are now ground between stones. A cold paste made with the flour is placed on a wooden tray, covered with leaves, and taken into the hut; after one or two weeks it is placed in a jar. The final operation is to mix this paste with a little cold water. Sorghum beer, like some of the other northern Bira beers, is diluted with hot water at the time of consumption.

In Burundi sorghum grain is soaked one night, then ashes are added. Two or three hours later the grain is washed and covered with banana leaves to germinate. When it has germinated, it is pounded and winnowed, then put in a pot, and boiling water is mixed with it gradually to make a paste. The paste is put in cold water, and banana juice or sorghum flour is added; after the mixture has fermented twenty-four hours, the beer is ready (*154*, p. 202).

To make sorghum beer by the Lamba method, sorghum grain is sprouted, ground and dried; then part of it is boiled "for a long time" (*115*, p. 107). The remaining malt is mixed with sorghum flour and water, cooked, and cooled. The cooked malt is added, and the mixture is set to ferment.

Even simpler methods are reported for the Holoholo and for an unidentified area of Katanga. In Katanga about 2 kilograms of sorghum grain are soaked in 10 liters of water until they germinate; then they are pounded in a mortar, water is added, and the mixture is set to ferment two or three days and the process is finished (*244*, p. 153).

By the Holoholo method the grain is germinated, immediately pounded, cooked, left overnight to ferment, then consumed (*317*, p. 63).

The Mandja method is similar. The grain is soaked and allowed to sprout, then pounded into flour, mixed with water, and boiled two hours before being set to ferment (*150*, p. 145). Gaud suggests that beer is made from either sorghum or maize by this method (*150*, p. 145).

Among the neighboring Banda, a malt is made either of sorghum or of finger millet, a paste is made of this malt mixed with sorghum flour, and the mixture is allowed to dry for one day. When the brew has been filtered it is ready for consumption (*9*, p. 240).

Maize Beer. The Baya and Kaka make maize beer by soaking a portion of maize kernels about twenty-four hours and covering them with leaves until they sprout (about four days). Two days later the germinated grain is sun-dried and ground. In the meantime, about five times as much maize grain has been soaked twenty-four hours, ground without being allowed to sprout, and then lightly roasted over a fire. The final step is to mix the two kinds of maize flour, add about twice as much water as flour, and set the mixture aside for two days to ferment. (A number of variants of this process are followed by altering the proportion of flour from germinated maize. "The larger the fraction of germinated flour, the sweeter the beer is" [*295*, p. 48].)

The Mandja soak maize grain two days, then cover it with leaves until it sprouts (about three days). It is next dried in the sun and pounded. The resulting flour is boiled and let cool. The following day it is filtered. A sack woven from an unspecified wild fiber containing bits of an unidentified plant (called simply *debré* wood) and roasted maize ears is placed in the mixture to add flavor. Twelve hours later the preparation is ready to drink (*397*, p. 95).

Among the Mangbetu, maize is germinated, the germinated kernels are boiled, and the mixture is set aside to ferment one day (*221*, p. 127). A similar method is reported among the Tio and in parts of Katanga, except that in Katanga, at least, the germinated grain is pounded but not cooked, and is fermented as much as two or three days (*244*, p. 153, and *165*, p. 200). Among the Tio sugarcane juice may be added to make the brew stronger, and the drink is filtered to remove impurities.

Maize-Manioc Beer.   The Luba make maize-manioc beer by first preparing a weak manioc beer. The soot-covered scrapings obtained from dried manioc balls while making flour are mixed with water and allowed to ferment (*83*, p. 121). (This brew may be drunk, but usually it is not if any other kind of beer is available.) The next step involves germinating maize kernels, drying, and pounding them. They are then mixed with manioc beer and "the mixture is boiled and left to cool. The next day it is fermented" (*83*, p. 121). Alternatively, the sprouted maize that has been pounded is mixed not only with manioc beer but also with finger millet to produce a drink that is said to be preferred to maize-manioc beer.

The Kongo crush together dried, germinated maize and manioc, add water to the mixture, and boil it for twelve hours; it is strained, cooled, and set to ferment (*267*, 1:300; *412*, p. 92; *195*, p. 111).

Among the Baya beer is made by mixing crushed immature maize with manioc paste (*295*, p. 102).

Maize-Manioc-Bulrush Millet Beer. The northern Songe make a beer involving three starchy-staples, by germinating a mixture of maize and bulrush millet kernels, pounding them, and adding some manioc flour. A paste made of this mixture is put in jars and mixed with water; after a few hours a liquid made by adding pure manioc paste to water is admixed, and the pots are set to ferment for twelve hours. The brew is then filtered and left to ferment another twenty-four hours (*188*, p. 209).

Maize-Finger Millet-Sorghum Beer. The Bira soak maize grain three days, pound the kernels in a mortar, wrap the pulp produced in banana leaves, and bury it in the ground for about three or four weeks. When dug up, it is sifted. The coarser fraction is pounded again and the entire quantity of damp flour thus produced is spread in the sun for three days. At the same time, a much smaller quantity of stone-ground flour is made from a mixture of germinated finger millet and sorghum that has been made by soaking the two kinds of grain one day, spreading them on banana leaves until they sprout (about four days), drying the germinated grain in the sun two days, and grinding it between stones. Next boiling water is poured on the maize flour and a paste made which is placed in a jar. After flour from germinated finger millet and sorghum is made and added, the jar is filled with water and set to ferment three days. The mixture is diluted with hot water as it is consumed; the drinker puts some of the beer in his cup and adds hot water.

Manioc-Millet Beer. The Banda make manioc-millet beer by cutting peeled manioc roots in chunks and letting them ferment in a pot three days. Sprouted millet and water are added, and the mixture is left to ferment another two days, then boiled to a paste, and poured into another jar to cool. The next day water is mixed with the paste and the beer is ready to consume (*114*, p. 156).

Maize-Sorghum Beer. In Katanga a maize-sorghum beer is made by soaking 5 kilograms of maize two days, then leaving the grain to germinate (about five days). Four days later 4.8 kg. of sorghum grain are soaked in a mixture of water and wood ashes for a day, then drained and left to germinate. Next, 1.7 kg. of the 5 kg. of germinated maize is pounded and sifted, the two flours are mixed and added to 10 liters of water, and the whole is set aside for two days. The next step is to heat the mixture four hours and leave it to ferment twenty-four hours. Then 1.3 kg. of germinated maize and sorghum grain is pounded and added to the preparation. The mixture is left for another twenty-four hours of fermentation. Finally, the remainder of the germinated maize and sorghum grain is pounded and made into a cold paste, which is mixed with hot water, then cooled. Toward the end of the day this is added to the brew, and three hours later the beer is filtered. Six hours later it is ready for consumption (*50*, p. 22). The entire process requires at least twelve days.

Other Beers.   Other beers mentioned but not described are manioc beer among the Mandja (*150*, p. 145), maize-sugarcane beer in the Brazzaville area (*40*, p. 35), and bean beer around Kamina in Katanga (*50*, p. 24).

In Katanga a beer is made by crushing the stalks of nearly ripe maize, soaking them in hot water, and letting the mixture ferment (*50*, p. 24). Another Katanga beer is produced by cooking the grinding offal from maize, adding munkoyo root, and letting the mixture sit twelve hours (*50*, p. 24). Beer is made from various wild fruits in the same area by merely crushing them, adding water, and letting the mixture sit three or four days (*50*, p. 23).

Mead.   In Rwanda-Burundi mead is made fairly simply by boiling a mixture that is four-fifths water and one-fifth honey for a long time and letting it keep warm by the fire a few days.[7] This preparation is then placed in the sun a day for final fermentation (*258*, p. 92).

Among the Azande and "their subject peoples" honey is merely mixed with water and left to ferment (*193*, 2:612). The process is similar in the Jadotville area of Katanga; the honeycomb is plunged into hot water and squeezed to extract the honey; then the mixture is strained to remove wax and larvae and left to set one to three days (*50*, p. 21).

Lamba methods of making mead are more complex. Intoxicating honey beer is produced by adding mashed bee larvae to maize flour and water and letting the mixture ferment one day. Then watered honey is added, and the brew is set in the sun a day to ferment. In the evening it is placed near the fire to keep it warm, and after a second day in the sun it is consumed. Doke observes that this drink is "violently intoxicating" (*115*, p. 108). (A nonintoxicating mead is produced by leaving watered honey in the sun one day and consuming it at nightfall.)

The Mandja mix water with honey and heat the mixture until it thickens, then add more water. After this procedure has been repeated two or three times the mixture is allowed to cool, and a little wood from the Guinea peach (*Sarcocephalus esculentus*) is added. The preparation is then left to ferment; we are not told how long. Alternatively mead may be produced by cooking flour made from an oilseed gourd (*Cucumis melo*) with mushroom roots until a paste is obtained. This paste is mixed with honey and with some of the paste obtained from the other type of mead. The new mixture is cooked and set to ferment (*397*, p. 97).

A drink made by adding banana wine to honey is mentioned for Rwanda-Burundi, but no description is provided (*21*, p. 137).

Distilled Drinks. Few descriptions of distillation techniques are available; most accounts of tribal food-processing techniques neither mention distillation nor deny that it is known. The best account of distillation is De Schlippe's for the Azande (*108*, p. 247): "A still consists of a boiling-pot (*rugusi*) covered with a lid (*wagadi*) made tight with gum from *Grewia mollis*, from which a hollow bamboo or pawpaw stem takes the steam through a cooler (*buza*, lit. pouring water) made of a yapa pot or of a bottle gourd. The condensed spirit is collected into a smaller bottle gourd."

Some of the neighboring Mangbetu distill palm wine and maize or finger millet beer with a similar apparatus using either a hollow reed, a bamboo stalk, or the muzzle of a rifle (*388*, p. 172; *221*, p. 128). The northern Songe let maize–manioc–bulrush millet beer ferment six days, then run it through a still which has a rifle barrel for tubing (*188*, p. 210). The Bwaka of former French Equatorial Africa sometimes use gasoline cans to construct stills for producing alcohol from maize (*341*, p. 21). The Sundi and Kunyi distill a mixture of maize malt and manioc or sugarcane juice (*331*, p. 54).

Livestock Products

Accounts of techniques for processing livestock products are available for the Bashi, Rwanda-Burundi, the Lugbara, and Lendu.

The Bashi. Small children drink fresh cow's milk; and the milk obtained the first five or six days after calving is cooked and eaten as a solid. Otherwise milk is made into butter or curdled.

Butter is made by pouring sour milk into a large calabash, then shaking the container until the pitch of the slosh indicates butter has formed. Butter is not eaten; it is used mainly as a skin lubricant — which, according to Carlier, means that the Bashi often have a rancid smell (*69*, p. 792). It is also used to soften animal hides.

Carlier states that after use the churn is washed with hot water (*69*, p. 792); Colle says it is rinsed twice — once with water and once with cow's urine (*84*, p. 679).

To coagulate milk, it is put in a jar, covered with a banana leaf and left (*69*, p. 790); a little whey may be added to hasten the process (*84*, p. 679).

Bull calves and diseased or old animals are regularly butchered by cutting their throats, care being taken to save the blood to cook later with the meat (*84*, p. 680). Animals that die of natural causes are also eaten.

Animal hides are stretched and staked to the ground in a sunny spot, then covered with a thin layer of wood ashes. R. Roy states that when dry they are stretched over a rope; the sides are staked to form a tent, then scraped with a knife. If a skirt is to be made, the next step is to measure the size of leather needed, and to cut out the garment. The garment is then stretched out on a bed of herbs, hairy side down, and rubbed with curdled milk. Then it is rubbed with butter, and finally rolled up, put in a basket, and stored in the hut a few days before being worn (*310*, pp. 344–45). Two skirts can usually be made from the hide of a mature animal.

Rwanda-Burundi.   Milk processing appears to be the same as among the Bashi, except that some of the Rwanda add a little urine [8] to milk to make it curdle, and in Burundi a little juice from a citrus fruit called *nongo* is used for the same purpose.

Blood, another liquid product that can be taken regularly without destruction of the animals, is also of some importance. Blood is obtained with a special short-tipped arrow from a wound made in the jugular vein of bulls. Several men hold the animal by its horns, and the arrow is shot from a bow held a short distance from the jugular vein, "whereupon the blood spurts out (*258*, p. 67). Meyer says it is then caught in a pot. Both Meyer and Czekanowski state that some of the blood is drunk fresh; Everaerts and Gorju say it may be sucked directly from the wound (*132*, p. 338; *154*, p. 203). According to Meyer the wound closes by itself when "two to four liters" have been collected (*258*, p. 67); Czekanowski states that a rope tourniquet is tied around the animal's neck below the wound (*91*, p. 27). Gorju reports that 2 to 3 liters are taken at a bleeding and that animals may be bled every three or four months (*154*, p. 203). The blood not consumed fresh is boiled until it solidifies; then salt, beans, peas, and "other ingredients" are added (*258*, p. 67). Gorju mentions only beans (*154*, p. 203).

When animals are slaughtered almost nothing is wasted, even the entrails and hide being consumed (*132*, p. 338; *326*, p. 346).

The Lugbara and Lendu.   According to Willaert, the veterinary of Uele District, former Belgian Congo, in 1909, cattle are slaughtered rarely, and milk and butter are virtually the only products obtained from them.

In making butter, cow's urine is mixed with milk to make it sour more rapidly. Butter is stored in earthen pots and eaten rancid (*422*, pp. 13–14).

Oil Extraction

The fruit of the oil palm is the primary source of oil in forest areas, but is replaced by peanuts, sesame, and oilseed cucurbits in most of the nonforest zones.

Oil Palm. The simplest technique for extracting palm oil is the fermentation process of the Yombe (*139*, p. 1276). Pits are dug and palm fruit is placed in them to ferment for three months; then it is crushed (probably in a mortar, but crushing is not described).

In the Kwilu River area sometimes oil is extracted by simply boiling the fruit and then squeezing it by hand or by putting it in a rolled mat and twisting the ends (*276*, p. 230). The Lele appear to know a similar method (*119*, Figure III b, p. 66).

In the Kisangani area, the pulp is heated on an inclined trough, then put in a torsion press made of the fibrous bark of *Sacrophrynium* and pressed (Figure 10-1). Finally, the oil extracted is filtered, and heated to evaporate any water that remains (*257*, pp. 340–43).

A similar process is employed by the Bwaka of former French Equa-

FIGURE 10-1   Palm Oil Extraction, Kisangani Area

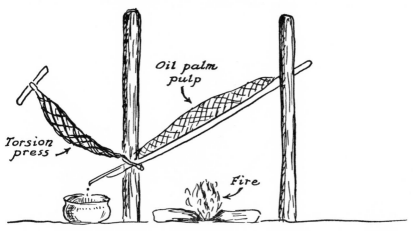

Based on M. Mestdagh, "L'Exploitation des palmiers Elaeis à la station expérimentale de Gazi (Stanleyville)," *Bull. Agr. du Congo Belge*, June, 1921, p. 343. Figure: Food Research Institute.

torial Africa, except that there is no mention of a fire under the inclined trough (*341*, pp. 10, 12). The Babwa are said to use a torsion press, but no information is given on the apparatus, if any, to which the press is attached (*68*, p. 223).

The Kuba and Lulua build a pit press for extracting palm oil. A triangular pit is dug about 60 cm. deep, and the walls are strengthened with logs (Figure 10-2). Spaces between the members of the walls are packed with leaves and debris. Black earth is mixed with palm oil and then applied to ensure that the walls are well sealed (*345*, p. 553).

Palm fruit is placed in this pit and covered with leaves, stems, and debris. The fruit begins to ferment; after two or three days the cover is removed and the fruit is pounded with a pestle. The next day, a hole is opened in the center of the pulp with the pestle, palm nuts heated over a fire are inserted, and the mass is pounded again. When this work is finished, a hole about 10 cm. in diameter is made in the center of the pulp with a pestle, and a cylinder of bamboo wattle is inserted. Weights are then placed on the pulp to squeeze out the oil. Under pressure, the pulp gradually is reduced and oil collects inside the wattle; it is dipped out and used as it is (*345*, p. 513).

Among the Kutshu and Songo-Meno an even more elaborate apparatus is employed which Maes describes (*241*, pp. 100–101):

FIGURE 10-2   Kuba Palm Oil Processing

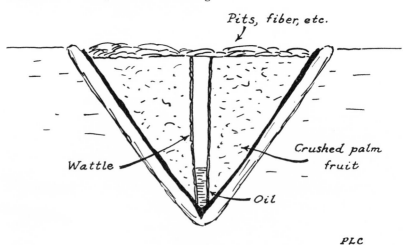

Based on L. Tihon, "Le palmier à huile au Kasai," *Bull. Agr. du Congo Belge*, Sept., 1924. Figure: Food Research Institute.

each village has a special installation for making palm oil. This very primitive factory usually stands slightly apart from the dwellings. Everyone has access to it, and it belongs to the entire community, but each family uses it individually.

It consists of a large hole in the form of a truncated cone. The diameter of the upper part varies from 60–70 centimeters, . . . and the depth varies from 60 to 80 centimeters. The bottom and sides are lined with pieces of raffia stems, placed . . . side by side with their rounded surfaces facing the interior of the pit. The nuts, which have been slightly boiled, are poured into this funnel, which serves as a mortar. The outer part is separated from the nut with a large wooden pestle. The kernels are discarded. The pulp is taken from the hole and tightly pressed between the hands to squeeze out the oil.

Near the funnel-shaped mortar dug in the ground, there is a bench made of two or four forked stakes, graduated in height, over which the natives place large sections of tree bark. The woman throws the pulp from which she has extracted the oil on this bench, spreads it out, and lights a small fire under the wide sections of bark, which serve as drain. Under the influence of the heat, part of the oil remaining in the pulp flows out slowly and is caught in the earthenware vessel placed at the lower end of the drain. Finally, whatever palm oil remains in the pulp is squeezed out by the torsion method. For this purpose, the native has set up a large stationary bar, very strong, to which he attaches one end of a pressing apparatus made of young lianas and fine rattan plaited together. The pulp, still hot, is placed in this press and wrung very tightly to extract every last drop. . . .

Oil presses are also used around Kongolo, but description of them is not given (*22*, p. 254).

Among the Kuba, Kutshu, and Songo-Meno, oil-pressing apparatuses are used only when large quantities of oil are needed; otherwise the simpler technique, described earlier, of pounding in a mortar, boiling, and hand squeezing the oil-bearing pulp is used.

Descriptions of palm nut processing are available only for the Tetela, the Kuba, and the Kisangani area. The Tetela simply break open the palm kernel and crush the almond in a mortar (*344*, p. 22). Among the Kuba, the almonds are crushed in a mortar and soaked in water two to four days; then the mass is pounded, the paste is placed in water and agitated until a scum forms. This scum is skimmed off and the residue is repounded, then again thrown into water to form scum. The scum collected is heated until all the water in it evaporates and a clear oil is obtained (*345*, p. 555). Alternatively, the almonds are roasted — crushed or not — in a pot until they release their oil. In the Kisangani area the palm almonds are first roasted in a pot, then pounded, and the paste is thrown in boiling water. "When the cooking is judged sufficient," the pot is taken off the fire, and the oil is skimmed off after the water cools (*127*, p. 708).

Coconut Palms. Oil is derived from coconuts in some parts of Équateur Province, former Belgian Congo, by letting the coconut lie in the sun several days — until the flesh withdraws from the shell — then breaking the shell, beating the flesh, crushing it, throwing it in a pot of boiling water, skimming off the oil that rises to the top, and finally heating the oil so obtained to purify it (*217*, pp. 943–44; *19*, p. 341).

Other Palms. In the Kwango area raphia palm and "marsh palm" fruit are buried in hot sand to make them soft, then the fruit — at least of the marsh palm — is beaten with a stick and the pulp is grilled on a bamboo grate. Next, the pulp is dried in the sun, then cooked without water for thirty minutes. Finally, it is squeezed in a basket press made of vines (*52*, p. 29). Extraction methods for raphia palm fruit are not given (*4*, p. 504).

Other Oil Trees. The Tetela, Kela, Rega, southern Buye, and Dzem, at least, extract oil from trees other than palms. Delhaise reports that among the Rega oil is obtained from the fruit of a forest tree called *busezi*. This tree produces small fruit about the size of a cherry, which are gathered, stripped of their hulls, and dried in the sun for two or three days, until they crack open. The kernel found inside them is put in a dug-out log about 1.5 meters long and is pounded. During the pounding hot water is added (*102*, p. 143). This process is not explained further, but the oil undoubtedly floats to the top of the hot water and is skimmed off. Busezi oil reportedly is used only for oiling the body; its strong flavor prohibits its use in cooking.

The Tetela extract oil from *Pentadesma butyracea*, the butter tree or tallow tree of West Africa. Two holes are dug about 1.5 meters apart, one lower than the other, and are connected by a small tunnel. A framework of sticks is placed over the higher hole. Chopped fruit of *P. butyracea*, in pieces about 12 to 15 cm. long and 10 cm. in diameter, are placed in a banana leaf and set on this framework. Then a fire is started in the lower hole, and the heat and smoke travel by the tunnel to the upper chamber. As the heat reaches the upper chamber, the oil-bearing fruit is turned. When the fruit is dry, it is placed in a mortar and pounded, and the paste produced is put in boiling water. As oil comes to the surface of the hot water it is skimmed off (*14*, pp. 579–80).

The Basuka and Mbole, who are adjacent to the Kela on the west, and the Ngombe extract oil from *P. butyracea* by drying the fruit in the sun, pounding it in a mortar, and boiling the pulp, then skimming the oil off the top of the water (*3*, p. 181).

The Tetela also extract oil from a tree called *baleko* (*Ongokea Klaineana*) that is reportedly widely found in the forest zone. The fruit, about 3 cm. long, is stirred into boiling water; then the mixture is put into pots to cool somewhat. While it is still warm but the oil and water have separated, the oil is poured off (*76*, pp. 75–76).

Around Eala the fruit of *O. Klaineana* is let ripen several days after harvest, then the flesh and pit are separated (presumably by pounding, but the technique is not specified). The pulp is let sit another ten days so that some of the moisture in it will evaporate, then boiled "several" hours and cooled. The accumulated oil is reheated to remove impurities (*155*, p. 85).

Mestdagh describes an oil extracted by the Kela which they trade to other tribes. The local name for the tree bearing the fruit this oil comes from is *usudi*; Mestdagh says it is a tree about 10 to 15 meters tall that had not been scientifically identified at the time of his writing (1912). The fruit is cut up and sun-dried; then a fire is made in a pit about 1 meter long, 40 cm. wide and 50 cm. deep. The chopped fruit is placed on a grill over this fire for a second drying. The final step is to place the fruit on the top of a clay mound which has a rim leading to a small trough that runs down one end. With the fruit on top of this structure, "a fire is made there" (*14*, p. 578). When the fruit is heated, the oil oozes out and runs down the trough into a pot or calabash.

Among the southern Buye, and possibly the Tabwa, oil is extracted from the fruit of a tree locally called *pafu* [*safou*?]. The fruit is said to be about the size of a prune and to taste something like an olive (*22*, p. 254).

The Dzem obtain an oil variously known as *dika* oil, *oba* oil, or wild mango oil, from the *dika* nut, *Irvingia Gabonesis*, by breaking open the fruit, then grilling and crushing the kernel (*40*, p. 42).

Pieraerts reports that oil is usually extracted from the oil-bearing members of the genus *Irvingia* in the former Belgian Congo by pounding the fruit and mixing the pulp with boiling water to produce a butter than can be used in cooking or to make soap (*291*, p. 53).

V. Gossens describes extraction of oil from the nut of the tree *Allanblackia floribunda*. Around Eala the process of extracting oil is the same as that for *Ongokea Klaineana* in the same area discussed above (p. 00), except that it is the kernel, not the flesh, of the fruit from which oil is obtained. After flesh and kernel have been separated, the kernel is cut into small bits and pounded; the mass is boiled "several" hours, cooled, and the oil on the surface is collected, then reheated to purify it (*155*, p. 85).

A. H. S. Landor states that oil is extracted from the fruit of the wild date (*Phoenix spinosa*) along the Uele River, but he does not describe the technique (*214*, 2: 36–37).

Oilseed Processing

The Azande roast peanuts, Bambara nuts, and the seeds of certain gourds, then pound them in a mortar to extract oil. In the Inzia Valley of Kwango the same procedure is followed with peanuts, except that after pounding the pulp is thrown into hot water and the oil that comes to the surface is skimmed off (*4*, p. 504). The Kongo, too, employ this technique, but the pounded pulp may be held in the hands, then hot water is poured on it and the pulp squeezed (*267*, 1: 132).

Among the Tetela, oilseed cucurbits are broken open and the seeds washed free with boiling water and dried. The dry seeds are placed in a sack, flailed with poles, and then winnowed. The kernels are mashed in a wooden mortar until a paste is formed. This is thrown into a pot of boiling water, and the oil that floats to the top is skimmed off (*15*, p. 646).

Sesame seeds are crushed in most of the grassland areas, but the only description of the process available is for the Bwaka of former French Equatorial Africa, who roast the seeds, then pound them in a mortar (*341*, p. 20). According to a generalization by the Department of Agriculture of the former Belgian Congo, the seeds typically are roasted, then pounded and thrown into boiling water, as described earlier for oil palm fruit (*17*, p. 263). The southern Kongo appear to omit the preliminary roasting, and grind the seed by stone, then add the pulp as flavoring in cooking (*267*, 1: 134).

Bark Cloth Production

In Rwanda-Burundi, when the bark is removed from the bark cloth tree, the exposed surface of the tree trunk is immediately plastered with banana leaves to protect it until new bark grows. The section of bark that has been removed is scraped, then beaten on a stump until it is flexible (*187*, p. 489).

Burton describes a similar, but somewhat more complex, technique at Ujiji on the eastern shore of Lake Tanganyika (*63*, 2: 64, 65):

This article, technically termed "mbugu," is made from the inner bark of various trees, especially the mrimba and mwale, or huge Raphia-palm. The trunk of the full-grown tree is stripped of its integument twice or thrice, and is bound with plantain-leaves till a finer growth is judged fit for manipulation. This bark is carefully removed, steeped in water, macerated, kneaded, and pounded with clubs and battens to the consistency of a coarse cotton. Palm-oil is then spirted upon it from the mouth, and it acquires the colour of chamois-leather. . . . Though durable, it is never washed: After many months' wear the superabundance of dirt is removed by butter of ghee.

The Banda make no attempt to aid the new growth of bark when wild trees are harvested, but are careful to cut the bark only half way around when harvesting cultivated trees. "A long time afterwards" the other half is harvested. With cultivated trees the surface exposed by removal of bark is carefully covered with a straw preparation to aid regrowth of bark (*346*, pp. 250–51).

Differences in Foodstuff Processing between the Congo Basin and Other Parts of Tropical Africa

Substantial differences in methods of processing manioc, maize, and palm oil in the Congo Basin and in other parts of tropical Africa have been documented, but other major foodstuffs have not yet been widely enough studied to allow more than conjectures.

Manioc

In western tropical Africa manioc meal and tapioca are important products, while wrapped manioc is made much less than in the Congo Basin. Manioc meal is made by peeling fresh manioc roots, then grating them on a sheet of tin or iron that has been roughened on one side by making holes in it with a nail or punch, or on a board with nails or spikes stuck in it. The pulp collected is put in a cloth bag and set in the sun to drain and ferment, then is put under pressure for three or four days. Pressing is often achieved by simply piling stones or logs on the bags containing the pulp. Sometimes simple mechanical presses of logs are used, but torsion presses of the sort found in the Congo Basin for palm oil are apparently never employed (*195*, p. 112).

When pressing is finished, the pulp is sieved, placed in a shallow bowl, and dried over a low fire. As the meal dries it is constantly stirred, and palm oil may be added to prevent burning (*195*, p. 113).

As noted earlier, we have record of manioc meal being made in the Congo Basin only by the Teke group of the Kuba (p. 198). Thus it is interesting that peoples with torsion presses do not press manioc pulp to expel the prussic acid quickly, as is done in Brazil, the area from which manioc seems to have been first brought to Africa, but instead follow the longer, soaking process. Yet, in western tropical Africa the practice of pressing was learned, but efficient pressing techniques were not. The peoples of western tropical Africa who learned to press manioc in the nineteenth century from freed slaves returning from Brazil apparently did not also learn how to make fiber presses of the sort used in Brazil. How and when torsion presses were introduced to the Congo Basin is not known, but since they are used in palm oil processing, and since manioc meal is commonly made just outside the Congo Basin in parts of Angola, it is curious that production of manioc meal and use of fiber torsion presses as part of the process have never been adopted.

The Brazilian *tipiti*, a cylindrical fiber press that contracts as the two ends are pulled apart, has been introduced to the southern Sudan on the northern edge of the Congo Basin in recent years and is said to have led to a considerable increase in the popularity of manioc meal there [9] (*195*, p. 109).

Tapioca, produced principally in Togo, from manioc, is obtained by a partially mechanized process that can easily be converted to production of manioc meal. A tapioca factory consists of a small hand-fed grater powered by a gasoline engine, a series of concrete tubs for settling out starch, and pans or bowls for drying the product. The pulp collected after grating is pressed and squeezed to free the starch, which is then allowed to settle in vats and finally is deposited in the drying bowls and slowly heated until dry (*195*, p. 114). The starch may be sifted prior to being dried to make the size of the tapioca granules more uniform.

Where manioc is important in Africa east of the Congo Basin, its processing is typically fairly simple. Most varieties grown are not toxic and can be eaten without being soaked first. (Even for toxic varieties soaking may be omitted.) Often the roots are dug, dried, and ground or pounded into flour. They may also be boiled or roasted fresh, or first dried, then boiled (*195*, pp. 116–17).

Maize

Regional differences in methods of processing maize appear to be roughly similar in terms of variation in the number of products made; the Congo Basin seems to be in an intermediate position between western and eastern tropical Africa (*264*, pp. 101–10).

Important maize products found in western tropical Africa and not in the Congo Basin are fermented, cooked paste; cooked starch; flavored flour; and a dish made from immature maize.

Paste is made in southern Dahomey as follows. Maize grains are soaked for a day; at the end of this period, when they are swollen with water, they are taken out for a light pounding in the mortar to remove the pericarp. They are soaked for a second period to ferment. After twenty-four hours, they are taken from the water and ground between stones. The resulting product is poured into water to float off the bran; then, by means of a calabash sieve, the remaining solid is separated from the liquid. This solid, called *ogi*, is used in a number of other preparations.

To make fermented paste, the procedure is the same as in the preceding instance, but the fermented liquid is exposed to the air after straining the paste from it. Liquid and paste are kneaded together; and the mixture is left to ferment another twelve hours. Hot water is then added to stop the fermentation.

If a cooked paste is made, a little flour is mixed with cold water in a bowl; a pot of water is heated, and when it begins to boil, the flour-water mixture is poured in and stirred into the hot water with a wooden paddle. This gruel is simmered for ten to fifteen minutes until it bubbles well; then a small quantity of it is dipped out with a small bowl and left to cool. To the remainder are added handfuls of flour until the mixture is doughlike. (A little gruel is poured into the mixture from time to time to aid in getting the desired consistency.) When the paste is quite stiff, it is ready to eat, and will be consumed with a sauce or relish of vegetables, meat, or fish (*1*).

In southwestern Nigeria two maize starch products, *ogi* and *agidi*, account for the bulk of maize consumed. To make ogi, dry maize is soaked from one to several days, depending on the variety of maize and the urgency of need for the product. A minimum period seems to be three days with the flour types — varieties of a harder starch take longer — though if hot water is used twenty-four hours may suffice. After soaking, the grains are washed and ground. (Many areas have mechanized milling, but lacking this, grinding is between stones as described for the Congo Basin.) The product from the mill or grindstone is put into clean water and passed through two sieves, one finer than the other, to remove bits of pericarp. This by-product of the operation is usually fed to poultry or livestock. The primary product, which is almost pure starch at this stage, is placed in pots of water to settle; it can be stored so for several days, provided the water is changed every day or two.

At this point the product is called ogi; boiled and eaten hot it is *eko* or *pap*; wrapped in banana or similar leaves and cooked, it is agidi. (Agidi is the principal maize dish in Sierra Leone (*57*, p. 49); I have not found reference to it elsewhere outside Nigeria, however.)

A fermented steamed mush called *kenkey*, the principal staple made from maize in Ghana, is prepared as follows: whole grain is washed and soaked one to two days, then is ground into dough and let stand another day or two. The dough is divided into two parts, one of which is cooked and then combined with the uncooked portion. The whole is divided into balls of a pound or so each, which are wrapped in dried maize husks or plantain leaves and steamed for about two hours. They are now ready to eat.

Two flavored flour preparations are reported for southern Dahomey: roasted maize flour is mixed with sugar; or palm oil, salt, and ground chilies may be added instead of sugar.

A product made from immature maize not reported elsewhere is made in the same area. The immature grains are cut from the ear, piled in a cloth, and pressed to extract the white liquid they contain (sometimes this is obtained directly by grating the ear). When the quantity of liquid needed has been procured, a little water and sugar are added and the mixture is poured into a cooking pot and placed on a fire. A sack of cloves is introduced to give additional flavor. The mixture is stirred with a wooden paddle to obtain a light consistency. Finally, after the preparation has boiled, it is poured into shallow plates which serve as molds. When cold, it thickens to the consistency of gelatin, and is eaten that way.

In Ghana, Ethiopia, and the Sudan unleavened bread is made from maize. Detailed description of the process is available only for the Balanda of extreme southern Sudan.

The Balanda produce flour for the flat bread they make by lightly pounding dry grain, adding water during the pounding, winnowing the product, and placing it in water overnight, then grinding and sieving the pounded grain. To this flour enough cold water is added to make a mixture the consistency of thick cream, which is left to stand a day. This slightly sour batter is finally mixed with a little boiling water and poured wafer-thin on a hot greased iron sheet (*88*, p. 15).

For porridge the flour is made differently. The grain is soaked overnight (sometimes the water is heated to about 40°C. first), and the swollen grain is rubbed through a sieve in order to separate the flour into two fractions. The fraction passing through the mesh (about 47 percent of the original grain by weight) is used for making porridge or steamed cakes. The coarser fraction, after being ground and dried in the sun, is used in making beer.[10]

To make steamed cakes, stiff dough (plain or mixed with honey or mashed ripe bananas) is shaped into long rolls, wrapped in banana leaves, placed in warm water, covered with additional leaves, and boiled about an hour.

The Balanda have four methods of making beer from maize:

1. Maize is sprouted, ground wet, soaked two or more days, dried in the sun, and the lumps are ground down and boiled several hours; then malted millet is added and the brew is set to stand overnight.

2. Mixed maize and sorghum grain is sprouted, ground wet, put in a basket two days, and then dried and stored. To brew, the dried lumps are ground, boiled, and left to stand twenty-four hours. (No malted grain is added.)

3. Maize is soaked forty-eight hours, ground wet, mixed with malted millet, and the mush is put in a pot and left three days to sour, then dried. To brew, the dried lumps are ground, added to malted millet and boiled, and put to stand one or two days.

4. Maize and sorghum are mixed and sprouted, ground wet, soaked for two days, dried, and ground. The flour is mixed with just enough water to keep it from burning and is cooked from fifteen to thirty minutes; it is then added to boiling water and cooked and stirred for a few minutes. Finally, cold water and either sorghum or millet malt are added, and the brew is set to stand until the next day.

Other variations in maize processing are found in the Mozambique portion of the Limpopo Basin. In the valley areas there are three methods of grinding maize: *cucila, tinzoho,* and *tiove;* in the hills one technique, a variation of tinzoho, is practiced. By the first method maize is pounded, sieved, soaked forty-eight hours, drained, and ground in a jar with a pestle until a flour is obtained. The second method differs merely in requiring only two to three hours of soaking in the valley areas, twenty-four hours of soaking in the hill variation. The third method too is like the first, except that after soaking the preparation is boiled two hours and combined with pounded peanuts. The maize-peanut mixture is then boiled lightly before it is served (*246,* p. 69).

Maize processing in Kenya is exceptional because of the use of water-powered mills in some areas, but accounts of foods consumed suggest no important maize dishes other than those found in the Congo Basin.

Palm Oil

Two methods of unmechanized extraction of palm oil found in Nigeria and the Ivory Coast differ from those of the Congo Basin. By the more complex method palm fruit is said sometimes to be boiled in a large pot overnight, then pounded in a wooden trough. Water is added and the water-oil mixture is skimmed off, filtered, and boiled about eight hours to separate the water and oil. Finally the pure oil is skimmed off (*38*, p. 30).

Alternatively, the pulp may be collected in a cloth which is twisted at each end with sticks to expel the oil. The residue left is boiled and the oil is skimmed off the top of the water.

When the simpler method is employed the fruit is placed in the end of an inclined canoe, covered, and allowed to ferment a few days. The heap is then mashed with the feet, and the canoe is tilted to allow the oil released to flow to the other end. A second and third fermentation and treading may follow; the remaining matter is boiled until an oil-bearing scum is obtained (*38*, p. 30, *123*, p. 44).[11]

Nigeria also differs from the Congo Basin in the extent to which African peasants have mechanical presses. Hand-operated screw mechanisms and "pioneer mills" — small, steam-powered centrifuges — are fairly widely operated by Nigerian peasants, who produce oil in quantity either for local markets or for export. In the former Belgian Congo such a development was precluded at an early date by a monopoly on mechanical processing given to plantations.

As the following tabulation shows, in Nigeria manual methods are considerably less efficient than mechanized processing, extracting only 45 to 60 per cent of the oil the fruit contains, compared with 60 to 65 percent for the presses, 85 percent for the pioneer mills, and 93 percent for the large plantation factories (*286*, p. 65, and *163*, p. 11):

Method	Percent of oil extracted
Manual	45–60
Hand press	60–65
Pioneer mill	85
Factory mill	93

Mechanically processed oil is also of higher quality because less fermentation is required to soften the fruit so that it can be pressed. This is of importance not only when oil is to be exported but for African housewives as well. In the southern Ivory Coast, at least in areas where I have done field work, consumers are willing to pay a premium for palm oil with a low free fatty acid content because food cooked with it tastes better to them.

PART III Technological Change

11

Major Technological Changes by Period

It is not possible to determine with any accuracy the date when various technical innovations were adopted by the various peoples of the Congo Basin, but the nature of the changes can be determined and some of the forces responsible for them sketched in this chapter. The next chapter examines changes in more detail by tribe or area.

1500–1830

In the earliest period for which we have information on the economies of the Congo Basin, the only innovations that can be documented are the introductions of exotic crops. When the Portuguese reached the mouth of the Congo River late in the fifteenth century after sustained voyages of explorations down the African coast, about a third of the thirty-six principal commodities now produced in the tribal economies were probably not known. Said to have been introduced by the Portuguese are manioc, maize, sweet potatoes, peanuts, some varieties of beans (*Phaseolus vulgaris* and *P. lunatus*), tobacco, pineapples, sugarcane, lemons, papayas, chilies, swine, pigeons, and ducks.

Direct evidence, such as statements of early Portuguese voyagers that they made these introductions, has not yet been uncovered; but traditions of African tribes, the names they have given these plants and animals, and what is known by botanists about the region of their origin, coupled with the lack of convincing evidence of pre-Columbian contact between the New World and Africa, suggest that these were introduced to the Congo Basin by the Portuguese sometime before the nineteenth century.

More can be established about the spread of maize and manioc, two of the more important new crops. Maize appears to give considerably higher yields in calories per acre than other cereals in much of the humid grasslands of the Congo Basin, whereas manioc generally gives yields superior to those of any other starchy-staples in the forest areas (*264*, ch. 11; *195*, p. 259). Both maize and manioc appear to have been introduced to the Congo Basin before 1600 (*195*, pp. 61–63; *103*, pp. 29–30).[1]

Portuguese voyagers reached the mouth of the Congo River in 1482 and established amicable relations with the ruler of the Kingdom of Congo, which extended from the mouth of the Congo River to about the present city of Kinshasa (Leopoldville). Within twenty years the Kingdom of Congo was sufficiently influenced by the Portuguese for the Pope to recognize it as a Christian state.[2] In 1521 the son of the king of Congo, who as a boy had been sent to Portugal for education, was made the first bishop of Congo (*89*, p. 213; *195*, p. 61). Thus any superior crops that the Portuguese knew about at this time could easily have been introduced either by the Portuguese or by Africans sent to Portugal during this period.

1830–84

In the five decades before the founding of the Congo Free State there was apparently a continued spread of new crops eastward and further crop introductions by foreigners (Appendix Table). Arab slave traders began to penetrate the Congo Basin from the east and north in the first part of the nineteenth century and by the 1850's had well established themselves in the area around Lake Tanganyika (*162*, ch. 1). Arab influence was still spreading westward when the Arab slave traders were crushed by the forces of the Congo Free State in the 1892–94 campaigns (*339*, p. 142).

Arabs, as traders or agents for traders, settled in a number of areas in the eastern Congo Basin and sometimes attained enough influence to control small kingdoms. Wherever they went they propagated their culture, building houses of their own design, attempting to spread their religion, and taking African wives. Viscount Mountmorres gives the following description of some villages in the northeastern Congo Basin that had been "Arabized" *(271*, pp. 37–38): "The Arabised villages form a startling contrast; exceedingly well-built in an Arab style of architecture, the large white houses with their deep verandahs supported on white pillars are scrupulously clean. . . . All the better houses have a central open hallway with raised daïs around it, on which mats are spread, giving the whole a typical Moorish air. . . . The chiefs and notables are intelligent. . . . They all read and write, and are well versed in the Koran. . . . Mohammedan schools are established, attendance at which is compulsory on all the children, by order of the chiefs and notables."

With the new religion and architecture came a new cuisine necessitating introduction of a number of commodities not available locally. The Arabs are said to have introduced some thirty-six commodities to eastern Africa, nine of which are also credited to the Portuguese in the western Congo. In one part or another of the eastern Congo Basin, the Arabs are said to have introduced rice, millet, sorghum, one type of manioc, wheat, sweet potatoes, some types of bananas, beans, peanuts, sesame, oilseed gourds, eggplant, tomatoes, onions, garlic, chilies, cucumbers, sugarcane, mangoes, papayas, guavas, lemons, limes, grapefruit, avocados, pomegranates, bullock's-heart (*Annona reticulata*), tobacco, hemp, indigo, pigeons, ducks, cats, and improved breeds of small livestock, cattle, donkeys, and mules *(333*, 2: 123; *339*, p. 180; *171*, p. 17; *422*, p. 19; *209*, p. 331; *193*, 2:600–609; *170*, p. 220; *72*, p. 40; *17*, p. 92).

Little is known about the Arabs' methods of establishing new crops, but in some instances they used coercion to effect adoption of rice, if not other crops. Tharin states that as late as 1885–90 the Arabs forced the Africans under their suzerainty near Kasongo to grow rice *(339*, p. 207). F. Hargot, speaking of the area between Lowa and Kasongo, in an article published in 1955, states that rice was introduced by the Arabs in the second half of the nineteenth century and that they compelled the Africans to grow it *(171*, p. 17).

Production methods credited to the Arabs are extraction of peanut oil and palm oil and distillation, but there are almost certainly others for which they are responsible *(102*, p. 70; *121*, p. 708; *388*, p. 172).

The only references to non-Arab introductions in this period that I have found are a statement by Sir Harry Johnston that the German explorer Pogge introduced rice to the south-central Congo Basin in 1875 or 1876; a statement by Auguste Chevalier that a German introduced papaya to the northeastern Congo Basin in 1875; a reference by Édouard Dupont in a book published in 1889 to the introduction of coconuts to the Bas-Congo area by a Dutch trading company "only a few years ago"; and a comment by Edmond Leplae that although several wild varieties of coffee were known when the first Belgians arrived in the Congo Basin, Liberica coffee was introduced and grown at Kinshasa in 1881 (*193*, 2: 601; *346*, p. 243; *124*, p. 539; and *23*, p. 6).

1884–1908

European exploration and administration in the Congo Basin from the founding of the Congo Free State in 1884 until its end in 1908 led to crop introductions in some areas and to fairly sharp changes in the structure of tribal economies. Explorers such as Wilhelm Junker and Emin Pasha tell of their efforts to introduce new varieties of crops (*198*, p. 174; *70*, p. 275) in the northern Congo Basin; and it is likely that administrators and missionaries often did likewise.

Lieutenant Storms introduced Irish potatoes along the southwestern shore of Lake Tanganyika while he was commandant of a post there (1883–85); and missionaries in the same area introduced manioc, wheat, a second variety of Irish potatoes, coffee, and vanilla (*73*, p. 49). Bananas were reportedly introduced to the Alur on the northern end of Lake Albert by Europeans sometime before 1909 (*422*, p. 7). Fernand Gaud reports in a book published in 1911 that Europeans had encouraged banana growing among the Mandja of French Equatorial Africa and that this crop was hardly found except near European posts (*150*, p. 210). Constant de Derken, a missionary, notes in a book published in 1900 that in the Luluabourg area pineapples and papayas were a recent introduction, and that papaya was then seen mostly at European posts although a few Africans were beginning to plant it in their villages (*97*, p. 229). J. Pieraerts introduced sunflowers in 1906 (*290*, p. 87).

Breadfruit was apparently introduced in this period, if not earlier. A list of the useful plants of the Congo Free State published in 1894 by Alfred Dewèvre notes that at the time of writing — apparently after 1889 since Dupont is cited — breadfruit was found at certain posts of the State, principally those between Kinshasa and the Atlantic Ocean (*111*, p. 21).

It was the policy of the Congo Free State to introduce and disseminate all crops that appeared to have commercial value or which could be used to provision posts. The State established two botanical gardens and stocked them with promising plants from such places as Indonesia and Brazil (*236*, p. 199).

By 1903, if not earlier, all posts were required to plant a given quota of rubber yearly — particularly *Futumia elasticia* — and to grow sugar-cane, kola nuts, and oil palms around posts where they were lacking but could be grown (*130*, pp. 13, 23, and 24). Coffee was also encouraged, and after 1894 state agents were paid a premium for each tree planted (*229*, p. 8).

A vigorous effort was also made to introduce certain foodstuffs and expand production of others in the vicinity of posts. Each post was directed to grow vegetables from Europe — cabbage, eggplant, lettuce, tomatoes, radishes, and onions are mentioned in instructions distributed to posts — to assure supplies of vegetables that the white personnel of the state administration were accustomed to (*130*, p. 23). Some posts received seed from Europe every three months, and all were urged to make new plantings every fifteen days to assure a continuous supply and presumably also to minimize difficulties of storing seed (*214*, 2:104 and *130*, p. 23). Staple foodstuffs such as "maize, rice, beans, etc." were also to be grown but in much larger quantities, sufficient to provision all personnel, including nonwhites, that the post had to feed.

It is of considerable interest that a number of the agricultural enterprises said to have been introduced to the tribal economies around the mouth of the Congo River by the Portuguese well before 1830 had not penetrated far into the interior by the time the first posts of the Congo Free State were established. Note has already been made of the absence in the eastern Congo Basin until after Arab influence of six agricultural enterprises — peanuts, sweet potatoes, some varieties of beans, sugarcane, papaya, and ducks — said to have been introduced by the Portuguese in the extreme western Congo Basin. Similar unevenness of introductions was also noted elsewhere and for some areas even closer to the area of Portuguese occupation. Captain Coquilhat was puzzled that among the Ngala, near Coquilhatville on the middle portion of the Congo River, he found no peanuts, beans, peas, Bas-Congo sorrel, onions, avocados, oranges, citron, or guavas, crops then common on the lower portions of the river (cited in *124*, p. 639). Father C. Tisserant (p. 256 below) documents the introduction of mung beans, pigeon peas, guavas, avocados, mangoes, citrons, and other crops to the Banda, found north of the Ngala, well after the coming of European rule. Other evidence (see Ch. 12) suggests that in the 1880's peanuts, guavas, lemons, oranges, papayas, and unspecified vegetables were unknown or only recently introduced to the Logo and Alur in the extreme northeastern corner of the Congo Basin.

Part of the process of transferring new or more efficient agricultural enterprises from one tribal economy to another was accomplished by the efforts of the State and motivated by the desire to improve efficiency in provisioning posts. *Chefs de poste* were instructed that rice seed could be obtained from the *commissaire* of Équateur District or the *chef* of Stanley Falls post. Orders were issued to encourage tobacco in areas where hemp was grown, in a effort to combat the habit of hemp smoking (*130*, pp. 24 and 109). Post administrators were directed to make efforts to replace local chickens and ducks with superior breeds. The Stanley Falls varieties of African chicken and Barbary ducks were recommended (*130*, p. 38).

There were also important livestock introductions during the period both by administrators and by private parties and missionaries. In addition to a policy of encouraging the production of chickens, ducks, and pigeons at all posts, certain posts were designated as livestock posts and were to introduce types of livestock not found, particularly cattle, and to improve the breeds of existing livestock. The State directed that implementation of livestock policies include post regulations prohibiting the slaughter of female animals by Africans; provision of breeding stock to chiefs; and programs for training cattle to be draft animals (*130*, p. 32). Commandant Rennette attempted to introduce the M'Bayrd breed of horses in the northern Congo Basin in this period, but failed after three years because of disease (*348*, p. 438). Commandant Hanollet introduced both cattle and horses in the northwestern corner of the Congo Basin, but we are not told the degree of his success (*55*, p. 329). Cattle — from Angola and Southwest Africa, in the main — were also introduced elsewhere by the administration beginning as early as 1886 and by 1905 the total number of cattle at state posts was more than 4,000 head (*347*, p. 424, *250*, p. 59, and *124*, p. 199).[3] But, unlike efforts with crops, the evidence suggests that livestock policies were generally unsuccessful. There is no evidence that training cattle for draft purposes was ever vigorous or successful or that breeding stock was in fact provided to chiefs. Most of the animals introduced remained on state farms and, in any event, appear not nearly to have offset cattle killed in the Arab campaigns fought in the eastern and southern Congo Basin, or cattle confiscated by agents then and later (see pp. 273–75).[4]

Livestock introductions by missionaries and private parties started as early as 1888. By that date the Dutch trading company in the Congo Basin had a herd of over 50 head of cattle as its post in Bas-Congo (*250*, p. 62). In 1891 the White Fathers attempted to introduce cattle from Urundi to missions at Kibange–Lavigevie Ville, Kilwa (on Lake Mweru), and Mpala in extreme eastern Congo Basin, but were unsuccessful because of difficulties with bovine pests. In 1893 efforts directed by Father Roelens at Baudouinville were successful, and by 1908 the herd there numbered 150 animals (*100*, p. 17). From 1896 to 1899 the Reverend Fathers of Scheut introduced cattle near the mouth of the Congo River; by the latter year they had a total of 34 animals (*140*, p. 199). The Société d'Agriculture et de Plantation au Congo simultaneously made introductions in the same area; and in 1905 Mr. Jacques, a colonist and former officer of the Congo Free State, imported 50 head of cattle of the Dahomey breed.

Changes in the structure of most tribal economies were considerable for several reasons. A large increase in the quantity of cloth, hoes, knives, and axes imported from Europe — all products that were superior to or cheaper than competing local commodities — must have greatly reduced the number of smelters, smiths, weavers, and barkcloth beaters. At the same time tribal economies became exporters of labor to meet the new administrations' needs for bearers, common laborers, soldiers, and clerks. Finally, within the agricultural sector of the tribal economies there was a shift from livestock to crop production as the number of domestic animals needed by Europeans to feed laborers became larger than the number of animals they imported (*317*, p. 109; *369*, p. 203; *400*, p. 22; *83*, p. 215; *370*, pp. 584–85; *268*, p. 57; *238*, p. 32; *150*, p. 216). In some cases the Africans' animals were bought; in others they were confiscated.

The 1884–1908 period, in the Congo Free State, at least, was one of sizable increase in the output of export industries with little or no change in production techniques — although there was some increase in efficiency of transportation. Increments in export output were almost entirely achieved by a shift of labor to the export industries from others; and it is not unlikely that the amount of labor input per unit of output increased — i.e., productivity decreased — while exports were expanding.

The main objective of the Congo Free State administration was to expand exports as much as possible. Some 112,000 square miles — an area about the size of Arizona — was Royal Domain, where the State had a monopoly on exploitation. Most of the remainder was leased to companies such as the still-operating Union Minière of Katanga. District officers or company agents, the sole authority in the areas they administered, were paid bonuses which were tied to the size of the export output of the district in order to encourage a maximum of production. The methods employed by such administrators varied, but coercion was common.

African villages were required to supply provisions and labor needed by administrative posts (*61*, pp. 429–32; *236*, p. 29);[5] they could also be required to serve in the Force Publique or work on public projects such as roads. In addition to these obligations, the equivalent of forty hours of labor per month could be legally imposed (*61*, p. 430), and apparently the taxes actually exacted frequently exceeded the legal limit. In some areas each able-bodied male was required to collect a specified quantity of produce, typically palm fruit, oil palm nuts, or rubber. The individual would usually be paid for whatever he brought in, at rates determined by the state or company official in charge of the area (*61*, p. 429). If a worker's output was below the assigned quota he might be flogged or given more severe punishment. An alternative system was to assign the quota to African *capitas*, or foremen, often from tribes foreign to the area where they worked. Capitas were left to secure their quota from producers under their control by whatever means they chose; murder or mutilation of delinquent producers was not uncommon (*238*, pp. 27–33; *61*, chs. 3 and 4; *268*, chs. 11 to 21; *61*, pp. 431–32).

Thus African producers were forced to translate as much of the economic surplus as possible into export production, and exports grew fairly rapidly at first. Total crop exports from the Congo Free State increased from 4,024 metric tons in 1888 to 12,395 metric tons in 1900 (Chart 11-1).

However, most of these gains came from commodities for which there is no record of introduction of superior production methods in this period; and the commission appointed in 1904 by King Leopold to investigate administrative practices in the Congo Free State suggests, in its report, that there were none (*238*, p. 31): "The Commission has noted with surprise how little contact with the white has modified native methods. The European has limited his education to a few industries, such as printing; shoemaking, etc., but he has done nothing to improve the native industries. . . ." Moreover punitive raids, the holding of village women as hostages, floggings, and other disciplinary measures must have decreased considerably the efficiency of producers.

There is evidence that toward the end of the period the limit to output increments that could be obtained by Congo Free State methods was approached. Most of the increase in crop exports came prior to 1900; and exports of rubber, the commodity for which the most bloody forms of coercion have been documented, actually fell between 1900 and 1908 (Chart 11-1).

CHART 11-1   Congo Free State Crop Exports, 1888-1908
(thousand metric tons)

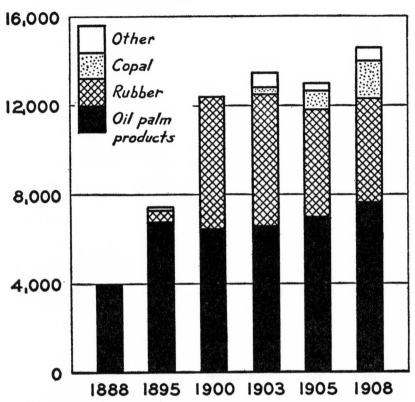

Data from W. H. Wack, *The Story of the Congo Free State* (London, 1905), 280, and Belgium, Ministère des Colonies, *Agriculture Congolaise* (Brussels, 1954), p. 6. Chart: Food Research Institute.

In the non-Belgian areas of the Congo Basin policies varied. In the Portuguese portion of the area, as in the Congo Free State, forced labor and other forms of coercion were the major tools of economic policy (*148*, 286–89). In the British part of the Congo Basin coercion was less common, more reliance being put on taxation. Coercion was not part of policy in the French Congo until after 1899, when trading companies were granted concessions (*84*, p. 13) and began to employ methods much the same as those in the Congo Free State (*342*, p. 14). Public opinion at home led to reforms in 1906, but in some areas abuses continued until World War II. In the French Congo, for example, an entrepreneur called "Le Barbu" (The Bearded One) grew so powerful from wealth derived by monopolizing the coastal trade in gold, ivory, and hides that in the 1930's he "employed a small army, acquired a concession of several thousand hectares . . . ruined his rivals, and was able literally to get away with murder" (*342*, p. 19)

1908–17

In 1908 the government of the bulk of the Congo Basin passed from the hands of the Congo Free State to Belgium, and what had been King Leopold's toy became the Belgian Congo. From this date until imposition of obligatory acreages in 1917, the growth of crop exports in the Belgian portion of the Congo Basin was rapid, the increase being from 13,691 metric tons in 1910 to 62,831 metric tons by 1920 (*46*, p. 12). These data slightly overstate export production by tribal economies since they are aggregates for plantations and peasant production, but the larger items — oil palm products and copal, which together accounted for 96 percent of crop exports in 1920 — are almost entirely African production; hence growth of African-produced crop exports must have been close to the rate of growth in aggregate crop exports.

Taxation and borrowing of techniques were the major features of agricultural policy in this period. With the change of administration came a shift of policy. While the administrators of the Congo Free State had emphasized exploitation of forest products, effected by the use of extreme coercion if necessary, the new administration came to the Belgian Congo partly because of desires abroad for new and less harsh economic policies.[6] Secondly, the new administration, unlike its predecessor, had objectives other than economic ones. Whereas officials of the Congo Free State had little interest in areas poorly endowed with exportable commodities, the administrators of the Belgian Congo were charged with bringing the Belgian system of justice — indeed, Belgian civilization — to the subjected Africans, whether or not there was immediate economic gain. In short, the administration of the Belgian Congo was willing to undertake investments slow to give returns, and was restricted in the sorts of coercion it could employ; the Congo Free State officials had been preoccupied with immediate gain and were encouraged to employ extreme coercion if necessary.

Persons in the employ of the Congo Free State introduced some new crops, as we have seen, but there is no evidence that they systematically taught the Africans how to grow and process them. Nor was there much incentive to do so. Food crops were not exportable and were of value mainly in feeding soldiers and others in the service of the State. There was no need to attempt to meet needs for provisions by increasing the productivity of farmers when village granaries could be raided with little fear of reprimand or reprisal.

Not only were such practices forbidden to the new administration, but its greater size plus increased activity in extending the communications network, in mining, and in plantation agriculture considerably augmented the need for food supplies outside the tribal economies. Some 450 kilometers of railway, for example, were built between 1884 and 1908, compared with about 1,200 km. between 1908 and 1917 (*173*, p. 17; *105*, Map 25). Except for gold, mining was not begun until after 1911 (*173*, p. 20).

Another impetus to increasing productivity came from dreams of developing in the Congo Basin export crops such as cocoa, coffee, cotton, and rice, which were already being profitably grown in similar climates elsewhere in the tropics. The Congo Free State had been attracted by the prospects of developing coffee production, and after 1896 Africans were forced to grow the crop in some areas (*55*, p. 287). About 2,000 hectares of coffee were eventually planted in aggregate; but because of the inexperience of the agronomists in charge of coffee, plantings got too little care and some were established in areas with an unfavorable climate. Yields, therefore, were not impressive. This, coupled with a slump in world coffee prices, eventually led to abandonment of coffee as a major enterprise (*25*, p. 378). By the time the Congo Free State was abolished, the prospects for coffee were again good, and one of the first acts of the Department of Agriculture of the Belgian Congo, established in 1910, was to create a coffee experiment station near Leopoldville (*25*, p. 378).

In 1914 Sakellarides, an Egyptian variety of cotton, was introduced into the Kasai area, but results were not encouraging (*85*, p. 15). Successful yields of the Triumph Big Boll variety at the Nyangwé experiment station in 1914–15 led to its distribution among African farmers in that area. In 1915 trials were also made with American varieties in Kasai, and beginning in 1916 these were disseminated to Africans. In 1919 similar trials were made in the northern Congo Basin and, under the direction of Commissaire Général Landeghem, production by 1922 exceeded that of the southern cotton zone (*85*, p. 16).

But although there was some agricultural research, the major response to the food crop needs and the prospects for export crops was, in this period, wholesale borrowing. A number of new varieties of various crops were introduced to the botanical garden at Eala on the Congo River for observation or to agricultural stations for dissemination. For example, a mission sent to Asia brought back "numerous varieties of bananas, rice, maize, sorghum, manioc, taro, and other important food crops," according to a report submitted to the Belgian legislative body about 1910 (*11*, p. 17); and the *Bulletin Agricole du Congo Belge*, the journal of the newly created Department of Agriculture which was sent free to all missionaries and settlers, carried articles discussing agricultural methods that seemed promising in other tropical countries.

Toward the end of the period — during World War I — taxes and produce prices were set by the state in the Belgian Congo at levels designed to press Africans into producing more of the crops that the state wanted (*226*, p. 208; *31*, p. 44). In the British portion of the Congo Basin policy makers ignored the possibility of developing export crop production among Africans and depended on settlers for most of the desired agricultural development. French administrators left agricultural development to the trading companies and made little attempt to improve techniques until after World War II (*342*, p. 162). Except for cotton, coffee, and cocoa — crops these companies were exporting — there was apparently very little technical change outside of unofficial efforts by missionaries and possibly other individuals.

1917–33

From 1917 to the establishment of large scale agricultural research in 1933, borrowing continued to be important in the Belgian Congo,[7] but was reinforced by new methods of effecting adoption of innovations.

Immediately before and during World War I, Belgian leaders became concerned with the slow development of agriculture; a mission was sent to Africa in 1915–16 to study means of increasing agricultural production in the colony (*230*, p. 667). When this mission returned it argued that Congolese farmers had been in a state of indolence for centuries and did not produce enough food for even their own nourishment. It was further argued that Congolese farmers would not respond to price incentives. In February 1917 legislation was passed which authorized the imposition of compulsory acreages wherever local administrators deemed them necessary. Rice, manioc, maize, oil palms — practically all food crops — were made objects of this policy in one area or another; and production of such things as coffee, cotton, and other fibers for the world market was also made obligatory in some regions.

Similar use was made of compulsory acreages in the French areas of the Congo Basin from the early 1920's (*342*, p. 163, and *346*, p. 224), and in some districts villages were relocated near roads to make evacuation of production easier (*283*, p. 128 and *346*). Legislation of 1928 authorized obligatory acreages in the Portuguese portion of the Congo Basin, according to Leplae, but his discussion suggests that such measures may have also existed earlier (*227*, p. 475). The Portuguese still operate a system of obligatory labor. In British areas of the Congo Basin compulsory planting of food crops as a measure to prevent food shortage was authorized in 1929 (*227*, p. 474), but there is no evidence that compulsory acreages were ever used extensively.

In the early part of the period shortage of hoes, axes, and machetes among African farmers was singled out as a major obstacle to expansion of production (*226*). Beginning with 1925, the government distributed free hand tools to Africans or made tools available at low prices (*230*, p. 647). In a few areas attempts were also made to introduce plows (*24*, p. 627).

1933–59

Only a brief sketch can be given here of the changes between 1933, the date at which Belgian policies in the Congo Basin shifted from a search for innovations developed elsewhere to research in the Belgian Congo itself, and 1959, the last year of colonial rule. Prince Leopold, after visiting the Belgian Congo and the Dutch East Indies in 1930, gave his support to the establishment of a vast agricultural research organization in the Belgian Congo (*46*, pp. 8–9). Three years later l'Institut National pour l'Étude Agronomique du Congo Belge (INÉAC) was created. Some thirty-eight research stations were eventually established in the Belgian Congo and Ruanda-Urundi (*325*, pp. 121–31). The volume, scope, and quality of the resulting research is unparalleled in tropical Africa, and in some instances productivity was increased impressively. By 1952 INÉAC efforts had raised potential yields under peasant conditions by an estimated 87 percent for beans, 125 percent for cotton, 150 percent for peanuts and oil palms, 233 percent for rice, and 380 percent for manioc (*199*, p. 8).

About 1950 Belgian administrators began to implement schemes for resettling and reorganizing African villages as a supplementary measure to obligatory acreages, which had come to be regarded as an insufficient means of effecting adoption of new methods. In the resettlement schemes — called *paysannats indigènes* — families were relocated in an effort to place their fields in a systematic layout and to set the center of the community nearer existing roads. The intent was to further the use of machinery; to facilitate the introduction of fertilizers, pesticides, superior crop rotations, and superior varieties; and to make supervision and guidance easier. By the late 1950's some 120,000 families had been grouped into paysannats to form the nucleus of what the Belgians hoped would be the means for a major productivity breakthrough.

In the French and British areas agricultural research was considerably expanded, although most of the research emphasis came after World War II (*342*, pp. 161–62).

12

Technological Changes
by Tribe or Area

Evidence of technological change among specific tribes is uneven. Enormous change can be documented for some groups; there is nothing, or very little, in literature on others. Evidence we do have suggests that traditional agriculture is much less static than has usually been assumed.

The Kuba

Evidence presented by Torday and Joyce suggests that large changes in the technology of the Kuba have been achieved by deliberate introduction of innovations by their rulers. According to oral tradition, Shamba Bolongongo, one of the popular rulers, introduced manioc, tobacco, and oil and raphia palm products. The date of these introductions is not known, but using the eclipse of March 30, 1680 — the only eclipse of the sun visible in this area in the seventeenth and eighteenth centuries (*358*, p. 36) — as a benchmark, Torday and Joyce estimated that manioc was introduced during a period of food shortage between 1600 and 1620. Before this period the staple food is said to have been maize; and before maize "millet, bananas, and yams" were the base of the diet (*358*, p. 131).

Shamba Bolongongo is said to have been interested in other realms as a boy and to have requested permission to travel: "Since the king is the largest of men, he must be the wisest; if I rest here, I will learn nothing that the Bushongo [a group of the Kuba] do not know" (*358*, p. 25). Although his mother thought travel risky and doubted if it were prudent to allow the heir to risk his life, she gave Shamba Bolongongo three slaves and provisions and he journeyed westward, visiting the Bunda, a group of the Pende, the Dzing, and the Binji group of the Kuba. Upon his return, he introduced a number of innovations.

Whether he introduced manioc immediately upon his return is not clear; the tradition as given by Torday and Joyce states merely that "During one season of his reign the harvests of the Bushongo were completely destroyed by locusts and the people were in danger of starving. But they were saved by Shamba Mikepe [i.e. Shamba Bolongongo], who showed them the use of manioc, which could not be destroyed by any amount of locusts" (*358*, p. 249).[1]

Shamba Bolongongo is said to have obtained tobacco from a man called Lokono Lon Pene, which Torday and Joyce explain means "Lokono of the Pende" (*358*, p. 26). Production of raffia cloth is said to have been learned from the same tribe. Shamba Bolongongo is also credited with teaching the Kuba to utilize the oil palm; Torday and Joyce found the oil palm called Shamba's palm (*itokolo Shamba*) but the source of his knowledge of it is not given (*358*, p. 249).

An innovation during the reign of Bom Bosh, the third ruler after Shamba Bolongongo, was possibly as important as the introduction of manioc growing.

When manioc was first introduced, the method of processing it was merely to cut up the roots and boil them.[2] During Bom Bosh's rule the technique of making manioc "bread" (wrapped manioc paste) was introduced by a woman named Lukanya, belonging to the Bienge group of the Kuba, a group that had learned from the west the use of manioc, but apparently through a different means than some of the other Kuba.

A woman ruler of the Bienge, Shema Shunga, is said to have learned of manioc and peanuts in the west and to have introduced them to the Bienge sometime before 1650 (*358*, p. 28). Thus it is not clear whether Shema Shunga introduced manioc before or after Shamba Bolongongo introduced it. Possibly the Bienge had manioc before the time of Shamba Bolongongo but were not in the Kuba kingdom until his rule, or between his rule and Bom Bosh's. Otherwise, manioc was reintroduced to the Kuba by either Shamba Bolongongo or Shema Shunga — unless the tradition presented by Torday and Joyce is inconsistent.

Some of the western groups of the Kuba apparently were little affected by either Shamba Bolongongo's or Shema Shunga's introductions, for Wolf, the first European to visit the Kuba, penetrating their territory from the southwest as far as Ibanshe (*358*, p. 28), said the Kuba grew principally maize in 1884 and did not have manioc (*402*, p. 728; *358*, p. 28). Torday and Joyce further state that the utilization of manioc was not common among the western Kuba until 1904 (*358*, p. 28).

The Kete group of Kuba appears to have had a number of crops introduced by missionaries about the turn of the century.[3] J. L. Kellersberger reports that about 1905 A. L. Edmiston, a missionary, enthusiastically attempted to bring a number of new crops from Europe, but at first failed, "for the seeds he so carefully selected and ordered from Europe deteriorated along the way and, when planted, failed to propagate. This condition was remedied as soon as every packet came sealed in a tin . . ." (*202*, p. 79). We are not told specifically which crops were introduced, only that they included garden vegetables and citrus fruit. Edmiston apparently worked energetically not only to introduce the crops but to assure that, once available, they were rapidly and widely adopted. He organized clubs to promote a number of enterprises — the raising of manioc, maize, fruit trees, chickens, and goats — and gave prizes.[4]

Bas-Congo

Drachoussoff's study of two areas in the Bas-Congo (*120* and *121*), the most detailed investigation of intervillage differences available for the Congo Basin, suggests that there has been considerable infusion of new crops within living memory. Information given to Drachoussoff indicates for the Bangu area that 20 of the 78 varieties of major crops that he describes, or 25.6 percent, have been introduced in living memory, while for the Inkisi area a somewhat larger proportion — 25 of 72 varieties, or 34.7 percent — are said to have been introductions. Four of 12 manioc varieties in Bangu and 12 of 14 manioc varieties in Inkisi are recognized as introductions.[5] But for plantains, gourds, Bambara nuts, and pigeon peas there is no memory of introductions in either area.

Missionaries and traders were the principal agents of introduction in Bangu, in instances where the agent of introduction is remembered. In Inkisi, it is mainly Africans who are remembered to have brought new crops. In both areas, a large proportion of introductions came from communities having a mission station or government agricultural station. Places to the east and south — Kionzo, Kasi, Banza Manteke, Kitobola,

Tumba, São Salvador, Bazombo, Kisantu, and Luvituku — are mentioned for the Bangu area (Table 12-1). Places north, west, and south are more frequently cited in Inkisi, where the following locations are referred to: Madimba, Gombe Matadi, Thysville, Kimpese, Kisantu, Kitobola, Bazombo, Boko, and Cadulac (Table 12-2).

The unevenness of introductions is striking. Even within the same sector some villages grow varieties that have never been adopted by other villages. For example, Kinbewa village in Inkisi sector has three varieties of bitter manioc and four of sweet manioc of which Sumba village some 10 kilometers south is ignorant. Congo-Botongo village in the Bangu sector has five varieties of bananas, two of which were introduced from the east and one of which came from the south; while Kisende village near Kitobola, source of the southern introductions, has only one variety of bananas, that introduced from Kitobola.

Improved breeds of poultry have probably come from European farmers, for Drachoussoff refers to the purchase of eggs of European poultry by Africans in Sumba and Kilumbu villages, Inkisi sector. In the Bangu area, improved poultry have been purchased "from the Manianga," a tribe, or possibly a clan, that I have not been able to identify.

Growth of cattle production in the Bas-Congo since the founding of the Congo Free State is fairly well documented. In 1897 the State and missionaries began attempts to introduce cattle to the area between Leopoldville and the mouth of the Congo River. The Société d'Agriculture et de Plantation au Congo sent animals from Tshela to Temvo to be acclimatized, and the Reverend Fathers of Scheut brought 3 animals to Boma in the same year (*140*, p. 199). In 1898 the same missionaries brought 12 animals from Zambi. By the end of 1899 religious orders in the area had a total of 34 animals.

In 1904 one Jacques, a colonist and former officer of the Congo Free State, imported 50 head of cattle of the Dahomey breed from Dahomey. In 1912 another 25 Dahomey cattle were imported by the Zambi agricultural station, while the Scheut missionaries imported another 15 head, 13 of which soon died of disease.

From 1927 on the Société de Colonization Agricole au Mayumbe built up herds of cattle; five years later they began selling cattle to African farmers who wanted them, but sales lagged behind the goals of the Société. By 1933 the herds of the Société were large enough to do considerable damage to coffee, cacao, and young oil palm plantations, and steps were taken to reduce them by loaning animals to Africans.

TABLE 12-1 Varieties of Crops Introduced to Bangu Sector, Former Belgian Congo, within Living Memory

Crop	Variety	Agent of introduction	Area whence introduced	Village to which introduced
Bitter manioc	nsielele	missionary?	Kionzo	Kinsende Manilonde Lukamba
	mputuandobe	?	Kitobola	Manilonde Lukamba
Sweet manioc	vanda	missionary	Kimpese	Kinsende
	lundala	missionary?	Kasi	Manilonde Lukamba Congo-Botongo
Tomato	mondele bbala	M. Arnould	?	Vunda-Nkama
Banana	dinkondo dia mputu	traders	Upper Congo River	Manilonde Congo-Botongo
	kinsiesie	?	Kisantu	all villages
	kimbangala	?	Kitobola Banza Manteke	Lukamba Congo-Botongo Vunda-Nkama
	kivuazi	?	Kitobola Banza Manteke Tumba	Lukamba Congo-Botongo Vunda-Nkama
Yam	kuamukongo	?	Angola	Lukamba Congo-Botongo
Taro	totolo	?	?	Vunda-Nkama
Peanuts	mputu	?	Kitobola	Kinsende Manilonde Lukamba
Beans	diniania	?	Tumba	Kinsende Manilonde Lukamba
	loanza	?	Loanza River	Kinsende Manilonde
	salvador	?	Angola	Kinsende
	carte	?	Saõ Salvador Angola	Kinsende Manilonde Lukamba
	kondua ntu	?	Bazombo	Kinsende Manilonde
Maize	kitobola	?	Kitobola	Vunda-Nkama
Tobacco	mputu	?	Luvituku	Vunda-Nkama

Data from V. Drachoussoff, "Essai sur l'agriculture indigène au Bas-Congo," *Bull. Agr. du Congo Belge*, Dec. 1947, pp. 798–806.

TABLE 12-2   Varieties of Crops Introduced to Inkisi Sector, Former Belgian Congo, within Living Memory

Crop	Variety	Agent of introduction	Area whence introduced	Village to which introduced
Bitter manioc				
	lundombe	?	Madimba	Sumba Banza-Nsundi Kinkewa
	kinsumba	?	Gombe Matadi	all villages
	kinvuama	?	Madimba Thysville Kimpese	all villages
	kingela	?	Kisantu or Madimba	all villages
	mpelubuya	?	Kimpese Madimba	Banza-Nsundi Kinkewa
	kudi	?	Kimpese	Kinkewa
	kidamo	?	Kisantu	Kilumbu
	belegi	?	Kisantu	Kilumbu
Sweet manioc				
	ngangan-tombe	Africans	Madimba	Banza-Nsundi Kinkewa
	kambi	Africans	Madimba	Kinkewa
	bungua diaku or *kimeya*	?	Kisantu Madimba	Kinkewa Kilumbu
	kinsasa	?	Kisantu	Kilumbu
Banana				
	kionzo	Africans	Madimba	Banza-Nsundi
	dinkondo dia mputu	traders	Upper Congo River	Kinkewa Sumba
	mafuta	?	Kisantu	all villages
Yam				
	mbele	Africans	Madimba	all villages
Sweet potatoes				
	maweti	?	Kisantu	Kilumbu
Maize				
	ntendezi	?	Cadulac	Banza-Nsundi
Beans				
	diniania	?	Boko Bazombo	Banza-Nsundi Sumba
Peanuts				
	bizeleketi	?	Kisantu	Kilumbu
	mfoko		Kitobola Kisantu	all villages

Table 12-2 (*Continued*)

Crop	Variety	Agent of introduction	Area whence introduced	Village to which introduced
	malunguba	traders and others	Kitobola Bazombo Kisantu Boko	all villages
Sesame				
	wangila	local administrator	?	Banza-Nsundi
Tomato				
	mputu	?	Cadulac	all villages
	tomatu portugueza	?	Bazombo	Sumba

Data from V. Drachoussoff, "Essai sur l'agriculture indigène au Bas-Congo," *Bull. Agr. du Congo Belge*, Dec. 1947, pp. 798–806.

In 1933 three head of cattle were loaned to a chief who was especially trusted by the Société, and the next year 25 animals were loaned out. By 1938 a total of 237 animals were loaned on contracts with the following provisions:

a. all animals remained property of the Société;

b. the borrower was required to keep cows near his village at calving time and to feed them from his own fields;

c. the Société was to be notified of all births, deaths, or illnesses in herds on loan;

d. any animals borrowed were to be replaced by the borrower eventually;

e. half of the offspring were to be the property of the Société; the other half belonged to the borrower;

f. at the expiration of the contract, the Société was to claim as many animals, of approximately the same quality, as it had provided; the rest of the herd was to be divided into two groups of equal number, one for the Société and one for the borrower, the Société retaining the right to choose which animals were to be included in its share;

g. the contract was to have no fixed duration, but could be terminated by either party on a month's notice;

h. the local administrator was to be the arbitrator in case of disputes.

Two somewhat similar systems, called *twadi* and *kutwila bibulu*, had long been practiced by the Africans for loan of goats and other small animals. The twadi was essentially a loan of money, guaranteed with an animal; the lender kept as interest all offspring of the animal (*141*, p. 654). Under twadi the loan was typically half the value of the animal given as security.[6]

Under the kutwila bibulu arrangement the borrower paid only four out of every five of the animal's offspring to the lender as interest.

The opportunity to obtain animals at a rent of but half the offspring and without money payment, through the contracts with the Société de Colonization Agricole au Mayumbe, had a great deal of appeal. According to Flamingi, by 1948 there was a tendency to raise the return under the kutwila bibulu arrangements between Africans from the traditional one-fifth to one-third, possibly in reaction to the superior terms offered by the Société de Colonization Agricole au Mayumbe (*141*, p. 654).

The Kamba Group of the Sundi in the Niari Valley

An early-maturing variety of peanut was introduced after World War II by Governor General Reste, with the result that the traditional varieties were abandoned (*313*, p. 75). Traditionally all sequences began with crops of pigeon peas, but now peanuts are often planted at the head of the crop sequence.

Three of the four existing varieties of bitter manioc were "recently" introduced by administrators. However, efforts of the administration to introduce European varieties of maize have been unsuccessful (*313*, p. 78).

The Tio (Teke)

French rule forced several changes in the Tio agriculture. Villages were moved near roads to facilitate control of disease and to aid recruitment of labor (*283*, p. 128). Huts on former village sites were torn down or burned. The French administration organized the production of manioc in order to provision Brazzaville and other cities, and it ordered that bananas-plaintains and coffee be cultivated. (The very slight importance of bananas-plantains before French rule is documented by Léon Guiral, who traveled over much of Tio country in 1881, including the Koukouya Plateau, and explicitly noted that bananas-plantains were rarely found [*165*, p. 151].) Irish potatoes and improved varieties of tobacco were distributed among the Tio for planting, and their production was encouraged. Papy says that in some areas relatively high tobacco prices have caused a reduction of manioc production (*283*, p. 131).

Oil palms have apparently become considerably less important among the Tio than they were in the 1880's. Guiral noted that oil palms were cultivated in small amounts for oil, wine, and construction materials, but although the Tio may still occasionally plant oil palm trees, Jan Vansina's informants remember that oil palm production used to be considerably more important (see p. 00 above).

A possible explanation for the apparent decline in the importance of oil palms is felling of groves to meet the rising demand for palm wine in the urban centers that rapidly developed after the advent of colonial rule — especially Brazzaville and Leopoldville. J. Van Lancker devoted an article in 1935 to discussion of means of slowing down the destruction of oil palm groves in the area around Leopoldville, and notes that, in addition to the difficulty of enforcing laws prohibiting the felling of oil palm trees that had been passed soon after Belgium took over the colony, a tax of 300 francs had been imposed on all palm wine sellers in the *District Urbain de Léopoldville* (382, p. 153). Van Lancker's prediction was that this measure, too, would be ineffective.

Lake Leopold II Area

The most important cultivated cash crops — urena, rice, and cultivated oil palms — are all recent innovations. Urena was introduced to the Banningville territoire in 1935 and into Kutu and Inongo territoires in 1938 by the Belgian administration (*306*, pp. 665–66). Production had expanded to 3,054 metric tons by 1946, but in ensuing years it declined (*306*, p. 665):

Year	Urena production (metric tons)
1935	15
1937	163
1938	412
1946	3,054
1947	1,729
1948	2,683
1949	2,017
1950	2,807
1951	1,590

In the forest region generally urena never became an important crop, but elsewhere it was the main cash crop by 1952 (*306*, p. 666).

In the area between the Kwango and Kasai rivers the production of rice, one of the principal cash crops prior to 1935, declined in the face of competition from urena (*306*, p. 674).

In some areas urena production was expanded by coercion. In the eastern part of Banningville territoire, the principal maize area of the region, local agricultural authorities decided that the maize, manioc crop sequence being following caused excessive destruction of the soil; they required that the maize be followed by urena instead of manioc (306, p. 676). Total maize production from Banningville territoire fell from an estimated 3,778 metric tons in 1950 to 360 metric tons in 1957 (*306*, p. 671; *185*):

Year	*Maize production (metric tons)*
1947	1,784
1948	2,150
1949	3,594
1950	3,778
1951	3,200
1956	252
1957	360

The introduction of oil palm cultivation came sometime after 1952. Robert stated then that a program was planned for establishing 960 hectares of oil palms among African producers over a period of three years (*306*, p. 679).

R. de Beaucorps, in a booklet published in 1933 on the Yanzi, the major tribe in Banningville territoire, states that swine which were "formerly rather widespread have disappeared. The largest herds of goats have been reduced to a few animals" (*94*, pp. 21–22). No explanation of these changes is given.

The Sanga

The Bangi reportedly have introduced techniques for making palm wine to the Sanga sometime before 1911 (*302*, p. 274).

The Mongo

The Arabs are said to have introduced rice to the Mongo (*383*, p. 548). That villages are apparently moved less frequently now than formerly suggests a decrease in the period fields are rested in forest fallow. Van Moesieke states that formerly the ratoon crops [7] from the plantain were not harvested for "the cultivations were moved with the village" *(383,* p. 535).

The Mandja

Gaud states that bananas are grown only near European posts, where they have been encouraged by Europeans *(150,* pp. 215–16). He also comments that before 1902 poultry were common among the Mandja, but that they had almost disappeared by the time of his writing (1911) because they had been sold to Europeans.

A. M. Vergait's account of the Mandja (published in 1937) states that the "old Mandja" grew manioc in pure stand for three successive years and then abandoned the field, whereas by the 1930's a sequence had been adopted of millet/beans/oilseed gourds, followed by millet/manioc the second year, and terminating in a pure stand of manioc *(397,* pp. 116–17).

Ubangi District

Beginning in 1924, the Belgian administration required each male taxpayer to plant ten oil palm trees per year *(224,* p. 54). About the same time, each adult male not paying taxes in the forest areas was required to grow from 0.10 to 0.25 hectares of cotton, while in savanna areas the imposition was from 0.15 to 0.40 hectares *(224,* p. 52). Total cotton production increased from 192 metric tons in 1924–25 to 2,529 metric tons in 1930–31 *(224,* p. 61):

Year	*Tons of cotton harvested*
1924–25	192
1925–26	604
1926–27	1,029
1927–28	735
1928–29	1,193
1929–30	1,286
1930–31	2,529

In 1930 and 1931 invasions of migratory locusts (*Locusta migratoria migratoroides*) originating in French Equatorial Africa caused severe damage in some areas and prompted the Belgian administration to increase compulsory acreages of manioc and bananas-plantains, crops little bothered by locusts. The Bwaka are said not to have known manioc before this, and to have grown few bananas (*224*, p. 55).

The Baya

Maize is said to have been introduced by the Bimore, and sesame by the Hausa (*295*, p. 110).

The Banza

Comparison of Torday's description of Banza agriculture around the turn of the century with that by Léontovitch in 1933 suggests a shift toward manioc during the intervening years. Torday says manioc is grown "in small quantity." Léontovitch, however, says manioc and maize were the major staples of the Banza about 1933 (*224*, p. 51).

The Banda

Father Tisserant gives a detailed account of crop introductions that occurred while he was among the Banda or within the memory of those then living. Of the sixty crops cultivated, at least thirteen — and most of the important ones — are known introductions; and for four others new varieties have been introduced. The major sources of new crops were tribal migrations; non-African travelers, missionaries, or traders; European administrators; and African soldiers.

Tisserant's informants say sorghum and castor beans came from the Sudan as a result of migrations. Manioc came from the opposite direction but by similar means. According to Tisserant it was known only among the extreme western Banda until a group of the tribe migrated to the Ubangi River sometime before World War I. He observes that it had spread throughout the Ouaka River basin by 1914 but was not known east of the Kotto River; i.e. was unknown to the eastern two-thirds of the Banda tribal areas (*346*, p. 215). In 1917, soon after Governor Lamblain arrived, agents were placed in all Banda villages to force manioc cultivation, and it was quickly established throughout areas that had not known it previously (*346*, p. 268).

Tisserant's evidence clearly suggests that European travelers, missionaries, or traders introduced Cerea rubber (*Manihot Glazionii*), papayas, mangoes, and some other varieties of bananas; and they must have also been the source of rice, guavas, plantain, and common hemp. Auguste

Chevalier, a French professor who did pioneering work on African botany, is said to have introduced Cerea rubber at Fort Sibut, about 175 kilometers northeast of the city of Bangui, in 1903; Governor Lamblain had it spread throughout the colony after his arrival in 1917 (*346*, p. 225). According to Chevalier, a German had introduced papaya to the area a little over a quarter of a century earlier (1875), and it easily spread because the seed from the fruit readily sprout and grow in the Banda area, as in much of tropical Africa, without cultivation (*346*, p. 243). Mangoes were planted by white traders on the Bangui River around their trading posts, for their own consumption, well before the colonial period; later they spread to administrative posts, then to the courtyards of the chiefs, and finally to the gardens of other Africans (*346*, p. 243). In 1914 a missionary referred to simply as Frère Gillete introduced apple and silver bananas (*346*, p. 228).

Tisserant states that rice was introduced after European penetration, and that in 1911 it could be seen mainly around European posts, where Senegalese soldiers, "who were very numerous at that period," were found. By 1917 rice, like manioc and Cerea rubber, was forced on Africans by Governor Lamblain; but at first they refused to incorporate it into their diet and sold their production to Europeans or administrators. Only after migrant Banda workers who had been employed on railway construction in the French Congo returned with a taste for rice did the Banda widely begin to consume it (*346*, p. 224).

Common hemp possibly came through European traders. Tisserant notes that it arrived about 1910 on river boats and was called "Kasai tobacco" (*346*, p. 254). He says that plantain was introduced "after arrival of the Europeans," but does not provide more information (*346*, p. 226).

The introduction of guavas is clearly attributed to Europeans, but no data are given. Tisserant suggests its spread was unusually rapid because the seed will pass through the intestinal track undamaged. Africans quickly became fond of guavas, and after 1917 involuntarily spread them to newly established Cerea rubber groves, which were favorite places for defecation (*346*, p. 244).

Cotton was introduced in 1930 and forced on Africans by Governor Eboué. Because sorghum and cotton planting times coincided, sorghum acreages had to be greatly reduced to meet cotton quotas (*346*, p. 225). As a result manioc took the place of sorghum as the dominant dietary staple.

Successful introductions credited simply to "Europeans" — presumably administrators — are one white variety of sweet potatoes, and pineapples (*346*, p. 231). Several other attempted introductions by administrators are known to have been unsuccessful. Pigeon peas were introduced in 1914 to alleviate food shortages that had developed in the wake of an intensive campaign to increase rubber collection. Because pigeon peas required much longer to cook than familiar pulses, they were soon abandoned (*346*, p. 235). Attempts to introduce mung beans were also unsuccessful, but no information is provided on the causes of the failure (*346*, p. 235). Sisal was introduced about 1920 and for a while widely grown under coercion, but now only a few plants are to be seen here and there (*346*, p. 249). Repeated attempts were made to introduce avocados, until it was finally established that this crop is unsuited to the climate except in parts of the south. Attempts to introduce citrus fruits have been successful only where care of the seedlings was carefully supervised. Only citron, which is hardy in the Banda area, is widely grown. One of the problems of growing fruit trees was said to be lack of incentive on the part of the Africans to plant trees prior to 1915 because the homestead was moved at least every eight years, and sometimes more frequently.[8] In 1915 the administration regrouped villages in fixed locations along roads (*346*, pp. 242 and 267). Coffee was introduced in the early 1930's but grew well only under close supervision and finally had to be abandoned in 1938 because of disease problems (*346*, p. 225).

Other introductions may have been a result of the efforts of administrators, but Tisserant's account is not clear as to the agent of introduction. Chinese bananas were introduced about 1911, but we do not know the source. Red bananas are said to have been introduced from the south (presumably the Belgian Congo) "towards 1930." A large root variety of sweet potatoes was introduced in 1917 from French Cameroons, but it soon degenerated in its new environment (*346*, p. 232). Hausa or Madagascar potatoes, *Coleus dysentericus*, were introduced from the "lower river" toward 1911 and reintroduced about 1918 as Chad potatoes without ever having disappeared in the intervening seven years (*346*, p. 233). Sugarcane was known only on the lower Bangui River in 1911, but since that time has, by some means, moved up the river and been disseminated among the Banda (*346*, p. 241).

Soldiers are credited with bringing a variety of taro previously unknown home with them when they returned from a tour of duty in French Cameroons during World War I. However, as with large-root sweet potatoes, which were introduced about the same time and by an unidentified source, the new variety of taro quickly degenerated and is no longer grown (*346,* p. 230).

The Azande

According to Pierre de Schlippe's informants, a fundamental change in field types and crop sequences of the Sudan Azande was brought about during the 1930's by introduction of an earlier maturing variety of peanuts known locally as *abiranga* or *mangirima,* brought from the Belgian Congo. Until this introduction, Azande in the southern section used field types and crop sequences reported in the 1950's among the Azande of the Central African Republic (see Ch. 3). With more slowly growing traditional varieties, the peanut harvest was too late for sowing finger millet, hence the peanut-finger millet succession could not be established and the number of possible crop combinations was reduced.

European administration is directly responsible for disappearance of a fairly important field type — the dry season maize field — and for decline in the importance of courtyard maize gardens. The Azande usually located their homesites near streams, and dry season maize was grown in valley bottoms or along streams where there was enough residual moisture to produce a crop without rain. From 1921 to 1926 the Sudan Azande were resettled away from streams in an effort to control sleeping sickness, and since that time there has been a regulation prohibiting the cultivation of slopes within 100 yards of a valley bottom, in order to prevent soil erosion. Thus the dry-season maize field was eliminated by decree, and the gardens associated with the courtyard were moved to poorer soils where the microclimate was drier and less favorable. In the new location yields were poorer and the number of cycles in the garden crop sequence consequently fewer.

Among the Congo Azande, also, the dry-season maize field has been eliminated, but only indirectly because of action by the administration. A. de Calonne-Beaufaict's observations among the Azande in 1915 led him to the conclusion that maize was then the most important crop of the Congo Azande, and he notes that their agricultural year was divided into three periods for planting maize: *dume* (February), *bire* (April), and *bakusa* (July). Pierre de Schlippe says that these terms are still remembered, although they have lost their importance since maize is now far from the most important crop in the southern Sudan; he suggests that the same is true of the Azande in neighboring areas of the Congo (Kinshasa). It was the Belgian administration's efforts to develop cotton production that led to the disappearance of dry season maize, contributing to its displacement as the dominant staple in the diet. Cotton, introduced about 1921, was so vigorously encouraged, De Schlippe argues, that time required by cotton fields left the Azande little time to guard their valley maize fields from monkeys; hence valley maize became unprofitable and was abandoned (*108*, p. 232). In general, all courtyard crops received less attention among the Congo Azande after introduction of cotton, and De Schlippe reports that courtyards were therefore very much reduced in size.

The policy of both the Sudan and Belgian administrations toward bush fires considerably reduced the productivity of the Azande affected. Before European rule, they burned the small patches of bush early in the dry season to drive out game for hunting. Burning was controlled by firebreaks. In the 1930's the administration of the Belgian Congo became concerned with the fact that the burning of the bush increased erosion; bush fires were prohibited. As a result, fires started accidentally, often swept over large stretches of country in the absence of firebreaks made by hunters. In 1946 administrators of the Sudan Azande recognized the problem and initiated deliberate burning in the dry season.

Crop Introductions

Pierre de Schlippe and E. E. Evans-Pritchard provide a considerable amount of information on crop introductions among the Azande. Information given by Evans-Pritchard differs a good deal from that reported by De Schlippe, but this possibly reflects geographical or secular variations in the pattern of crop introductions. Evans-Pritchard did his fieldwork about twenty years before De Schlippe and studied a different group of Azande.

According to De Schlippe one of the ten manioc varieties now grown — *karangba*, a bitter type with red leaves and white skinned roots — was introduced from the Central African Republic by Major Wyld, at a date not given. "All other [manioc] varieties are said to have been imported from the Congo mainly by chief's messengers who were sent there to fetch poison for oracles" (*108*, p. 67).[9] But other evidence casts doubt on this. None of the four bitter varieties now found has the same name as the four bitter varieties the Dominican missionaries report among the Congo Azande in 1922 (*210*, 2:164). Moreover, De Schlippe's account is inconsistent, for after saying that all varieties except karangba came from the

Congo through quests for poison, he notes that two sweet (nontoxic) varieties came from the Bakango and Babua respectively, peoples who are found along the Uele River between 23° and 26° E. (*242*, p. 73).

Evans-Pritchard lists twelve varieties of manioc for the Gbudwe Azande, the most northeasterly group of the tribe; only five of these are mentioned by De Schlippe, who describes only one of them as bitter (*131*, p. 315). Five varieties are said to have come from the Ambomu; two from the Mangbetu; two from the Miangba; one from the Abubua; one from the Bakongo, and one from "the west." All of these varieties are said to have reached Gbudwe Azande via the Tembwe Azande.

De Schlippe says that peanuts appear to have become much more important since the turn of the century. Adolphe de Calonne-Beaufaict, who was in the Azande country from 1905 to 1915, reports that sesame was then the main oil crop and that peanuts were of only minor importance (*95*, p. 212). Three of the current varieties reportedly were introduced after World War I; all three varieties came from the Belgian Congo. *Agobu*, a slow-growing variety, was obtained about the time of World War I; abiranga or mangirima, the early-maturing variety, was brought in the 1930's; and *amadamu*, a white, fast-growing variety, was introduced "even later." There is, however, evidence that prior to 1922 the movement was in the other direction. The Azande-French dictionary published by the Congo Dominican missionaries in 1922 lists four peanut varieties not mentioned by De Schlippe and notes that one of these, *tembulë*, was introduced to the Belgian Congo from the north (*210*, p. 27).

One variety of bananas, *biro*, is reported by De Schlippe to be "a recent introduction from the Congo" (*108*, p. 71). Evans-Pritchard's informants state that eleven varieties of plantain came from the Uele River area (*131*, p. 316).

According to De Schlippe, the *basende* variety of sweet potatoes is an introduction from the Congo (Kinshasa); Evans-Pritchard says that five varieties were borrowed from the Ambomu; one variety came from the Mangbetu; and three reached the Gbudwe Azande "from the west" (*131*, pp. 315–16).

One of the nine sesame varieties grown is called *bungere* (literally, the cigarette from the Congo), which De Schlippe points out suggests it may have come from the Congo (Kinshasa). Evans-Pritchard attributes importation of sesame to the Ambomu, Baka, Adio, and Belanda (*131*, p. 314).

De Schlippe describes all rice as a "very recent introduction from 'wetwards,' i.e., from the Congo" (*108*, p. 55). Mangoes he reports to have been introduced from the Belgian Congo by Europeans sometime after 1910; in the Gbudwe area mangoes and pineapples were introduced in 1926–30 (*131*, p. 314).

Evans-Pritchard gives additional information on finger millet, sorghum, maize, taro, yams, Bambara nuts, cowpeas, hyptis, *gali* (an oil-bearing plant he could not describe), pumpkins, sugarcane, and pineapples. He was told that the Ambomu contributed a total of twelve varieties of these plants, the Amiangba nine; the Miangba four; Europeans three; and other groups of people nine. (*131*, pp. 318–21).

Other evidence suggests that the Azande may also have learned new processing techniques within the last eighty years. Gaetano Casati, who visited the Azande while exploring parts of the northern Congo Basin in 1880–83, describes a dish made by pounding almost ripe maize in a mortar, wrapping the pulp in banana leaves, and baking or boiling it (*70*, p. 248). This method was followed, he explains, because dry mature maize is hard to grind. Thus he suggests that in 1880 the Azande had not yet learned to use — as they do now — the wet process for grinding maize, which involves soaking the grain prior to grinding.

Evans-Pritchard reports that the techniques for producing a maize beer, a sorghum beer, and a manioc beer were learned from the Ambomu; that methods for producing finger millet beer and one manioc beer were taught by the Amiangba; that techniques for brewing one kind of maize beer came from the Congo (Kinshasa); and that banana wine production was learned from the Mangbetu. Arabs are said to be responsible for the introduction of distillation techniques (*131*, p. 321).

The Medje

There may have been exchange of banana-plantain varieties between the Medje and Mangbetu in times past. Casati listed seven banana-plantain varieties for the Mangbetu in 1881 (*70*, p. 177), and Lacomblez listed twenty-seven for the Medje about 1918, five having the same names as varieties Casati mentions (*208*, pp. 103–4).

The Mangbetu

Rice appears to have been a fairly new crop among the Mangbetu. Neither Shweinfurth nor Casati mentions it in his description of the Mangbetu agriculture in the 1870's and 1880's. But Captain Wacquez, who, after participating in an expedition to explore the Nile in 1897, commanded posts in the Mangbetu country, wrote during his administration that "rice, recently introduced, is expanding rapidly" (*221*, p. 133; *388*, p. 152).

Sometime after Georg Schweinfurth's visit in 1870, the Mangbetu apparently began to raise goats. Schweinfurth stated that "the only domestic animals are poultry and dogs . . . cows and goats are familiar by report, although it happens occasionally that some are brought in as the result of raids . . ." (*323*, 2:15–16).[10] It is not unlikely that so long as game was plentiful, or the Mangbetu could obtain livestock by resorting to war, they preferred to raise no goats rather than have the bother of keeping them out of fields. European rule ended raids, brought European hunters, and increased the availability of firearms, which cut off traditional sources of goats and probably greatly reduced the availability of game.

A statement attributed to De Rennette by Van Overbergh, but not documented, credits slave traders with introduction of distilling techniques (*388*, 172): "In some villages that were formerly closely associated with the slave traders and the Egyptians, [palm] wine and beer are distilled through the muzzle of a gun."

The Logo

M. H. Lelong says that long ago millet and sorghum were the principal crops of the Logo, but that maize later became dominant (*221*, 2:300). According to De Schlippe, introduction of the wet process of grinding grain sufficiently reduced the effort required in grinding to make maize the favorite cereal (*108*, p. 225).

Maize, says Lelong, was the principal staple foodstuff until after manioc was introduced by Europeans, and he points out that the Belgian officials required African farmers to plant manioc after a disastrous invasion of locusts that ruined most other crops in 1930 (*221*, 2:229).

Another crop said to have become more important during European rule is sweet potatoes, but no reason is advanced for this development (*221*, 2:229). They undoubtedly were one of the crops encouraged by Belgian agricultural officers as a famine reserve, as they were among the Alur some 200 kilometers to the southwest.

A number of varieties of fruits and vegetables were probably introduced by Emin Pasha, governor from 1878 to 1888 of Egypt's Equatoria Province, which included the northern portion of the Logo. Casati writes that Emin Pasha, "by encouraging agriculture and regulating the collection of tribute. . . . By distributing seed of all kinds, which he obtained from Egypt and Europe . . . promoted the cultivation of the soil; pawpaw, orange, and lemon trees, cotton, guava, grapes, and every kind of vegetable rendered the gardens . . . beautiful" (*70*, 1:257).

A fundamental change in the Logo agriculture was the loss of cattle, about which little is known except that it occurred sometime after 1909. Willaert, veterinary with the Logo in 1909, described them as cattle-keepers at that time (*422*, p. 7); and Gustin said the same in a note published in 1911 (cited in *12*, p. 469). Willaert suggested that raids from neighbors and shortage of suitable pasture were reducing the herds. De Schlippe found the Logo to be without cattle in 1946.

The Alur

Pauwels says that sorghum and finger millet were the original staple food crops of the Alur, but were displaced by maize sometime in the past. Emin Pasha noted in one of his reports sent to *Esploratore* that "Maize, from which very good alcohol may be obtained, flourishes all over the country, and its cultivation is on the increase" (*70*, p. 265).

Another comment in one of Emin Pasha's reports suggests that in the 1880's peanuts were fairly new to the Alur (*70*, p. 266): "The Sandeh [Azande] and Mangbettu are extremely fond of this nut, and now its cultivation is spreading eastward to Dutilé." Since the Alur are located between the Mangbetu and Dutilé, a town on the Nile, peanut culture spreading from the Mangbetu to Dutilé would have probably reached the Alur.

Early attempts to get the Alur to grow manioc apparently met with little success because the manioc could be obtained more easily by trade with peoples on the plains of Lake Albert (*237*, p. 2300).

The principal crop sequences appear to have been considerably changed in recent times, too. The traditional sequences described by Loeckx (*237*) were sorghum, finger millet, then a beans-sorghum succession; and a beans, finger millet, sorghum sequence. When the succession was followed, grass and trees were cut and burned in April or early May, and two weeks later sorghum was sown, often with a little amaranth and maize; the field was then hoed to cover the sorghum seed. Sorghum was harvested in December; and in April of the following year finger millet was sown — perhaps with some maize and amaranth — and harvested in October. The third season began the following March with the planting of beans;

FIGURE 12-1   Alur Crop Sequences

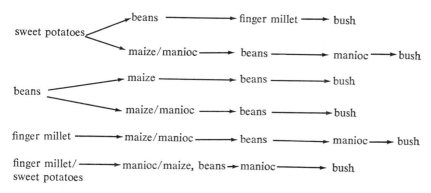

when these were harvested in June sorghum was again sown, finishing the cycle. Usually the soil was so exhausted by the end of two of these cycles that the field was abandoned for a few years.

The second principal crop sequence began with clearing the land in August or September and planting beans. The following season the field was sown with finger millet; the third season sorghum was planted;[11] and in the fourth season beans were again planted to start the cycle anew.

Today the Alur have not two but at least six major crop sequences; in these sorghum is only a minor crop; the crops of major importance are maize, manioc, and sweet potatoes (Figure 12-1). Beans or sweet potatoes are most commonly the first crop grown when a plot of land is cleared, but finger millet may also be planted at the head of the crop sequence. In the second season a mixture of maize/manioc is often planted; beans are commonly planted the third season. The beans, maize, beans and finger millet/sweet potatoes, manioc/maize/beans, manioc sequences are practiced "only on very poor or very rich soils" (*389*, p. 1543).

The Lugbara

Population growth has forced the central Lugbara to reduce their unfertilized outfields greatly and grow outfield crops on their fertilized infields, with the result that crop sequences on infields have been lengthening — but no details are provided (*260*, p. 13). Within fields there has been a progressive substitution of manioc — said to have been introduced as a compulsory crop in 1945 as a famine reserve — for other starchy-staples because it gives higher yields (*261*, p. 453). John Middleton and

D. J. Greenland, in a survey of the area in 1953, found that the importance of manioc was greatest where land shortage was the most severe (*261*, p. 455):

Group	Size of group	Average cultivated land per capita (square yards)	Percentage of cultivated land in manioc
Maraca	34	2,500	25.2
Omugo	48	2,450	36.4
Metu	52	2,420	42.1
Paidha	99	2,380	52.7

The Maraca, the group with the smallest proportion of land in manioc, still maintain a minimum of three years of fallow, but the Omugo and Paidha, both of whom plant a considerably larger proportion of land to manioc, no longer fallow land.

The Bira

The Hima, found at the south end of Lake Albert (not shown on Map 1-3), are said to have introduced cattle keeping (*378*, p. 53).

The Lese and Mamvu

The neighboring Bira are said to have introduced beans and sweet potatoes; and the Arabs rice, peanuts, a variety of manioc called *mokotayamba*, and a variety of tobacco named *kambatasitsi-kida* (*209*, p. 331).

Lacomblez observed that in 1924 the traditional tools were beginning to be replaced by machetes and hoes (*209*, p. 332).

The Bali and Budu

H. Van Geluwe states that the Ngwana tribe introduced rice to the Bali group of the Ndaka (*380*, p. 52). He reports that goats are much less numerous than they once were among both the Bali and Budu because of raids by Arabs (*380*, p. 53).

The Turumbu Group of the Lokele

In 1915 some farmers in the Turumbu area, a small zone around the present town of Yangambi, Congo (Kinshasa), were beginning to adopt new tools. According to Elskens: "Certain farmers have replaced their pre-historic two-edged knives used for clearing and weeding with the commercial machetes and, very rarely, with the small 'Bakusu' type hoe, tools which are presently made by river smiths" (*126*, p. 771). The Bakusu hoe was probably introduced by the Kusu, a group of Tetela who may also have introduced a method of extracting oil from palm nuts. Elskens says that the method used in the area directly across the Congo River from the Turumbu for extracting oil from palm nuts was introduced by Kusu slaves who were put there by Arabs (*127*, p. 708).

The Kisangani Area

M. Tharin, in an article published in 1915, credits the Arabs with the introduction of rice, millet, sesame, peanuts, oilseed gourds, beans, tobacco, and indigo (*339*, p. 147). He also states that two varieties of manioc, *tchuka* and *tchini*, were "recently" introduced by the Kusu.

The Mbole Group of the Ngandu

Raphia fiber was reportedly extracted by the Mbole, located across the Congo River from the Turumbu, until about 1885, when superior fiber was made available by Arab traders (*339*, p. 142).

The Beni-Lubero Area

Sorghum, finger millet, and taro appear to have declined in importance in recent decades. J. Claessens reported that these plus beans, Irish potatoes, and bananas-plantains were the major crops when he toured the middle and upper Beni-Lubero area in 1925 (*77*, pp. 19–20). Since that time sweet potatoes and wheat certainly, and possibly manioc, beans, Irish potatoes and bananas-plantains, have become more important. Wheat was being distributed by agricultural officers in 1924 and 1925 (*77*, p. 172). Van Daele says that taro declined because of the introduction of Irish potatoes, and that beans "have taken considerable extension" because of the market for them at nearby mines (*365*, p. 242).

Rwanda–Burundi

Pagès, in an article published in 1928, states that peanuts had been "recently" introduced and seem to have come from the Lake Victoria area and from the Ruzizi Valley of Congo (Kinshasa) (*281*, p. 120).

Other crops he lists as "recent imports" are manioc, wheat, chives, green peppers, tomatoes, and turnips. Almost certainly some of these were introduced by Europeans. Pagès notes that manioc was still spreading at the time of his observation and was still unknown in some areas.

Beginning in 1922 the Belgian administration, alarmed by food shortages in one part or another of the country during nine of the previous twenty-five years, first encouraged, then ordered, Ruanda-Urundi farmers to grow manioc, sweet potatoes, and Irish potatoes because they were relatively drought-resistant. Although there were instances when Africans tried to eat bitter manioc varieties without adequately processing them, and "a number" of people were "gravely poisoned" (*134*, p. 855), the campaign was intensified after a fairly severe famine was experienced in several regions in 1929 (*101*); compulsory acreages continued to be an important part of policy for at least two decades. Between 1928 and 1938 estimated acreage of manioc increased 43 percent; that of sweet potatoes 93 percent; and Irish potatoes 585 per cent (*132*, p. 592).

In the Busoni area, the compulsory planting of manioc resulted in a shift from sorghum to manioc, with sorghum being grown only for beer (*273*, p. 291).

The Belgian administration also aggressively extended coffee acreage, and production increased from 8 metric tons in 1923 to 3,200 metric tons in 1939 (*132*, p. 599).

The cotton campaign showed a similar but not so spectacular result. Cotton production stood at 114 metric tons in 1929 and had reached 3,675 metric tons by 1939 (*132*, p. 601).

Little information is available about the efforts to increase livestock production, except that in early years of Belgian administration in at least some areas the traditional custom of eating the hides of slaughtered animals was prohibited in an effort to increase their export (*326*, p. 346). Traditionally most bull calves were slaughtered, but the emphasis on selling hides led herdsmen to keep bull calves to maturity in order to get a larger hide. With a taboo on castration and no separation of bulls and cows, this led to a considerable degeneration in the quality of calves (*270*, p. 64).

The Bashi

According to Father Wattenye, coffee was introduced by the White Fathers from Baudouinville in 1906 (*406*, p. 939). Carlier states that the largest breed of chickens found is called "Arab chicken" — which suggests that they may have been introduced by the Arabs (*69*, p. 750).

In the Mumosho area manioc production was rare in 1948, but by 1952 was spreading at the expense of sweet potatoes (*216*, p. 80). In the Chigoshole area, however, a decline in manioc acreage was reported about the same time because of its poor yields at that attitude (*204*, p. 970). In the same region, and probably elsewhere, too, special gardens have been developed to grow European vegetables for market in Bukavu and other towns (*204*, p. 972).

The Rega

According to Delhaise's informants, the Ntata group of eastern Rega learned bean growing from the Rundi (*102*, p. 127). The Rega also told him that sometime in the past they attempted to import cattle from Urundi but failed. Delhaise explains this by a lack of pasture and "an unknown factor that kills cattle" (*102*, p. 129).

Before contact with the Arabs, the Rega bought palm oil from the neighboring Songola because of a local shortage of cooking oils. The Arabs reportedly introduced peanuts and taught the Rega how to extract oil from them, with the result that by 1906 purchase of palm oil from the Songola had almost stopped (*86*, p. 70).

The Tetela

Mestdagh, in an article published in 1912, reports the introduction of an oilseed cucurbit locally called *utelo*. This plant is said to have been introduced by a former soldier who brought it from the Uele basin (cited in *15*, p. 646).

According to Janssens the Tetela introduced rice to the Kasai area, and themselves acquired it from the Swahili — presumably Arabs, or Africans with Arab customs (*188*, p. 214).

The Kwango Area

Adriaens says that cultivation of the oil palm was taught to the Yaka, whose habitat lies mainly outside the natural palm oil zone, by the Tsumba sometime before European rule (*4*, p. 504): "Before the arrival of the Bayaka in the Kwango, the country was occupied by the Batsumba who introduced and propagated Elaeis. Thus well before European occupation, palm oil was known."

George Grenfell reported during his exploration of the Kwango in 1892–93 that development of rubber trade a few years before his visit had sharply altered agricultural practices on the plateau of the extreme southern Kwango. Sir Harry Johnston summarizes Grenfell's account (*193*, 1:212):

Such indigenous population as there was had become nomadic — they would settle in a likely spot for some months, building ramshackle, temporary houses and planting quick growing crops like manioc — then, unless they were already raided, they would move restlessly to another site which offered virgin soil for planting and greater security of position. Some of this restlessness was due to rubber trade, which had been introduced a few years before into these western Lunda countries. The rubber (native name, Nkwezi) was derived from the roots of underground branches of *Landolphia* (probably *L. Thollonii*). The natives were carrying on a reckless destruction of the rubber plant, and never for a moment considered the advisability of replanting.

During at least one later period the changes in world rubber prices caused a considerable reorganization of tribal economies of Kwango. Adriaens states that before the great depression of the 1930's rubber collecting was a major economic activity, and rubber revenues "were used in part to purchase food crops. They [the Africans] ate well because the companies [who bought the rubber] paid them partly in [gun] powder which gave them the opportunity to kill much game" (*3*, p. 231).

With the depression in the 1930's, rubber prices fell drastically and there was a substantial increase in agricultural activity.

At the outbreak of World War II rubber prices soared again and there was a reverse movement away from agriculture until 1946, when the rubber companies again stopped buying (*3*, p. 243).

There was probably a shift to fiber production at about the same time. In 1951 Adriaens reported that "some years ago fiber" (presumably *Urena lobata*) "was introduced into the gallery forest valleys of the Wamba and Bakali regions" (*3*, p. 242). The Belgian government introduced urena into the Banningville territoire, one of the territoires adjacent to the Kwango on the north, in 1935; and introduced it elsewhere as part of the war effort in World War II (see p. 254). It is not unlikely that urena was first brought to Kwango in the late 1930's or early 1940's.

Increased production of manioc, bananas, and palm wine may have been another adjustment stemming from termination of the rubber trade. Adriaens noted that in 1948 farmers often walked 20 to 30 kilometers to market loaded with 20 kilograms of dried manioc or a bunch of bananas; and he says that in southern Kwango a considerable amount of palm wine was sold.

A little evidence on the introduction of food crops is given. Rassel asserts that the present Kwango tribes brought sorghum with them when they migrated from the Zambezi to the Congo Basin, but that sorghum "has been progressively displaced by millet, which is less exacting" (*300*, p. 13). Rassel also refers to a recent introduction of an earlier maturing variety of peanuts, but gives no details (*301*, p. 15).

Some data are also given on changes in processing techniques. Adriaens suggests that Africans now crush oil from peanuts less than they did formerly. He found Kiamfu-Kinzadi in the Inzia Valley to be the only area he visited where peanut oil was produced in 1948. (The method was to roast the seeds lightly, pound them in a small mortar, throw the pulp in hot water, and then skim off the oil as it floated to the top [*4*, p. 504]. The residue was dried on hut roofs and later used as fish bait.)

Maize-manioc beer reportedly was introduced by soldiers coming from the Bas-Congo (*4*, p. 509). The Nkano, Mbeko, and Sonde — a group of the Luwa — are singled out as people who have "taken to the habit" of eating chickwangue, which suggests that chickwangue is a fairly recent introduction and that in 1948 it had not yet spread to all of the Kwango.

The Belgian administration introduced oranges and papayas, according to Adriaens.

Sir Harry Johnston notes that Grenfell rode an ox throughout his exploration of Kwango, and adds "The natives between Angola and Tanganyika and over Portuguese South-West Africa have trained oxen for centuries as riding-animals. This practice was apparently introduced by the Portuguese four centuries ago" (*193*, 1:216). Johnston also refers to herds of cattle among the Holo,[12] but Adriaens makes no mention of cattle anywhere in Kwango some fifty years later. Therefore, there has possibly been a decline in cattle keeping in at least some areas.

The Dzing

Rice was unknown among the Dzing until they were forced by the state to grow it, and as late as the 1930's some of the northern Dzing villages still did not grow it (*252*, p. 105).

The Lele

The Lele now annually plant two crops of maize, one of their principal crops, rather than one crop as they traditionally did, because of a large increase in the market for maize in cities and mining centers, and because of government programs. Mary Douglas argues that with more efficient tools and government programs for reorganizing agricultural work, clearings are larger and forest regenerates less rapidly than traditionally; *ceteris paribus*, this would decrease the effectiveness of a given time in fallow in restoring soil fertility and also reduce the time land is fallowed (*117*, pp. 814–15):

> The clearings were smaller; the Lele all-purpose tool, the double-bladed *mghalu* being much less efficient than the trade axes now everywhere in use. . . . and undoubtedly the destruction of the forests by burning was less than now, when the zeal of the native agricultural assistants forces the Lele to make a much more thorough job of cutting and hoeing. In the administrative program the forest clearing should be started at the beginning of the dry season, so that the cut wood can dry out and make a better conflagration. The Lele, by natural inertia rather than by design, used to spend the first two months of the dry season visiting, hunting, and weaving raffia, and then worked feverishly in their forest clearings, so they say, for only one month or six weeks before the rains. The firing of the newly cut wood, often only after the first rain storms had broken, presumably did much less damage to the big trees than the present method. Traditionally after they had harvested the first crop of maize, the Lele let the forest start to close in at once on their clearings. . . . The two maize crops a year mean the clearings have to be exposed for much longer than before.

A second major change was addition of oil palm cultivation to the tree crops (raphia palms) already grown. Traditionally the Lele did not give the oil palm special care, merely harvesting the fruit from wild trees. The palm oil supply was sufficient for local needs in cooking and lubricating the body. Development of palm oil as an export from the Lele area has apparently led not only to more intensive harvest of wild palm groves but to planting of oil palms as a cash crop (*117*, p. 815).

Other changes were almost complete replacement of Bambara nuts by peanuts, which were introduced by the Belgian administration at an unspecified date (*117*, p. 814).

The Lulua

Hermann von Wissmann, in describing his second trip to the Congo, clearly refers to his introduction of limes and swine to the area; and the narrative suggests he may also have been responsible for the introduction of tomatoes, cucumbers, carrots, cabbage, yams, beans, eggplant, and "foxtail" (*401*, p. 66).

The Southern Songe

According to Vermeesch, Arabs or Europeans introduced mangoes, lemons, bullock's-heart, and pineapples. Before arrival of the Arabs, bark cloth trees were cultivated, but now only a few are grown for shade (*400*, p. 22).

The southern Songe say that cattle were introduced from Angola by traders, and Vermeesch states that the cattle are of the Angola type (*400*, p. 23). He also reports that the numbers of both cattle and small livestock were greatly reduced after advent of European rule because of the demand for meat in urban centers. Among the relatively isolated Songe in the east, some herds of 500 to 1,000 head of small livestock were still to be found at the time of Vermeesch's observations (about 1924), whereas elsewhere herds were rarely larger than 20 or 30 animals (*400*, p. 24).

The Holoholo

Schmitz states that during the last quarter of the nineteenth century the Holoholo prospered as provisioners of trading caravans, but that with the crushing of the slave trade not only did they lose most of their market for foodstuffs but their domestic animals — especially their cattle — were confiscated by officials of the Congo Free State (*317*, pp. xxiv, 109).

Western Katanga

J. Vandersmissen, a Belgian agronomist, gives the following account of the rise and decline in cattle keeping among the Lunda and Chokwe of western Katanga between 1880 and 1943. About 1880, when the Chokwe began invading them, the Lunda did not have cattle. The first waves of the Chokwe were comprised of warriors in search of slaves and new hunting grounds.[13] Later cattle were brought to the Lunda country; they were common when the first administrative posts were established in the area in 1903 (*369*, p. 202). However, policies followed by the European officials brought about a drastic reduction in the size of the herds in the following years.

In 1910 the Belgian administration restored authority to the Lunda paramount chief, Mwata-Yamvo Muteba, who took advantage of this turn of events to exact a tribute from the Chokwe in the form of cattle; all of these were slaughtered for royal feasts or lost to the lions. About the same time most Chokwe were liquidating the remainder of their herds. Before establishment of European rule rumors had reached the Chokwe of confiscation of cattle by Europeans; therefore upon seeing firm establishment of European authority become a reality most Chokwe slaughtered their animals to keep them from European hands. It is estimated that by

1915 only 50 head of cattle remained and these were well hidden (*369*) p. 203).

Cotton was introduced as a cash crop by the Belgian administration in 1943, and it was decided at that time that plowing should be introduced to increase the productivity of the cotton farmers. In 1935 the Société Cotonnière Congolaise trained a few of the remaining cattle to the plow. A plow was given to the Bako chieftancy, and the local Belgian officials attempted to instruct the Africans in the use of it. However, because of suspicion among the African farmers this scheme was temporarily abandoned.

In 1940 attempts were again made to introduce plowing. In 1941, 15 fields were plowed in the Sandoa area; in 1942–43, 88 fields were plowed. According to the census of 1943, herds had been considerably rebuilt; the total number of cattle belonging to Africans was estimated at 500 in 1943 (*369*, p. 212).

The Luba

Verhulpen reports that the Bena Kalundwe, a group of the western Luba, had no manioc and depended mainly upon maize as their staple crop the last two decades of the nineteenth century. About 1885 Tambo Kanonge, ruler of the Bena Kalundwe, had manioc cuttings imported from the Lunda and made manioc cultivation compulsory for everyone under his rule (*399*, p. 232).

According to Verhulpen's informants, some of whom could well have witnessed their introduction, manioc was greeted with enthusiasm once people found that it could be harvested throughout the dry season, a part of the year when they had often been short of food. With the name of this new crop, *ludwe*, on the lips of everyone (*399*, p. 232) their neighbors called them Bena Kalundwe: "people of manioc."

Colle says that goat, sheep, and swine populations were large before European administration, but later became rare because of sales of animals to buyers who were supplying the railway construction crews (*83*, p. 215). The date of Colle's observations cannot be closely determined, but his monograph was published in 1913. He states that all cattle kept by the Luba were introduced by Europeans.

The Northern Tabwa

According to Roelens manioc was introduced to the northern Tabwa by missionaries in 1893 at the founding of Baudouinville mission, and has since displaced sorghum, the traditional staple food (cited in *73*, p. 39).

Wheat was introduced by missionaries in 1885 at Mpala, a neighboring mission (*340*; *73*, p. 54). Irish potatoes were introduced between 1883 and 1885 by Lieutenant Storms, who was in command of a post at Baudouinville at that time. About a decade later another variety of Irish potatoes was imported from Europe by Roelens, who was one of the local priests (*73*, p. 49). By 1925 wheat production had grown considerably, and 500 metric tons of wheat were sold by the African farmers. Beginning in 1929 traders paid relatively better prices for Irish potatoes; African production of wheat declined to about 50 hectares in 1932 and 20 hectares in 1934 (*340*; *73*, p. 54). From 1934 to 1939 the administration tried in vain to encourage wheat production. Only 13 and 17 metric tons of wheat were produced in 1938 and 1939 respectively (*73*, p. 54). New introductions of seed were made by the government in 1939, and production "regularly increased" from 44 metric tons in 1940 to 124 in 1947.

About the same time Irish potato production was declining because of disease problems. From a peak of 3,200 metric tons, marketing of potatoes fell after a blight struck in 1944 to about 650 metric tons in 1945 and to around 150 tons in 1952.

Wheat marketings expanded over the same period from 277 metric tons in 1949 to a peak of 638 in 1952, then declined slightly to an average level of 514 metric tons over the next five years (*73*, p. 54):

Year	Wheat marketings (Metric tons)
1949	277
1950	327
1951	329
1952	638
1953	580
1954	393
1955	593
1956	551
1957	451

The White Fathers report that in 1893 goats and sheep were abundant, but that by 1911 most herds were greatly diminished — for reasons not given (*232*, p. 210).

The Fipa

The early German administration of Tanganyika reportedly introduced long-horned Ankole cattle, obtained from the Ha, to the Fipa early in the 1890's (*32*, cited in *424*, p. 23).

The Luvale

According to the Luvale, bulrush millet was their staple food and finger millet was grown for beer at the earliest time for which they have oral tradition (*417*, p. 17). Now manioc is the staple, finger millet has almost disappeared, and bulrush millet is grown less and mainly for beer, C. N. M. White argues that this shift to manioc has lengthened the period that land can be cropped because manioc takes less nutrients from the soil than other starchy-staples. According to White, the fact that the land can be cropped almost continuously with manioc in much of the Luvale area, plus an increase in the price of manioc that came in the early 1940's with completion of roads linking the Luvale area with markets in other regions, has led to the substitution of manioc monoculture for traditional crop sequences in the last twenty-five years or so.

Traditionally one of three crop sequences was practiced. The simplest was bulrush millet followed by a mixture of bulrush millet and manioc. The third year the manioc planted the preceding year occupied the land alone, and the fourth year the field was returned to bush. In a more complex sequence, manioc was planted again in the fourth year or manioc and bulrush millet were planted; and the sixth year manioc was planted alone. By the eighth year the plot was returned to bush. Under the most complex sequence, cropping was the same as in the second sequence except that the field was fallowed from the eighth through the twelfth or thirteenth years and then a crop of manioc was planted. The fourteenth year the field reverted to bush.

Today manioc is planted immediately when a field is cleared. After about twelve months, gradual harvesting begins. The larger roots may be removed and the plant left growing, or the whole plant may be pulled up and new cuttings planted immediately; either way, mounds have a growing manioc plant on them at all times. This continual harvesting-planting operation continues until the soil is exhausted. In fifty fields that White surveyed in Kabompo District, 20 percent of the plots had been growing manioc continuously for over ten years; the oldest field had supported a manioc monoculture for twenty-nine years.

The Ndembu

Rice has been introduced and is cultivated in valley gardens as a cash crop. In the Ikelenge area, which is regularly visited by traders seeking foodstuffs, manioc is a cash crop and sometimes is planted two or three times in succession without the traditional regeneration of forest (*363*, p. 23). Finger millet cultivation has almost disappeared.

The Lamba

Allan shows that in the Mushiri area of the eastern Lamba, mining companies and European farmers have reduced the land available for Africans from approximately 2,200 to some 360 square miles, with the result that in some communities there was not enough land to permit abandoned fields to regenerate completely before they were cleared again. There was also a shortage of manpower in most villages because a large portion of able-bodied men were working in mines (*6*, p. 36). A second change was the development of new gardens. By 1940 a few men had begun to make special vegetable gardens in order to have produce to sell in the markets of the nearby mining centers (*6*, p. 37). The result expected from these two changes is longer crop sequences and possibly a change in cropping techniques. Allan's investigation gives some evidence of the adjustments that have been made. Gardens are being cultivated more intensively and manioc acreage is being increased (*6*, p. 20).

The Lala

Peters concluded at the end of his survey of Lala agricultural methods (*289*, p. 92) that the traditional Lala system of agriculture had capacity to support only about half of the prevailing population density and that in 1946 it was on the verge of breaking down. Other things being equal, one would expect that with the population expansion a larger area would need to be cultivated, and that the increment of woodland cut to supply ash fertilizer would be a multiple of the additional cropland required, since the chitemene technique requires that more land be cleared than cultivated. Thus, once the population density exceeds the carrying capacity of the land the area of woodland needed would exceed that available. Eventually this could lead to insufficient food per capita, followed by an increase in the death rate until the balance was restored. In the short run, however, cultivators might adjust by meeting part of their ash requirements with wood from woodland that is less than fully regenerated; but since immature trees furnish less wood per hectare than mature ones, such a move would increase the area of woodland that would have to be cleared to provide enough ash for a hectare of crops. It would also tend to reduce the size of plots burned and cultivated, for with a less dense timber stand wood must be carried farther. But if smaller circles are in fact made, there is a further loss in productivity because the portion of the plot being taken up by the relatively infertile border zone of the circle is increased.

Peters' survey led him to the conclusion that all of these changes were taking place. He reports that the average area of woodland cut per family has increased from 12 to 19 acres; that 75 percent of the trees cut for ash were not fully mature; and that the average age of timber cut was only seventeen rather than the thirty-five years required for complete regeneration. The proportion of the total area which is burned has fallen from 12 to 7 percent. "In addition, because of the reluctance to carry brushwood any distance greater than is necessary when fully regenerated trees are cut, the character of the garden is so altered that the proportion of the burnt area which is actually crop is reduced, for 'border wastage' is increased" (*289*, p. xiv).[14]

The most likely means of accommodating the increment in the population density is to find either a substitute for ash fertilizer, an alternative agricultural system that is equally productive and less dependent on the density of the forest, or more productive crops. Peters found some evidence of the last solution in greater dependence on manioc (*289*, p. 74).

Evidence of changes in animal husbandry was also found. Informants told Peters that "many years ago" greater numbers of cattle were kept, but that herds were depleted through raids by the Bemba and Ngoni (*289*, p. 84).

The Unga

Information provided by Mrs. Gore-Browne in 1933 and published by Audrey Richards suggests that on Chilubi Island in the Bangweulu swamps the Bisa reacted to mounting population pressure in the two or three decades prior to 1933 by replacing finger millet cultivation on chitemene with a system of continuous cultivation based on manioc (cited in *305*, p. 327). The Unga occupy a similar area and are also plagued with population pressure (*57*, p. 125–26); they probably have made a similar adjustment. Brelsford indicates that the Unga living on islands now grow little except manioc.

The transition from finger millet to manioc at Chilubi Island was made by planting a manioc/finger millet association the first two years after clearing the land, followed by three years of manioc grown alone, and repetition of the same succession the following five years; then the fields were fallowed two years. After this manioc was planted alone for three successive years, then peanuts were grown one year, followed by one year of fallow and repetition of the sequence. By 1933 only a little finger millet was grown for beer (*305*, p. 327).

Among the Unga of the sand banks adjustment to population pressure may have brought premature harvesting of manioc: "It is said that the [manioc] plants were formerly sometimes left in for two years but that no more than a year can now be allowed on account of prevailing hunger . . ." (*57*).

The Bemba

According to two of Richards' informants, the main crop sequence has changed considerably since around the turn of the century. Before that time, fields are said to have been abandoned after the second year. Now a millet or sorghum crop is planted followed by two or more crops of sorghum, beans, vegetables, manioc, or sweet potatoes. The Bemba, says Richards, "seem to have learnt" this practice from "the Lungu and other tribes to the west" (*305*, p. 317).[15]

Other innovations said to have been received from neighboring tribes are sweet potatoes, which informants claim Swahili traders introduced about the end of the nineteenth century, and manioc, which the Bemba say the Bisa taught them to grow (*305*, p. 20). The timing of the introduction of manioc is not given; but the Bisa had the crop at least as early as 1824, when the Portuguese planted fields of manioc near the Luangwa River in order to establish provisioning stations for parties journeying from Zumbo to Cazembe (*215*, p. 30).

Whether manioc has yet become a major crop cannot be determined with certainty, but this is the impression I gained from two Bemba men I encountered while I was doing field work among the Plateau Tonga and Nsenga in 1959. Whatever the current position of manioc in the diet, it is likely that it has become increasingly important as a foodstuff in recent decades. If population has increased fairly steadily since European rule, as it seems to have, other things being equal, this would have tended to bring about increased dependence on manioc, for its relatively high yields become increasingly attractive as land becomes scarce.

It is not unlikely that the Bemba have experienced a growing shortage of fully regenerated forest, just as the Lala have. And that there is a tendency to substitute manioc for finger millet as fully regenerated bush becomes scarce is suggested by an example Richards gives of a village on the Luansenshi River, where in 1933 the finger millet crop had been given up for the first time because, in the words of the informant (*305*, p. 328): "we have used up all the trees and we said 'Well! then let us turn into Bisa now,' " i.e. live on manioc.

Richards cites Kungu village near the government station at Kasama as being typical of three kinds of general changes that were occurring in Bemba agriculture in the early 1930's. At Kungu she found that the village had remained in one location ten years, about twice as long as usual; that there was a specialization in crop production; and that some individuals who had worked outside Bemba country had observed cattle raising and plowing, and were adopting the plow (*305*, pp. 322–23).

CONCLUSIONS

The scattered fragments of evidence available on technical change in the traditional economies of the Congo suggest that non-African influence has led to or accelerated growth of population, cash crop production, and in some areas, animal husbandry (in other areas, however, European rule for a while discouraged livestock production). Many traditional tribal agricultural systems have adjusted to forces of change by altering the composition of agricultural production. Some, perhaps many, African tribes traditionally produced certain crops partly, if not largely, for market; this production has expanded, and communities that formerly grew crops only for their own use now devote a large part of their efforts to production for market. Substitution of imported goods for products traditionally produced within the tribal economies may have freed labor for work in the fields and for carrying goods to market. There have also been changes in dietary staples. Such crops as manioc and maize have been substituted for other staples in several areas; and introduction of new varieties has almost certainly caused shifts in the position of other dietary mainstays for which we have no record.

Comparison of Maps 1-7 and 12-1 clearly suggests that bananas-plantains gave ground to manioc in the northern Congo Basin between 1900 and 1950. A similar trend can be observed for maize, but the evidence is not as strong — maize became less important in four areas because of gains by manioc or sorghum and more important in one; and remained unchanged in one. Over the same period, manioc and maize appear to have gained at the expense of bulrush millet in the Kasai area and among the Luvale. The Tetela seem to have substituted rice as well as manioc for bulrush millet.

MAP 12-1

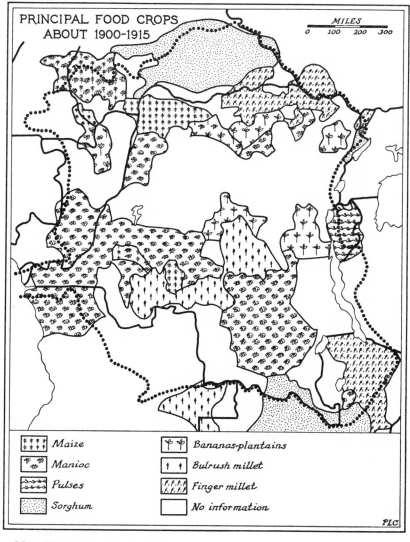

Map: Food Research Institute.

In the northern Congo Basin the reason for the growth in importance of manioc is not clear. Very little evidence is available, but a few fragments suggest that manioc has been widely known in the northern Congo Basin only for a hundred years or so.

In the southern Congo Basin, even less information is available about the reasons for changes in the position of maize, but there is considerable evidence that manioc has been relied on increasingly as a major dietary staple as growth of population pressure on land has forced adoption of a more productive crop.

Changes in tools are hinted at for a number of tribes, but the evidence is too thin to support generalization. For several widely separated portions of the Congo Basin we have evidence of striking changes in crop associations and crop sequences, many of which appear to be explained by introduction of new crops or new varieties of existing crops. The nature of the change in each instance, however, depends on so many variables that general patterns in the kinds of change cannot be detected in the information available.

Data on the mode of spreading crops point in a number of instances to non-Africans as agents of change; but in the few studies in which crop introductions have been investigated in some detail, the majority of crop introductions are credited to other tribes. Thus, there is suggestion that Africans clearly have been active in spreading innovations. However, without better information on the relative contribution of the various innovations to economic change, there is no basis for judging whether Africans or non-Africans have generally played the greater role in spreading means of increasing productivity from one tribal economy to another.

13

Conclusions

Contrary to the common belief that small scale agriculture in the tropics is simple and much the same the world over, agricultural production in the tribal economies of the Congo Basin is both complex and diverse. Productivity is indeed low absolutely and relative to that of most producers in the agricultural sector of developed countries, but agriculture is frequently much more complex in terms of the number and diversity of enterprises managed.

In the Congo Basin it is not uncommon for a farmer to grow thirty or more different crops — and as many as sixty are recorded — and to have several varieties of many of them. In addition to main fields, a number of special fields or gardens are often made in microenvironments suited to particular crops or crop combinations, e.g. courtyards, old village sites, riverine areas, and depressions. It might be expected, a priori, that diversity of farm enterprises stems largely from lack of a sufficient market to warrant greater specialization; but a great diversity of enterprises is common both to areas near to pure subsistence and to those with an intricate network of markets and an active commerce. The diversity of enterprises is probably largely related to the nature of the environment, as discussed in Chapter 7.

Perhaps the most striking feature of methods of growing crops is the wide variation in techniques of soil management among vegetation zones

283

and from tribe to tribe. Although some form of shifting cultivation is found everywhere, the stereotype of it frequently found in the literature — and heretofore presented as valid for tropical Africa as well as other parts of the tropics — is reported only in part of the forest zone. At least twelve types of shifting cultivation involving no attempt to restore soil fertility by human effort can be distinguished; and less frequently found, but prominent, are methods characterized by use of ash fertilizer (other than that created in the process of clearing fields), composts, and animal manure which are not reported in accounts of shifting cultivation outside of Africa. Part of the failure to report these more intensive types elsewhere may be traceable to lack of research or to the common assumption that shifting cultivation is too simple to vary much.

A particularly interesting variation in agricultural methods found is the amount of labor required of men (as compared with women) in field operations. This is of special interest because of the need of development planners to predict the impact of a system of rural-urban or rural-rural labor migration on agricultural production and productivity. (Both types of migration are common in tropical Africa, although the rural-urban case is the only one that has been analyzed. The rural-rural type of migration can be divided into two categories: employment of migrants by white farmers — as in common in Kenya, Tanzania, Zambia, Rhodesia, the Malagasy Republic, and Portuguese Africa — and employment of migrants by African farmers, e.g. in the forest belt of West Africa, and in the Sudan, Uganda, Kenya, and Zambia, where African farmers growing an export crop or cash crops for domestic markets commonly employ migrant laborers.)

Evidence from the Congo Basin demonstrates the error in the common tendency to assume that the effect of the migrant labor system on agriculture is the same throughout tropical Africa. The importance of men in the agriculture of the area they leave varies greatly not only because by custom men only clear land among some tribes (but participate in one or more other field operations among other tribes) but also because the significance of the tasks that men do varies. Where they help weed, for example, only one weeding is the typical practice in some areas while there is almost constant weeding throughout the growing season in others. And all detailed accounts of areas where weeding is done suggest that yields are strongly affected by weeding. Similarly, where men only clear land, the effect of a reduction of able-bodied males available is very different in areas where only land to be cultivated is cleared compared with

areas where ten or twelve times as much land is cleared as is cultivated —
the practice in the ash-dependent system (Chapter 4).

A puzzling feature of agriculture in the tribal economies of the Congo
Basin is the uneven distribution of certain agricultural enterprises or
techniques. The limited distribution of cattle is explained largely by the
distribution of the tsetse fly and difficulties of rebuilding herds once they
are decimated. However several peoples who had no cattle in 1950 are
outside the tsetse fly zone and had raised cattle earlier but lost them
through disease epidemics or confiscation by soldiers or administrators.

But no explanation is suggested in the literature for the uneven distribution of swine. Like goats, which are found everywhere, they are a threat
to crops. Swine are probably more destructive and less hardy than goats.

Kola nuts are carefully grown in some parts of the western Congo Basin
and are widely reported throughout the western forest zone. They will
grow throughout the humid forest, but are not mentioned in any of the
accounts for the eastern portion of the forest belt. There is a similar
geographical distribution of sugarcane and of use of the basket press in
squeezing palm oil and sugarcane pulp. Like kola nuts, sugarcane could
be grown throughout the eastern forest zone. Vines and fibers from bark
are available through the forest area, hence basket presses presumably
could be made.

Another interesting variation in techniques is the practice of felling
palm trees to get their sap for palm wine in some areas, use of tapping
techniques (which do not kill the tree) in others, and use of both techniques
side by side in a number of areas. No information is available on relative
yields by the two methods. The nature of property rights may be of some
importance. Oil palms may be owned even when the land on which they
grow cannot be, but there are no data on whether it is unowned trees
which are more commonly felled, as might be expected. The demand for
palm oil is clearly a relevant variable, too, but again the needed data are
not reported.

Similar questions arise with respect to the practice of bleeding cattle, and
the relative efficiency of various types of hoes found. Bleeding cattle
probably gives a far higher yield than slaughtering them, if the utility of a
pound of blood to the consumers involved is not greatly below that of
a pound of meat. Slaughtering an animal is the equivalent of consuming
one's capital, up to the point where herds are too large for available water
or pasture. A number of cattle-keeping peoples in the Congo Basin do

not bleed cattle, however, and the practice is nowhere reported for sheep or goats.

Much of the emphasis on introducing better tools in Africa has focused on replacing hoes with plows, but almost no plowing is found in the Congo Basin. Nor is there prospect of introducing plowing in most regions in the near future either because of the presence of the tsetse fly, because of stumps, or because of the damage done to lateritic soils when worked deeply.

Hoes vary by tribe from very small ones with short handles to large ones with long handles; the blade may be any of numerous shapes from rectangular to heart-shaped and may form various angles with the handle, from 90° to less than 45°. Some peoples have more than one type of hoe; and here and there in the literature there is mention that certain field operations are done with special hoes. It seems sufficiently likely that some tribes have hoes that are more efficient than those of others with a similar environment to warrant research by African countries into hoe design and problems of disseminating superior hoes.

Another area that would seem to justify research is the nature of the obstacles to adoption of more productive starchy-staples. Breadfruit, a major dietary staple in Africa only in the Comoro and Seychelles Islands, grows throughout the humid forest zone, appears to yield as many calories per acre where it will thrive as any starchy-staple now important in the diet, and — since it is a tree crop — can capture soil nutrients that escape annual crops. Reliance on breadfruit would therefore permit permanent field cultivation without introducing the use of fertilizers or other new techniques of soil management. Breadfruit appears not to be liked by African peoples when treated with the processing techniques they now employ,[1] but other African starchy-staples were similarly disadvantaged in some areas until appropriate processing methods were introduced. Manioc, now the dominant starchy-staple in much of the humid forest, was of minor importance in West Africa until Brazilian processing techniques were introduced by freed slaves returning to Africa in the middle of the nineteenth century (195, p. 78).

The literature on the Congo Basin yields substantial evidence of technological change in the tribal economies; and other evidence shows that much technological change in such predominantly preliterate agricultural economies is likely never to be recorded. Therefore total technological change probably exceeds by a large margin what has been reported.

As was seen in Chapters 11 and 12 and in the Appendix Table, a common type of technological change has been the introduction of new crops, or new varieties of existing crops, some of which can be of major importance. Introduction of a crop or crop variety that, say, doubles yields per acre without increasing the amount of labor required would mean a doubling of productivity for the amount of total economic activity that crop represents. In economies where production of starchy-staples appears to account for a majority of economic activity, as in the Congo Basin, introduction of a much more productive starchy-staple, such as manioc, can be an impressive technological advance.

It appears that in much of the Congo Basin manioc is frequently at least twice as productive in calories per acre as the next most productive starchy-staple (*264*, p. 207–15); and it clearly has been introduced to many of the tribal economies in the last hundred years. The relative productivity of other crops is less well established, but the record strongly suggests numerous crop introductions during the last 100 years.

This casts strong doubt on the proposition of Theodore W. Schultz that traditional agriculture in underdeveloped economies is stagnant at a low level.[2] As Schultz states it (*320*, p. 37): "The factors of production on which they [farmers] depend are known through long experience and are in this sense 'traditional'. . . . farmers of this class continue year after year to cultivate the same type of land, sow the same crops, use the same techniques of production, and bring the same skills to bear in agricultural production."

Schultz's point that there are "comparatively few significant inefficiencies in the allocation of factors of production" (*320*, p. 37) may well be correct, and is not here challenged; but serious errors may be committed in development planning, or the execution of plans, if it is assumed that African farmers are unaccustomed to choosing among alternative enterprises or factor proportions. If one assumes that farmers do the same things the same way their fathers and grandfathers did, it is easy to slip into the assumption that changing agricultural productivity is mainly a matter of supplying new techniques to farmers and providing them incentives to adopt them, as Schultz in fact argues (*320*, ch. 10). However, if the present low productivity of farmers is recognized to be concomitant with considerable technological change, the problem must be regarded as more complex. The question of why past technological change was insufficient to raise productivity to satisfactory levels must be faced.

If one believes that there has been very little or no technological change in the agricultural sector, it is easy to assume that there were no opportunities for change, and that just as there are no recorded successes, there were also no failures. If, however, change is admitted, the possibility of failures, of poorly introduced or ill-timed innovations, cannot be ignored; and planners are much more likely to give thought not only to what changes are desirable but also to the conditions under which a given desired change is likely to be adopted.

We know relatively little yet about why successful technological change came about in the tribal economies of the Congo Basin. Successes tend to be little discussed, much less analyzed, because they usually present no striking problems. More attention is given the failures, and it is largely to them that planners are forced to look for guidance.

Particularly instructive, perhaps, are such examples as the abortive attempt to introduce pigeon peas and soy beans to the northern Congo Basin without research into how pulses are processed by the peoples involved; attempts to introduce improved maize varieties that failed because of lack of research on consumer preferences as to hardness and color of the grain (*264*, pp. 231–32); and rejection of chemical fertilizers by farmers in eastern Nigeria because the fertilizers introduced caused their rice to develop too much straw and their yams to store poorly (*414*, p. 912).

Finally, agriculture of tribal farmers in at least the Congo Basin — but almost certainly in the rest of tropical Africa as well — not only is complex and changing over time but can be greatly different from area to area within national economies. The resource endowment, recent economic history, the system of property rights, the importance of agriculture relative to other economic activities, the degree of dependence on other economic units through exchange, the organization of agriculture (particularly as influenced by labor rights and obligations); the collection of crops, crop varieties, and noncrop enterprises known; tools, methods of tilling land, crop associations and sequences, care given animals, storage and processing techniques, and consumer preferences can all vary greatly from one tribal economy to another. Evidence from the Congo Basin strongly suggests that development programs which are suited to one tribal economy may well fail in another.

Because of the diversity of agriculture in African countries, those who want to assure rapid economic growth have the added development burden of having to do research on the nature of each tribal economy as part of development planning. Thus the cost of developing agriculture may be considerably greater per capita in tropical Africa than in much of the rest of the world both 1) because of added research required to identify similarities and differences in development problems and potential within rural areas and 2) because of the added cost of having to administer several — perhaps many — types of agricultural programs rather than one or two (except, of course, where research shows that there are only one or two large clusters of tribal economies and that there is enough homogeneity within clusters for the success of a given common development policy to be much the same from tribe to tribe within clusters).

We have much to learn about the tribal economies of tropical Africa, but it is becoming increasingly clear that a number of current stereotypes about them are in need of revision. Particularly important for development planning is the abundance of evidence from the Congo Basin that African agriculture is complex and variable over time — evidence which makes it no longer plausible to explain the low level of living now found in terms of indolence of unorthodox response to economic incentives by African farmers.

Reference Material

APPENDIX

Construction of Map 1-7,
Principal Food Crops about 1950

For the Belgian Congo, French Equatorial Africa, French Cameroons, and Angola, Map 1-7 is based largely on maps in Bruce F. Johnston's *The Staple Food Economies of Western Tropical Africa* (Stanford University Press, Stanford, Calif., 1958). Data on Sudan, Uganda, Ruanda-Urundi, Tanganyika, Northern Rhodesia, Southern Rhodesia, Nyasaland, and Mozambique are based on official estimates, where these are available, and on nonquantitative information elsewhere. The definition of principal crops — those with acreages at least 80 percent of that of the food crop most extensively grown — is the same as that employed by Johnston; but Map 1-7 differs from Johnston's maps in that it includes pulses as staple food crops.

For Uganda, Ruanda-Urundi, Tanganyika, Nyasaland, and Southern Rhodesia data can be obtained for sufficiently small administrative divisions to give a detailed account of the position of the principal food crops; the main deficiency is that (except for Uganda) estimates are incomplete and for only one year.

Methods of estimating acreage in Uganda are officially described as follows: "Statistics of acreage are derived from the annual sample survey. The survey is carried out by dividing the country into small areas and choosing a sample unit for each area. Within each sampling unit, crop acreages are measured by pacing" (*144*, see Uganda). Actually, two methods are used. In Buganda Province, for a single "representative" parish, all plots are measured twice a year (once in each rainy season); a count of population is taken, and acreage per taxpayer is calculated. This average is assumed to apply throughout the province, and is multiplied by the number of taxpayers to yield county, district, and provincial aggregates.

293

Outside Buganda Province there is a lack of uniformity of method, but usually the average size of plots in a small "representative" administrative area, not necessarily a parish, is calculated once a year. Chiefs are required to tour periodically and count the number of plots being cultivated. When planting is considered complete, and all chiefs have submitted their reports, the number of plots counted is multiplied by the average plot size measured earlier (*194; 238*).

In both Buganda and other provinces, when intercropping is encountered, as it frequently is, acreages are adjusted to "pure stand" basis, i.e. the equivalent acreage of the crop grown alone.

It is doubtful that Ruanda-Urundi data are more trustworthy than those for Uganda, although they are reportedly derived by some kind of census technique (*45*, p. 343).

A three-year average, 1950–52, was used in Uganda; district estimates are not provided for the 1939–49 decade. For Ruanda-Urundi, the estimates refer to a single year, 1949, the only date for which quantitative estimates, by district or geographical region, are available.

No geographical breakdown of estimates is available for Mozambique, Northern Rhodesia, and the Sudan, but there are detailed descriptions of agriculture by provinces; and for Northern Rhodesia and Mozambique published information was supplemented by correspondence with officials and authorities in Africa, and my own field work during the latter half of 1959.

In the main, data for this map were taken from: J. D. Tothill, ed., *Agriculture in the Sudan* (London, 1948); Pierre de Schlippe, *Shifting Cultivation in Africa* (London, 1956); Tanganyika, *Blue Book for the Year Ended December 31, 1946* (1948) and ibid., *1948* (1950); Tanganyika, East African Statistical Department, *Report on the Analysis of the Sample Census of African Agriculture, 1950* (1953); Tanganyika, Department of Agriculture, *Agriculture in Tanganyika* (1945); R. C. Jerrard, *The Tribes of Tanganyika, Their Districts, Usual Dietary and Pursuits* (n.p., 1936); R. E. Baker and N. W. Simmonds, "Bananas in East Africa," *Empire Journal of Experimental Agriculture*, Vol. 19, No. 96 (1951); Food and Agriculture Organization of the United Nations (FAO), *Report on the 1950 World Census of Agriculture* (1955); Frank Debenham, *Nyasaland* (London, 1955); Central African Statistical Office, *Statistical Handbook of Nyasaland, 1952* (1952); C. C. Taylor, *Agriculture in Southern Africa*, U.S. Department of Agriculture, Technical Bulletin, No. 446 (Mar. 1935); communication from the Northern Rhodesia Department of Agriculture; J. M. Winterbottom, "The Ecology of Man and Plants in Northern Rhodesia," *Rhodes-Livingstone Journal*, June 1945; Southern Rhodesia, *Seventh Report on the Agricultural and Pastoral Production of European Farmers, 1952–53* (1954); R. R. Staples and C. A. Murray, "Farming Systems in Southern Rhodesia," *Rhodesian Agricultural Journal*, Sept.–Oct. 1951; E. B. Jones, "Foods from Southern Rhodesia," in

Malnutrition in African Mothers, Infants, and Young Children (Great Britain, Colonial Office, London, 1954); Sir Frank Engledow, *Report to the Minister of Agriculture* . . . (Salisbury, 1950); Derwent Whittlesey, "Southern Rhodesia — An African Compage," *Annals of the Association of American Geographers*, Mar. 1956; C. F. Spence, *The Portuguese Colony of Moçambique* (Cape Town, 1951); and communication from R. Smith Simpson, American consul general of Mozambique.

Appendix Table

APPENDIX TABLE — Crop and Livestock Introductions to One or More of the Tribal Economies of the Congo Basin, 1830–1960, according to European Travelers, Administrators, and Missionaries*

Crop or animal	Scientific name	Agent of introduction and date	Source of evidence
Starchy-staples			
Maize	*Zea mays*	Bimore (. . .)	*295*, p. 110
"Millet"	. . .	Arabs (1830–80)	*339*, p. 149
"Sorghum"	. . .	Arabs (1830–80)	*111*, p. 22
Wheat	—	Arabs (1830–80) Belgians (1883–85; 1924–25)	*73*, p. 49; *77*, p. 172; *281*, p. 120
Rice	*Oryza sativa*	Arabs (1830–80) Tetela (. . .) Ngwana (. . .) Pogge (1875) Belgians, French (1880–1930)	*171*, p. 17; *339*, p. 149; *209*, p. 331; *252*, p. 105; *346*, p. 224; *380*, p. 52; *188*, p. 214
Irish potatoes	—	Lt. Storms (1883–85)	*73*, p. 49

296

Crop or animal	Scientific name	Agent of introduction and date	Source of evidence
Manioc	*Manihot utilissima*	Arabs (1830–80) Belgians (1883–1930) An African chief (1885) French (1917)	*17*, p. 92; *73*, p. 49; *346*, p. 215; *221*, p. 229; *237*, p. 2300; *399*, p. 266; *224*, p. 55; *281*, p. 122
Sweet potatoes	*Ipomoea batatas*	Bira (. . .) Arabs (1830–80) Europeans (1880–1930)	*171*, *193*, *221*, p. 229; *209*, p. 331
Plantain	*Musa paradisica*	Europeans (1880–1911)	*346*, p. 226
"Taro"	. . .	African soldiers (1914–17)	*346*, p. 230
Madagascar potatoes	*Coleus dysentericus*	Africans? (1911, 1917)	*346*, p. 233
Breadfruit	*Artocarpus incisa*	Europeans? (1875–85?)	*112*
Livestock			
Cattle	. . .	Rundi (. . .) Hima (. . .) Arabs (1830–88) Dutch (1886) Belgians (1891–1913) Germans (1890–1900)	*250*, p. 59; *124*, p. 199; *100*, p. 17; *378*, p. 53; *102*, p. 127; *83*, p. 215; *424*, p. 23
Sheep	. . .	Arabs (1830–80) Belgians (1910)	*72*, p. 40; *349*, p. 44
Milk goats	. . .	Belgians (1910)	*349*, p. 44
Goats	. . .	Arabs (1830–80)	

Crop or animal	Scientific name	Agent of introduction and date	Source of evidence
		Belgians (1870–1910)	*72*, p. 40; *221*, p. 133
Swine	. . .	Von Wissmann (1880–90?)	*401*, p. 66
Horses	. . .	Commandant Rennette (1884–1908)	*348*, p. 438
Mules	. . .	Arabs (1830–80) Europeans (1884–1908)	*348*, p. 435
Donkeys	. . .	Arabs (1830–80)	*348*, p. 435
Chickens	. . .	Arabs (1830–80)	*408*, p. 939
Ducks	. . .	Arabs (1830–80)	*171*
Pigeons	. . .	Arabs (1830–80)	*193*
Sources of fats and oils			
Oil palm	*Elaeis guineensis*	Tsumba (. . .)	*25*, p. 504
Peanuts	*Arachis hypogaea*	Arabs (1830–80)	*339*, p. 149; *209*, p. 331
Bambara nuts	*Voandzeia subterranea*	Arabs (1830–80)	*193*
Coconuts	*Cocos nucifera*	Dutch (1830–89)	*111*, p. 20; *124*, p. 539
Avocado	*Persea americana*	Arabs (1830–80) French (1880–1930?)	*72*, p. 40; *346*
Sunflower	*Helianthus annuus*	Belgians (1906)	*290*, p. 87
Sesame	*Sesamum indicum*	Hausa (. . .) Arabs (1830–80)	*339*, p. 147; *295*, p. 110
Oilseed gourds	. . .	Arabs (1830–80) African soldiers (1880–1912)	*339*, p. 149; *15*, p. 646
Sources of sugar			
Sugarcane	*Saccharum officinarum*	Arabs (1830–80) Africans (1911–50)	*193*; *346*, p. 241
Fibers			
Congo jute	*Urena lobata*	Belgians (1935–45)	*306*, p. 665; *3*, p. 242
Sisal	—	French (1926)	*346*, p. 249

Crop or animal	Scientific name	Agent of introduction and date	Source of evidence
Cotton	—	Europeans (1878–88 and 1921–30)	*70*, 1:257; *346*, p. 225; *108*, p. 232
Vegetables and condiments			
"Beans"	...	Bira (...) Rundi (...) Arabs (1830–80)	*339*, p. 149; *72*, p. 40; *102*, p. 127; *209*, p. 331
Mung beans	—	French (1917–30)	*346*, p. 235
Soya beans	*Glycine maxima*	Europeans (1930–50)	*108*, pp. 222–23
—	*Dolichos multiflorus*	Belgians? (...)	*112*
Pigeon pea	*Cajanus indicus*	French (1914) Belgians (...)	*346*, p. 235; *112*
—	*Soja hispida*	Belgians? (...)	*112*
Tomato	*Lycopersicum esculentum*	Belgians? (...) Arabs (1830–80)	*112*; *124*, p. 641
Cabbage	*Brassica oleracea*	Belgians? (...)	*112*
—	*B. scleroneora*	Belgians? (...)	*112*
—	*B. alta*	Belgians? (...)	*112*
Indian mustard	*B. juncea*	Belgians? (...)	*112*
Mustard	*Sinapis alba*	Belgians? (...)	*112*
Onions	...	Arabs (1830–80)	*72*, p. 40
Chilies	*Capsicum annuum* and *C. frutescens*	Arabs (1830–80)	*72*, p. 40
Garlic	—	Arabs (1830–80)	*72*, p. 40
Chives	—	Belgians (1920–30?)	*281*, p. 120
Eggplant	*Solanum melongena*	Belgians? (...)	*112*
Cucumber	—	Arabs (1830–80)	*72*, p. 40
"Green" pepper	...	Belgians (1920–30)	*281*, p. 120
Turnips	—	Belgians (1920–30)	*281*, p. 120
Fruits			
Orange	...	Arabs (1830–80) Europeans (1878–88)	*72*, p. 40; *70*, 1:257
Lemon	*Citrus limonum*	Arabs (1830–80) Europeans (1878–1910)	*400*, p. 22; *72*, p. 40; *70*, 1:257

Crop or animal	Scientific name	Agent of introduction and date	Source of evidence
Lime	C. aurantifolia	Von Wissmann (1880–1890?)	401, p. 66
Citron	C. medica	French (1890–1917?)	346
Papaya	Carica papaya	Arabs (1830–80) Europeans (1875–1900)	97, p. 229; 346; 70, 1:257
Mango	—	Arabs (1830–80) French (1880–1917) Europeans (1926–30)	72, p. 40; 346, p. 225; 131, p. 314; 399, p. 22
Guava	—	Arabs (1830–80) French (1880–1917)	72, p. 40; 346, p. 225
Pineapple	—	Europeans (1884–1908)	112, 97, p. 229; 346, p. 231; 401, p. 22
Bananas	Musa sapietum	Europeans (1884–1908)	422, p. 7; 150, p. 210
Chinese banana	Musa nana	Arabs (1830–80)	150, p. 210; 170, p. 220
Bullock's-heart	Annona reticulata	Arabs (1830–80) Europeans? (1880–1910)	399, p. 22
—	A. squamosa	Europeans? (. . .)	112
—	A. muricata	Europeans? (. . .)	112
Cape gooseberry	Physalis peruviana	Europeans? (1830–94)	111, p. 21
Pomegranate	Punica granatum	Arabs (1830–80)	72, p. 40
Passion fruit	Passiflora edulus	Belgians? (. . .)	112
—	Amomum citratum	Belgians? (. . .)	112
Grapes	. . .	Europeans (1878–88)	70, 1:257
Vanilla	—	Europeans (1906)	407, p. 1293
Stimulants			
Common hemp	Cannabis sativa	Arabs (1830–80) Europeans? (1880–1911)	346, p. 254
Tobacco	—	Arabs (1830–80)	339, p. 149

Crop or animal	Scientific name	Agent of introduction and date	Source of evidence
Coffee	. . .	Belgians (1883–85; 1906) French (1930)	73, p. 49; 346, p. 225
Liberica coffee	*Coffea liberica*	Belgians (1881)	231, p. 6
Dyes			
Indigo	. . .	Arabs (1830–80)	339, p. 149
Other			
Cerea rubber	*Manihot glazionii*	French (1917)	346, p. 225

*Introductions of new varieties of existing crops, discussed in some detail in Chapter 12 above, have not been listed here because spread of varieties seems to be greatly underreported and because of the difficulty of evaluating the impact of the varietal introductions so far recorded. Availability of a new variety of an existing crop may often contribute more to increases in production or productivity than introduction of new crops; and available evidence suggests that a number of known introductions did, in fact, considerably increase productivity. On the other hand a new variety, introduced experimentally by farmers or others, which has undesirable qualities — e.g. is too early or too late maturing, or stores or processes poorly — may cross with existing varieties and lower productivity before its characteristics are well known or fully understood. Once introduced, a hardy undesirable variety, like a weed, can be extremely difficult to control. The evidence suggests that in the tribal economies the effects of an undesirable varietal introduction which readily crosses with the local varieties cannot be corrected without an intensive, carefully directed campaign (see 264, pp. 230–33).

Note: Information not available: . . .

Negligible amount or none: —

Notes

1 Exceptions are some of the small tribes along the middle Congo River who produce only fish and exchange them for all other commodities needed. In the eastern Congo Basin a tribe that similarly specializes in hunting has been reported (*271*, p. 18; *368*, Books II and III, p. 728).

2 In the pages that follow the names "bananas" and "plantains" will be used interchangeably, because they usually cannot be distinguished in the literature. Most French and Belgian writers designate both cooking bananas (plantains) and dessert bananas as *bananes*.

3 The percentage of starchy-staple crop acreage would be even higher since pulses are not classified as starchy-staples.

4 Later writers say there were no marketplaces in Azande country at that time, or at any time before colonial rule; but the Azande occupy a large area, and it is possible that such observations come from the northern Azande and do not apply to the southern Azande that Calonne-Beaufaict describes (*303*, pp. 537–38).

5 The lack of variety in the foods consumed is possibly considerably exaggerated. During the wild fruit season the Lala of Northern Rhodesia used the juice of three different wild fruits (*Upaca* sp., *Parinari* sp., and *Anisophyneo* sp.) in making porridge (*350*, p. 45). The contribution of foodstuffs collected in the bush has been neglected in generalizations about the monotony of African diets; practices similar to those of the Lala may well be found more widely.

The Lala have two methods of making porridge with wild fruit. In one the fruit is pounded to remove the seed, put in cold water and boiled, then strained; the juice collected is mixed with flour and cooked. By the second method the fruit is boiled without pounding, and then cooked with flour (seeds of the fruit are discarded while eating).

Chapter Two

1 Also referred to as "slash and burn," swidden, *landang* (Malaya), *Kaingin* (Philippines), *togel* (Java), *ray* (Indochina), *taungya* (Burma), and *milpa* (Guatemala and parts of Mexico) (*39*, p. 693). Those writing about African agriculture frequently use the term *chitemene* as synonymous with shifting cultivation (e.g. *39*, p. 693; *37*, p. 72; and *34*, p. 169), but chitemene is a special type of shifting cultivation found only among the Bemba of Zambia and some of their neighbors and is unknown among the several hundred other tribes of tropical Africa who practice shifting cultivation. For a survey of the literature see H. C. Conklin, "The Study of Shifting Cultivation," *Current Anthropology*, 2 (1961): 27–61 and R. F. Watters, "The Nature of Shifting Cultivation," *Pacific Viewpoint*, 1:59–99. Conklin also provides an extensive bibliography.

2 Rights to specific secondary plots, such as former hutsites and gardens near them, do continue through the fallow period among a number of Basin peoples, but the volume of production from such gardens appears to be slight compared to main fields.

3 See Derwent Whittlesey, "Fixation of Shifting Cultivation," *Economic Geography*, 13:36–37, for maps showing the distribution of shifting cultivation in the tropics.

4 If goats are kept, the fields are often placed far enough away for them not to find the crops.

5 Some cultivators in humid forest areas prefer to clear secondary rather than fully developed forest because it takes less labor.

Chapter Three

1 The Bambara nut, or earthnut (*Voandzeia subterranea*), looks much like the peanut and has the same habit of developing its seed underground. Unlike the peanut, however, it usually has only one seed per pod.

2 *Mamba, limbali,* and *uduna.*

3 Bananas-plantains are planted in lines, with 1.5 to 1.8 meters between plants (*102*, p. 128).

4 It seems the machete is not used. Van Overbergh categorically states that "the only tools I have seen employed are the hatchet and the hoe" (*386*, p. 181).

5 Crop sequences differ from associations in that associations refer to combinations of crops in a given season and sequences show successive crop combinations that occupy given fields in two or more seasons. Sequences are like rotations but not as regular. With a rotation a repeating pattern of a given sequence of crops or crop combinations is followed with regularity. Among African farmers in the Congo Basin so many variables determine which crop or crop association will be planted any particular season that the regularity implied by the term crop rotation is not observed.

In this study separation of crop names with virgules (e.g., maize/manioc/beans) is the convention used to indicate crop associations. Dashes are used to indicate sequences (e.g., maize-manioc-yams-fallow, or beans/manioc-maize-beans-manioc/gourds-fallow).

A crop succession is two or more crops grown on the same field in a given season but one of them planted after the other is already growing. Thus crop successions like crop associations may be components of crop sequences.

6 The Vili, located on the Atlantic Ocean near the mouth of the Congo River,

occupy both forest and savanna areas. In forest they use the cut, burn, plant technique but in savanna areas follow Class 5 techniques (cut, burn, hoe, plant). We have arbitrarily placed them in the latter class (see p. 70 for discussion of their agricultural methods).

7 Both a large knife (blade 25 to 30 cm.) and a small knife (blade about 15 cm.) are illustrated, but Elskens does not state which is used in many of the operations.

8 Tharin, writing about the same time as Elskens, states that bananas-plantains are planted before manioc (*338*, p. 172).

9 Possibly several tribes in the central Congo Basin traditionally were without hoes. Descriptions of Turumbu agricultural methods make no mention of hoes; and S. Molin, in an article published in 1933, explicitly states that the Kela then used only the knife and hatchet in cultivation (*265*, p. 391).

10 Manioc is planted on mounds, but these peoples believe that maize planted on mounds will have less resistance to the wind, so they always plant it on the flat (*256*, p. 884).

11 Mestdagh's informants reported that two additional varieties are known on the eastern side of the Lomami River.

12 The Kuba and the Kongo of Thysville territoire who have both forest and savanna lands practice this technique in forest areas. In savanna areas the Kongo use a complex method of hoe and cut, then burn, with incineration sometimes preceding hoeing and cutting. Their agriculture is discussed under savanna techniques (pp. 69–109) because much more information is available on their savanna fields.

The Kuba employ a cut, burn, hoe technique in savannas but also plant tree crops. Their agriculture is discussed under Class 12 because planting tree crops is economically more interesting than the other methods they employ.

13 *Pachylobus edulis.* "In equatorial Congo it is found in almost all the villages" (*18*, p. 272). The fruit resembles a "large violet prune" and is boiled in water or baked in ashes under coals.

14 "Bananas" here probably also embraces plantains.

15 Mounds are not mentioned for the northern Bira, but since only a sketch is given of their agriculture mounding may have been overlooked (see p. 67).

16 Janssens lists a white, a purple, and a yellow variety of maize (*188*, p. 207).

17 Information on when fields are cleared is not given, so the time between burning and planting cannot be established.

18 Yams are planted and harvested in the dry season. The hole left when the tuber is dug out is left to fill gradually with debris. When the yam tuber is processed, the end with a bud is cut off and thrown in this hole. At the beginning of the rainy season the piece of tuber is covered with a little soil and left without further care until the next harvest (*400*, p. 19).

19 Colle gives manioc as the principal crop in a book published in 1913, and Schmitz gives maize as the dominant crop in a book published a year earlier (*83*, 1:97; *317*, p. 49); they may be talking about different segments of the tribe.

20 Verhulpen states that maize holes are spaced about 70 cm. apart (*399*, p. 316).

21 The only other crops for which harvesting techniques are discussed are peanuts and sweet potatoes, both of which are dug out with a hoe.

22 Crops reported are manioc, maize, bulrush millet, rice, sweet potatoes, Livingstone potatoes (*Coleus esculentus*), peanut potatoes, Irish potatoes, taro, yams, beets, carrots, turnips, peanuts, Bambara nuts, cowpeas, haricot beans, lima beans, peas, watermelons, both edible and nonedible gourds, cucumbers, pump-

kins, cabbages, onions, lettuce, eggplant, okra, sweet peppers, roselle, garlic, small hot peppers, mild chilies, cherry chilies, tobacco, castor beans, kidney cotton, sesame, sweet sorghum, sugarcane, mangoes, bananas, pineapples, cayenne pineapples, papayas, guavas, granadillas, Cape gooseberries, oranges, tangerines, and lemons.

23 Ten more varieties are known in some locations but not in others.

24 This field association may be characteristic only of the Pende and Mbunda. Rassel describes it as though it were generally characteristic of the plateau areas, but later comments: "The Pende and Mbunda south of Idiofa are the big consumers of millet. The other tribes are little or not at all fond of it because it is difficult to grind and furnishes a grayish flour" (*300*, p. 16)

25 In mixed culture several Bambara nuts are probably placed in each hole, but the holes are spaced "more widely" than in the Bambara nut/peanut association, for Rassel indicates this variation for Bambara nuts "planted with manioc" (*301*, p. 13), which could mean either in the manioc/bulrush millet field only or also in garden associations.

26 H. Vanderyst, in an article published in 1921, gives supplementary information on clearing around Kisantu, the first town east of Inkisi sector on the railroad. He reports that small trees are cut 0.60 to 0.80 cm. above the ground, and that large trees that bear nothing useful are killed by ringing (*372*, p. 540). Debris is burned at the end of the dry season.

27 Vanderyst reports that in planting maize at Kisantu holes are made in the soil (*372*, p. 541); Drachoussoff mentions use of a machete, but does not make it clear whether he refers to Bangu or Inkisi (*121*, p. 817).

28 See n. 5, p. 304 for definitions of the terms crop association, crop succession, and crop sequence.

29 Hyptis (*Hyptis spicigera*), a plant resembling peppermint which grows to some 150 cm. in height, bears a very small whitish oilseed (*108*, p. 61). It responds well to soil fertility and care, and will grow over a wide range of soils, but its yields are low in the northern savanna. At Yambio experiment station in southern Sudan it gives only about 0.24 metric tons per hectare, and at Kagelu station only 0.43 metric tons per hectare.

30 De Schlippe gives the following account of this cause for moving the homestead (*108*, p. 193): "If a wife dies, even one of several wives, the whole family must move to a new place. Quite a complicated rite obliges the widower to have all his buildings destroyed, all his belongings and crops abandoned. His other wives are allowed to come back to their fields and harvest them, but he himself never returns . . . . Under certain circumstances, however, the obligation to move, and the penalties . . . can be removed by a special magic . . . ."

31 This hoeing is combined with clod breaking, but the procedure is not described. Among the Logo of the northern Congo (Kinshasa) — a tribe that also uses the hoe and cut, burn, clean, plant method in which small grains are sometimes broadcast immediately after burning the field — women move over the plot as soon as the grain has been scattered and break any clods with an L- or T-shaped stick, using it as a mallet. De Schlippe describes a similar L-shaped tool for breaking clods in his chapter on Azande tools, but he does not explain its use other than to say it is employed in the first hoeing.

32 If a ratooning variety is planted, shoots from the cut stalks bear heads that ripen the following July or August, in normal years, or as late as the following November in moist years.

33 Chilies, or red peppers, a crop sown through the droppings of birds but cultivated and harvested by the Azande, survive only when they are planted in
favorable environments; hence De Schlippe includes them with ecologically
specialized crops.

34 In 1909 M. Willaert, veterinarian of the Uele District, which at that time
included all the Congo Azande, reported that "livestock among the Azande is
limited to some poultry; even goats are only very exceptionally encountered"
(422, p. 7).

35 The only other crop studied is Job's tears.

36 According to A. M. Vergait, in a study published in 1937, the main field is planted
with a millet/beans/oilseed gourds association, and manioc is not planted until
millet is "high," presumably at least a month later (397, p. 117).

37 ". . . among the Mandja of Dekoy this is practiced only with certain early-
maturing varieties of sorghum. The seed are sown thickly and the young plants
are later eliminated until the desired density is obtained" (150, p. 207).

38 Women also "cultivate fish-ponds," but no account is given of what this work
comprises (116, p. 3).

39 Mary Douglas uses the general term "raffia," which suggests she means Raphia
raffia, the palm known for its fiber. In some other parts of the Congo Basin
where R. raffia is cultivated, R. vinifera is also grown, to produce palm wine.
This is possibly also true of the Lele.

40 Torday and Joyce say that the Lele make a hole in the trunk of the tree and
lead the sap out via a leaf which is made to serve as a trough (358, p. 138).

Chapter Four

1 Probably some bulrush millet is mixed with the finger millet sown at this time.

2 The reason sowing calls for skill is apparently that the Bemba want the seed
spread in such a manner that the young millet plants will not need thinning.
Richards emphasizes the general reluctance of the Bemba to thin crops by
quoting a single farmer she remembered saying: "Yes, those plants are pressing
against each other. Each will steal the food of the other. But are we to throw
them away? Would not that be a slight to the spirits (ukutuke mipashi)? Is it not
they who gave us the food?" (305, p. 306). Richards here attributed the aver-
sion to thinning to religion, but it is also sound economics; thinning is not only
extra work but among the Bemba would come at a time when labor is urgently
needed to plant other crops.

3 Jessie Williamson describes Livingstone potatoes (Coleus esculentus) as "A herb
growing to about 2 ft. with opposite leaves and yellow flowers, with thickened
underground stems which grow like fingers of a hand from a central point"
(423, pp. 37–38). Trapnell says this crop is indigenous to Zambia and Rhodesia,
but does not provide documentation (361, p. 28).

Richards implies that coleus potato gardens are common among the Bemba,
but Trapnell found in his ecological surveys that this garden type is "hardly
ever encountered among the Bemba but it occurs among them in the northern
half of Kasama District" (360, p. 54). Richards refers to the Kasama area
several times in her book, and her descriptions of coleus potato cultivation
match Trapnell's for Kasama District; thus it seems likely that her observations
came only from the Kasama area.

4 This sequence is followed only if the first crop fails.

5 A plant grown for poisoning fish.

6 Around Abercorn the hoeing method is employed.

7 The Chisinga, Mukulu, and Swahili of Zambia are not recognized as tribes by Murdock, hence are not shown on Map 1-3. Murdock classifies the Chisinga and Mukulu as part of the Aushi. The Swahili referred to here are an enclave on the northwestern edge of the Lala.

8 There is great variation in crop sequences from place to place among the Tabwa; cf. *360*, pp. 60–61, for a detailed discussion.

9 Maize is not grown with millet, reportedly because of damage monkeys would do to the maize (*360*, p. 71).

10 Only 27 percent of cultivators had fences, and these cut an average of 0.86 hectares each for fences. Peters does not describe fence construction.

Chapter Five

1 In a number of forest areas hut or courtyard gardens — e.g. banana or plantain groves — are given compost, but there is only one reference to use of composts in main fields. The lower Bwaka, located in the forest between the Congo and Ubangi rivers, reportedly practice a type of permanent field agriculture with plantain, the preferred starchy-staple, based on regular application of composted weeds. During the dry season weeds and grass are collected, dried, and placed at the base of each plantain stalk. Every two years a new bundle of compost materials is added to the existing heap (*129*, p. 276).

2 Informants told Trapnell that sweet potatoes were formerly more important, their cultivation having "decreased greatly on account of depredations by wild pigs" (*360*, p. 57).

3 For description of Livingstone or coleus potatoes, see Chapter 4, n. 3.

4 Papy reports that this technique is also employed by the Bamiléké of Cameroun for growing yams (*136*, pp. 180–82, cited in *283*, p. 124 n.).

5 In some of the western parts of the Niari Valley, only maize is interplanted with yams (*313*, pp. 90–91).

6 According to H. Nicolaï peanut fields are given special preparation in the Luozi area. The field is hoed twice, rather than once, and is smoothed; then roots pulled out of the soil during hoeing are burned and the ashes scattered over the field (*275*, p. 40).

Chapter Six

1 Whether fallows exceed cropping periods in length cannot be determined from the data.

2 Among the Bashi certain unfertilized fields are not fallowed but instead are planted to bananas ten years to restore fertility. In the Beni-Lubero area sometimes peas are similarly grown in place of fallow.

3 Belgian agricultural experts identify twenty-two natural regions in Rwanda-Burundi, each with its characteristic food agriculture.

4 De Greef says compost is made by chopping up banana trunks and covering them with leaves and earth (*99*, p. 24).

5 H. L. Shantz reports that in Urundi maize grains are soaked for a day before planting (*326*, p. 352) Meyer states that the holes for planting any crop may be made with a reed or a stick, and in soft soil may be made with the hands (*258*, p. 73).

6 De Greef states that maize and bean kernels are placed in the same holes (*99*, p. 24).

7 R. P. Pagès states that in parts of northern Ruanda little tobacco is grown; people obtained it through trade with specialists from the Byahi Plain north of Lake Kivu. The "people who grow it largely make their living from this trade" (*282*, p. 294).

8 Shantz and De Greef, writing only of Urundi, say that irrigation systems are often complex and that the construction of the irrigation network is done collectively (*326*, p. 350; *99*, p. 25). De Greef and Meyer indicate that maize is the major crop irrigated in some areas, and mention that sometimes two or three crops of irrigated maize are grown per year (*99*, p. 24; *258*, p. 78).

Chapter Eight

1 J. D. Tothill translates *harīqa* from Arabic as "conflagration" and suggests *harīq* cultivation might be called cultivation with the help of fire (*353*, p. 292). It is reported for Kordofan, Blue Nile, Kassala, and Upper Nile provinces of the Sudan.

2 Protection of fallows is said to be an important village obligation. Fields suitable for *harīq* may be protected by cultivating a strip around them, by clearing strips to serve as fire breaks, and by controlled burning of short grass on all nonharīq fields (*62*, p. 293). Harīq fields must also be protected from animals, not only to assure maximum growth of the grass but also to prevent trampling of it, which impedes proper burning (*62*, p. 292).

3 Night soil is very little used as a fertilizer. It is reported only among the Hill Pagans of Dikwa Emirate and among the Ezzas of eastern Nigeria and some of their neighbors (*404*, p. 91 and *419*, p. 132).

Chapter Nine

1 About 1956, according to Kevers, 5 percent of herds in the Walungu area consisted of six or more animals, 35 percent of three to five beasts, and 65 percent of less than three animals (*205*, p. 1255). Total 105 percent (*sic*).

2 In the Uvira area, adjacent to the southern Bashi, two types of lending arrangements are practiced with cattle. Under the first, called *gabia*, usually a practice between a man with a number of cattle and one with none, the owner of a heifer or cow receives a heifer when the animal he loaned has calved three times. (If a bull is loaned a heifer is returned when the bull has sired four or five living offspring). Under the second type of arrangement (*nekesba*), usually practiced between a man with a few cattle and his cattle herder, the keeper of a cow gets a heifer when the animal borrowed has calved three or four times, but the owner gets all subsequent offspring (*426*, pp. 224–25).

3 These three types are further described as follows (*18*, pp. 239–40):

"Long horned race — Zoological characteristics: This race, which is the largest, attains an average height of 1.4 meters at the withers. The length of the horns varies between 70 centimeters and 1 meter. The hump at the withers is often absent or little developed. These animals are badly nourished and give little milk. The dominant color is red. Piebald red is also found.

"Short horned race — Zoological characteristics: The height at the withers attains 1.3 meters. The horns are short and scarcely pass 30 centimeters in length. The fetlock is very developed; the withers carry a small fatty hump. The dominant hide is black or red, mixed with white to form a red or black piebald. The milk aptitude is satisfactory.

"Hornless race — Zoological characteristics: The average stature attains 1.2 meters at the withers, the fetlock is very developed; the hump at the withers in contrast is little developed; horns are completely lacking; the hide is varied, red, black red, or black piebald. The milk aptitude is developed; the race has a certain propensity towards stoutness."

4 Guyaux gives fear of theft as the reason for enclosing cattle at night, and states that cattle and people are separated in the hut by a partition (*169*, p. 113).

5 Symptoms reported are fever, the passing of blood in the urine, the inability to stand, and groaning (*69*, p. 794).

6 Meyer says that the herder tears the epidermis of the horn off with his teeth (*258*, p. 65).

7 Meyer says that from time to time the milk vessel is "cleaned" with human urine (*258*, p. 66), and he adds: "It is possible that this custom has ritual meaning aside from the practical experience that urine acts as a mild disinfectant."

8 Tickling the cow's vulva to induce her to release her milk is reported, although there is no mention of introducing medicine into the uterus for the same purpose, as the neighboring Nkole in Uganda do (*211*, p. 46), or of blowing air into the cow's vagina, as is reported for the adjacent Haya and several eastern and southern African cattle-keeping tribes (*211*, p. 47).

9 For swine the cavity is also filled with sand (*354*, p. 402).

10 Gustin reports that in the Nile Valley of northern Uganda hives are not destroyed after being robbed, but are replaced in trees. In this region hives are typically made of hollow logs 70 to 80 cm. in diameter and 1.2 meters long (*168*, p. 470).

11 According to a description of another species of the honey guide, *Indicator indicator*, by Walter N. Verheyen, the honey guide attracts attention by his cries and by repeatedly flying in the direction of the hive he has discovered, changing his cry once he arrives at the hive (*398*, p. 8).

The honey badger (*Mellivora capensis*) is the principal animal that works with *Indicator indicator*; it may initiate a bee robbing expedition by uttering noises that attract the honey guide. Africans sometimes also attract the honey guide by imitating the call of the honey badger.

The appetite of the honey guide for wax is sufficiently strong that it reportedly sometimes invades churches and eats the candles. However, when fed solely wax in captivity it loses weight and dies (*398*, pp. 7–9).

12 C. M. N. White reports that the Luvale currently make hives out of bark (*418*).

Chapter Ten

1 Richards does not discuss the use of bark among the Bemba; but the Senga, Nsenga, and Plateau Tonga, who have most, if not all, the same species of trees available, strip the cambium layer from the bark of certain species whenever they need a binding. Freshly cut, this material is flexible and tough, and can easily be separated into narrower bands if a small binding is needed. Dry fiber is made flexible by soaking it in water. Bark is known to have been an item in the traditional trade of the Plateau Tonga of Zambia (*263*, p. 41); it was possibly an important item in the traditional trade of other tribes in woodland areas.

2 Some of the Alur build mortars out of stone and earth. A flat stone is placed just below the surface of the soil to serve as the bottom of the mortar, and earth is built up around the edges of it to form walls. Dried manioc roots are cut up and pounded in this receptacle with a wooden clublike pestle (*10*, p. 121). Finally meal produced in the mortar is ground between stones to produce a flour.

3 In some areas the two techniques are found side by side among neighboring tribes in the same vegetation zone. The Bunda, and the Pende who border them on the south, both inhabit tall grass savanna containing gallery forests; but the Bunda grind millet between stones and the Pende pound it in a wooden mortar (*276*, p. 237).

4 Among the Songo-Meno, found adjacent to the Tetela in the extreme eastern part of the zone, there is variation at an earlier stage in manioc processing. The northern Songo-Meno peel manioc before soaking it; the southern Songo-Meno peel it after soaking, as do their neighbors to the south and east, with the exception of the Kete group of the Kuba (*368*, Books II and III, p. 775; *41*, pp. 71–72).

5 While I was in Katanga and Zambia investigating market structure in 1959 salted fish were sold in some of the urban markets of Katanga, but rarely in Zambia. This difference seems to be partly explained by the existence of a number of non-African fish traders in Katanga, but not in Zambia, who may salt fish. Fish appear not to have been salted in traditional tribal economies because of the relatively high cost of salt.

6 At the time this vat is made the help of other villagers is enlisted — as when a house is constructed — and beer or food or both are provided at the end of the task. Beer-work parties are not associated with work in fields, however.

7 Gorju gives the proportions as one part honey and three parts water in Urundi and gives two to three days as the period the brew is kept by the fire (*154*, p. 201).

8 Presumably cow's urine.

9 According to William O. Jones this is the most popular fiber press used in manioc processing in Brazil (*195*, p. 30).

10 The portion used for beer is about 22 percent of the original grain; the remainder — 31 percent — is reportedly waste (*88*, p. 94).

11 In the southern Ivory Coast a vine press like that used for expressing palm oil in the western Congo Basin may be used in some areas (*123*, p. 44).

Chapter Eleven

1 Maize must have spread slowly in some areas. In the northern Congo Basin it seems to have been still spreading at the beginning of the nineteenth century. The powerful Azande who were pushing southward in the early 1800's are said to have introduced maize to the Medje (*208*, p. 105). Maize did not reach Uganda, and possibly adjacent eastern areas of the Congo Basin, until sometime between 1863 and 1900. (Capt. J. A. Grant, a member of Speke's party which explored Uganda in 1861–62, took copious notes on the plants found, and commented that maize was "very rare as the equator is approached [from the south]; and quite unknown beyond it northwards to 5° N." [cited in *332*, p. 651].) After Grant's note there is no further reference to maize in Uganda until 1901, when Sir Harry Johnston, then the governor, reported to the Foreign Office concerning the potential of the Protectorate: "Wheat, oats and barley, grow well in some districts, Indian corn everywhere . . . ." (*191*).

2 See L. Kochnitzky, *Negro Art in the Belgian Congo* (New York, 1958),

pp. 4–11, for an excellent discussion of the relations between the Portugese and the Kingdom of Congo.

3 The only reference I have found to deliberate introduction of small livestock is introduction of goats and sheep of the milking type to the post of Zambi, Ruanda-Urundi in 1910 (349, p. 444).

4 No evidence has been found to suggest that breeding stock were distributed to chiefs anywhere to start herds, although some chiefs apparently did receive animals as a reward for their assistance in the campaigns to crush the Arabs in the 1890's. Roger d'Hendencourt says that "the celebrated Lupungu" and chiefs Mutambo, Mukulu, and others in the Katanga area received animals as a reward for their military assistance in the Arab wars but that small chiefs got none (100, p. 16). He also states that those who received cattle had no idea how to care for them and were not shown, with the result that some 300 to 400 animals were left to become semiwild.

5 The Leopoldville area, for example, was divided into three approximately concentric zones around the city, whose outside radii were 19, 27, and 50 miles, respectively. Some 100 hours of work per month in food production was required for each able-bodied woman in the first zone; 50 and 33 hours were required in the second and third zones, respectively (238, p. 30).

6 See R. Slade, "King Leopold II and the Attitude of English and American Catholics towards the Anti-Congolese Campaign," Zaïre (June 1957), pp. 593–612, for a fairly full account of the development of public opinion against the methods employed in the Congo Free State.

7 An important failure was the attempt to spread breadfruit growing. Experiments at the botanical garden at Eala in 1921 showed yields of 48 to 60 metric tons of fresh fruit per hectare (156, p. 904), a yield more than twice that of manioc in most of the Congo Basin (195, p. 258); the margin of superiority over other starchy food crops is even greater. Beginning in 1924 breadfruit trees were planted at military camps in Lusambo, Luebo, Charlesville, Bandundu (Banningville), and in several other areas (324, pp. 905–9). Despite these efforts breadfruit never was adopted as a major foodstuff, probably because of failure to introduce ways of making the fruit into a food acceptable to the African palate.

Chapter Twelve

1 An adoption of manioc similar to that of the Kuba is said to have been made by the Bena Kalundwe group of Luba, located some 200 miles southeast of the Kuba, about 1885 (399, p. 232). According to oral tradition, the ruler at that time, Tambo Kanonge, sent to the neighboring Lunda realm to the west for manioc cuttings and made cultivation of this crop compulsory.

2 Whether they were soaked first is not stated.

3 I am indebted to Jan Vansina for bringing this material to my attention.

4 Edmiston arrived in 1903, but the mission burned in 1904 and was not reoccupied until 1905. The account suggests that manioc was already known, but was not an important crop, when Edmiston arrived. He states that with encouragement of its production the area not only became self-sufficient but developed a surplus that could be sold to developing administrative centers such as Luebo.

5 As early as the last years of the Congo Free State, Africans in the Madimba territoire, adjacent to that containing Bangu and Inkisi, were forced to send supplies of manioc to Leopoldville and the shipyards of Bas-Congo (66, p. 226).

Inkisi, which is on the railway, probably came under that same regulation. It is likely that it was during this period that a number of new manioc varieties were introduced.

6 A. Flamingi notes that a similar loan arrangement involving cattle is found in Italy (*141*, p. 654).

7 The plantain which has been planted is cut down at harvest, and new growth that stems from its base grows large enough the second year to produce fruit. Harvest from these stems is called the first ratoon crop. Plants that develop when the first ratoon crop is harvested are the second ratoon crop. In this area there are apparently never more than two ratoon crops.

8 This is not consistent with the fact that the Banda were planting bark cloth trees in the precolonial period. When the village moved, the rights to bark cloth trees remained with the planter even though he had abandoned the surrounding fields and thus lost the rights to the land. The importance of bark cloth trees is suggested by the fact that a slave was sometimes left to live in an abandoned village and look after the trees after the owners had moved on (*346*, p. 251).

9 At another point De Schlippe suggests that Major Wyld introduced more than one manioc variety (*108*, p. 223).

10 The Mangbetu depended mainly on the Babukur, a small tribe found just within the Congo (Kinshasa), almost due north of the Mangbetu, for goats. Of the technology of the Babukur, Schweinfurth says only that "they have established a system of agriculture and give great attention to the breeding of goats" (*323*, 1:257).

11 J. Vanden Plas describes a somewhat similar traditional crop sequence for the Kuku, a neighboring tribe in extreme southern Sudan (cited in *299*, p. 425). The principal crop sequence of the Kuku differed only in that it consisted of a beans-finger millet succession followed the second year by a sorghum-beans succession, instead of crops being planted separately in each of four succeeding seasons. Among the Kuku, beans were planted at the beginning of the agricultural year; after three months they were harvested and finger millet planted. The next season the field was planted with sorghum at the beginning of the rainy season; after four months this was harvested and beans were planted.

A second crop sequence was a peanut-sesame sequence.

The Kuku are also of interest because they fertilized their fields with cattle manure carried there in baskets and spread before planting. The only other reference to this practice among the other cattle-keeping peoples of the northeastern Congo Basin is for the Lugbara.

12 M. W. Hilton-Simpson, who crossed the northern Kwango in 1909, also found no cattle in the northern areas, but states that they were present then in the south (*179*, p. 274): "In the whole year's journey domestic cattle are not to be found. . . . Further to the south, however, near the Portuguese frontier, the natives breed a certain number of these animals, and also sheep."

13 A similar invasion of the Lele by Chokwe warring parties looking for ivory and slaves is described by Hilton-Simpson (*179*, pp. 334–38).

14 Border comprised, on the average, 33.7 percent of the area of 2,876 circles measured in 1946 (*289*, p. 89).

15 There has apparently also been some extension of Bemba methods to some of their neighbors. D. U. Peters reports that C. G. Trapnell "points out that aerial photographs of South Mpika district [Bisa area lying between the Bemba

and Lala] show how small circle *chitemene* has there been recently modified (by Bemba influence) in the direction of the making of much larger circles by the Bisa" (*289*, p. 74).

Chapter Thirteen

1 In addition to the dislike of breadfruit reflected in the Belgian efforts to establish it in Congolese diets (Chapter 11), similar evidence comes from informants in Nigeria, the Ivory Coast, Liberia, and Sierra Leone. In all these areas people who eat breadfruit lose social status; for example, among the Kru of Liberia one of the worst insults is to be called a "breadfruit eater." In Sierra Leone the Creoles are said to dislike breadfruit because it is associated with the period of their history when they were slaves in the West Indies.

2 Schultz specifically excepts Japan, Mexico, and Taiwan from his hypothesis because agriculture has developed there (*320*, p. 1017); and he also excepts certain areas of other countries from his definition — those which are adjusting to serious adversity of nature (floods or drought) followed by famine; to major man-made alterations of the environment (new roads or railroads, large dams irrigation canals, structures to control floods and to reduce soil erosion); to large political changes (e.g. partition, recruitment of many men into the armed services, or destruction of resources by war); to large changes in relative prices of products because of outside developments affecting the terms of trade; and to advances in knowledge useful in agriculture (*320*, pp. 37–38). None of these exceptions appears to apply to more than a small portion of the farmers in any tropical African country, and most are not found anywhere. Moreover, in the Congo Basin, contrary to Schultz's hypothesis, there is record of considerable change in techniques under circumstances not covered by his exceptions.

For additional discussion of the validity of Schultz's hypothesis see George L. Beckford, "Transforming Traditional Agriculture: Comment," and Theodore W. Schultz, "Transforming Traditional Agriculture: Reply," *Journal of Farm Economics*, Vol. 48, No. 4, Pt. 1 (Nov. 1966), pp. 1013–15 and 1015–17.

Citations

1 Adandé, A. "Le Maïs et ses usages dans le Bas-Dahomey," *Bulletin de l'Institut Français d'Afrique Noire*, Vol. 15, No. 1, Jan. 1953.

2 Adriaens, E. L. "Le *Pentadesma Butyracea* du Congo Belge," *Congo*, Feb. 1934.

3 ———. "Recherches sur l'alimentation des populations au Kwango," *Bull. Agr. du Congo Belge*, Belgium, Ministère des Colonies, June 1951.

4 *Ibid.*, Sept. 1951.

5 Allan, William. "African Land Usage," *Rhodes-Livingstone Journal* (Manchester, Eng.), June 1945.

6 ———. *Studies in African Land Usage in Northern Rhodesia*, Rhodes-Livingstone Papers, No. 15. Oxford, 1949.

7 ———. *The African Husbandman*. New York, 1965.

8 Alldridge, T. J. *A Transformed Colony, Sierra Leone*. London, 1910.

9 Angladette, A. "La Production vivrière en Afrique Équatoriale Française et au Cameroun," *Bulletin de la Mission d'AEF*, Cameroun, June 1958.

10 Annaert, J. *Contribution à l'étude géographique de l'habitat et de l'habitation indigènes en milieu rural dans les provinces Orientale et du Kivu*, Académie Royale des Sciences d'Outre-Mer, Classe des Sciences Naturelles et Médicales, Mémoires in 8°, N.S., Vol. 10, fasc. 3. Brussels, 1960.

11 Anon. "Rapport présenté aux Chambres par le Ministre des Colonies," *Bull. Agr. du Congo Belge*, Nov. 1910.

12 ———. "Situation actuelle de l'apiculture au Congo Belge," *ibid.*, Sept. 1911.

13 *Ibid.*, Dec. 1911.

14 ———. "Note relative à deux arbres à fruits oléagineaux du Congo Belge," *ibid.*, Sept. 1912.

15 ———. "Renseignements sur l' 'Utelo' plante à graines oléagineuses," *ibid.*, Sept. 1912.

16 ———. "L'Apiculture au Kasai," *ibid.*, Dec. 1912.

17 ———. "Agriculture indigène au Congo Equatorial," chap. 6 in *18*.

18 ———. "L'Agriculture du Congo Belge," *Bull. Agr. du Congo Belge*, Mar. 1913.

19 ———. "Note sur la palmier Elaeis dans le District de l'Équateur," *ibid.*, June 1914.

20 ———. "Le Ruanda-Urundi," *ibid.*, June 1921.

21 ———. "L'Agriculture indigène dans le territoire d'Udiji et dans le Ruanda-Urundi," *Congo*, Jan. 1922.

22 ———. "Rapport sur la situation économique du District du Tanganyika-Moero pendant le premier trimestre 1922," *ibid.*, Feb. 1923.

23 ———. "L'Agriculture du Congo Belge," *Bull. Agr. du Congo Belge*, June 1924.

24 ———. "Rapport sur l'agriculture dans l'Ituri en 1924," *ibid.*, Sept.–Dec. 1925.

25 ———. "Le Congo Belge, producteur de café," *Congo*, Mar. 1935.

26 ———. "Les Élevages au Congo Belge en 1935," *Bull. Agr. du Congo Belge*, Dec. 1937.

27 ———. "L'Agriculture du Congo Belge en 1937," *ibid.*, Sept. 1938.

28 ———. "Les Élevages au Congo Belge en 1937," *ibid.*, Dec. 1938.

29 ———. "Les Élevages au Congo Belge en 1938," *ibid.*, Mar.–Dec. 1940 (Brussels ed.).

30 ———. "Développement de quelques activités au Congo Belge, durant la période 1939 à 1945," *ibid.*, Mar. 1946.

31 ———. "Volume jubilaire 1910–1960," *ibid.*, 1960.

32 ———. Sumbawanga District Book [Tanzania].

33 Arbulot, M. Information provided by him in *12*.

34 Baldwin, Robert E. *Economic Development and Export Growth* . . . . Berkeley, 1966.

35 Bambui Government Farm (British Cameroons). *Annual Report 1945*.

36 Barber, W. J. "Economic Rationality and Behavior Patterns in an Underdeveloped Area: A Case Study of African Economic Behavior in the Rhodesias," *Economic Development and Cultural Change*, Apr. 1960.

37 ———. *The Economy of British Central Africa*. Stanford, 1961.

38 Barnes, A. C. "Chemical Investigations into the Products of the Oil Palm," *Special Bulletin of the Department of Agriculture*. Ibadan, Nigeria, 1924.

39 Bartlett, H. H. "Fire, Primitive Agriculture and Grazing in the Tropics," in W. L. Thomas, ed., *Man's Role in Changing the Face of the Earth*. Chicago, 1951.

40 Bascoulergue, P., and J. Bergot. *L'Alimentation rurale au Moyen-Congo*,

French Equatorial Africa, Service Commun de Lutte contre les Grandes Endémies, Section Nutrition, 1959.

41 Bateman, Charles S. L. *The First Ascent of the Kasai* . . . . London, 1889.

42 Baudouinville. Information from the archives of the territoire of Baudouinville.

43 Baxter, P. T. W., and Audrey Butt. "The Azande, and Related Peoples . . . ," International African Institute, *Ethnographic Survey of Africa*, Vol. 1, Pt. 9. London, 1953.

44 Beguin, H. *La Mise en valeur agricole du Sud-Est du Kasai*, Belgium, Institut National pour l'Étude Agronomique du Congo Belge (INÉAC), Série Scientifique, No. 88. Brussels, 1960.

45 Belgium, Ministère des Colonies. *Plan décennal pour le développement économique et social du Ruanda-Urundi*. 1951.

46 ———. *Agriculture congolaise*. N.p., 1954.

47 ———. *Aperçu sur l'économie agricole de la Province de Léopoldville*. N.p., 1955.

48 Bélot, R. "L'Apiculture indigène: Les Améliorations possibles," *Bull. Agr. du Congo Belge*, Dec. 1935.

49 Berg, Elliot H. "The Economics of the Migrant Labor System," in H. Kuper, ed., *Urbanization and Migration in West Africa*. Berkeley, 1965.

50 Bernier, G., and A. Lambrechts. *Étude sur les boissons fermentées indigènes du Katanga*, Académie Royale des Sciences Coloniales, Classe des Sciences Morales et Politiques, Mémoires, in 8°, N.S., Vol. 9, fasc. 7. Brussels, 1959.

51 Bertrand, J. *Le Congo Belge*. Brussels, 1909.

52 Bervoets, W., and M. Lassance. *Modes et coutumes alimentaires des Congolais en milieu rural*. Brussels, 1959.

53 Bloch, M. R. "The Social Significance of Salt," *Scientific American*, Vol. 200, No. 1.

54 Bois, D. G. J. *Les Plantes alimentaires chez tous le peuples et à travers les âges*. Paris, 1927.

55 Boulger, Demetrius C. *The Congo State or the Growth of Civilization in Central Africa*. London, 1898.

56 Bourgeois, R. *Banyarwanda et Barundi*, Académie Royale des Sciences Coloniales, Classe des Sciences Morales et Politiques, Mémoires in 8°, N.S., Vol. 15, fasc. unique. Brussels, 1957.

57 Brelsford, W. V. *Fishermen of the Banqweulu Swamps*, Rhodes-Livingstone Papers, No. 12. Livingstone, Northern Rhodesia, 1946.

58 Brewin, D. R. "Kilimanjaro Agriculture," *Tanganyika Notes and Records*, No. 64, Mar. 1965.

59 Bruel, G. "Les Populations de la Moyenne Sanga, les Pomo et les Boumali," *Revue d'Ethnographie et de Sociologie*, 1910.

60 Buchanan, K. M., and J. C. Pugh. *Land and People in Nigeria*. London, 1955.

61 Buell, Raymond L. *The Native Problem in Africa*. 2 vols. New York, 1928.

62 Burnett, J. R. "Crop Production," in J. D. Tothill, ed., *Agriculture in the Sudan*. London, 1948.

63 Burton, Sir Richard F. *The Lake Regions of Central Africa*. 2 vols. New York, 1961.

64 Bylin, Eric. *Basakata*, Etudia Ethnographica Upselensia XXV. Uppsala, Sweden, 1966.

65 Cambier, E. "Culture en collaboration avec les indigènes," *Bull. Agr. du Congo Belge*, June 1930.

66 Cambier, P. *Missions en Chine et au Congo*, Vol. 1, N.p., 1890.

67 Cameron, Verney L. *Across Africa*. New York and London, 1877.

68 Canisius, E. "A Campaign amongst Cannibals," in G. Barros, *The Curse of Central Africa*. London, 1903.

69 Carlier, F. "L'Élevage au Kivu," *Bull. Agr. du Congo Belge*, Sept.–Dec. 1912.

70 Casati, Gaetano. *Ten Years in Equatoria and the Return with Emin Pasha*, Vol. 1. London, 1891.

71 Central African Republic, Mission Socio-Économique, Centre Oubangui. *L'Emploi du temps du paysan dans une zone de l'Oubangui central 1959–60*. Paris, Nov. 1961.

72 Ceulemans, P. *La Question arabe et le Congo (1833–1892)*, Académie Royale des Sciences Coloniales, Classe des Sciences Morales et Politiques, Mémoires in 8°, N.S., Vol. 22, fasc. Brussels, 1959.

73 Chambon, R., and M. Alofs. *Le District agricole du Tanganyika*. Belgium, Ministère des Colonies, 1958.

74 Charreau, M. P. *Un coin du Congo. Le Cercle de Kundé*. Cherbourg, 1905.

75 Chevalier, Auguste, "Les Îles du Cap Vert," *Rev. Bot. App. et Agr. Trop.*, Oct.–Nov. 1935.

76 Claessens, J. "Grains de Baleko," in Belgium, Ministère des Colonies, *Quelques plantes oléagineuses du Congo Belge*. Brussels, 1929.

77 ———. "Du Lac Albert au Lac Kivu . . . ," *Bull. Agr. du Congo Belge*, Mar. 1929.

78 Clark, A. S. "The Warega," *Man*, Vol. 30, 1930.

79 Clayton, Eric S. *Agrarian Development in Peasant Economies*. London, 1964.

80 Clement, J. M. "L'Agriculture dans le District du Sankuru — Réflexions sur son développement," *Bull. Agr. du Congo Belge*, Apr. 1953.

81 Clozel, F. J. *Les Bayas*. Paris, 1896.

82 Colback, H. "Notes sur les races bovines du Ruanda-Urundi et sur l'élevage," *Bull. Agr. du Congo Belge*, June 1929.

83 Colle, P. *Les Baluba*. 2 vols. Brussels, 1913.

84 ———. "L'Organization politique des Bashi," *Congo*, Dec. 1921.

85 Compagnie Cotonnière Congolaise. *Trent années de culture cotonnière au Congo Belge, 1918–1948*. Brussels, n.d.

86 Constance-Marie, Rev. Sr. *Babira. Essai d'adaptation*. Editions Grands-Lacs. N.p., n.d.

87 Coquilhat. "Le Haut-Congo," *Bulletin de la Société de Géographie d'Anvers*, Vol. 10, 1886.

88 Culwick, G. M. *A Dietary Survey among the Zande of the South-western Sudan*. Sudan, Ministry of Agriculture, 1950.

89 Cuvelier, J., and L. Jadin. *L'Ancien Congo d'après les archives romaines (1518–1640)*, Académie Royale des Sciences Coloniales, Section des Sciences Morales et Politiques, Mémoires in 8°, Vol. 36, fasc. 2 et denier. Série Historique. Brussels, 1954.

90 Czekanowski, J. *Forschungen im Nil-Kongo Zwischengebiet*. Leipzig, 1924.

91 ———. *Investigations in the Area between the Nile and the Congo*. Human Relations Area Files. New Haven, 1960.

92 Darby, H. C. "The Clearing of the Woodland in Europe," in W. L. Thomas, ed., *Man's Role in Changing the Face of the Earth*. Chicago, 1951.

93 De Bauw, A., "Le Coton dans l'Afrique Centrale," *Bulletin Périodique*, Société Belge d'Études et d'Expansion, Feb. 1931.

94 de Beaucorps, R. *Les Banyanzi du Bas-Kwilu*, Collection Africana, No. 1. Louvain, 1933.

95 de Calonne-Beaufaict, A. *Études Bakongo*. Liége, 1912.

96 ———. *Les Azandes*, Brussels, 1921.

97 de Derken, Constant. *Deux ans au Congo*. Antwerp, 1900.

98 Conde de Ficalho, F. M. C. *Plantas uteis da África portugueza*. Lisbon, 1947.

99 de Greef, G. "Monographie agricole de la région de l'Urundi," *Bull. Agr. du Congo Belge*, Mar.–Dec. 1919.

100 d'Hendencourt, Roger. *l'Élevage au Katanga*. Bruges, Belgium, 1953.

101 de l'Épine, Baron Ch. "Histoire des famines et disettes dans l'Urundi," *Bull. Agr. du Congo Belge*, Sept. 1929.

102 Delhaise, Commandant. *Les Warega*. Brussels, 1909.

103 Denis, Jacques. "Ngombe ya Tumba, village Holo du Haut-Kwango," *Bulletin de la Société Belge d'Études Géographiques*, Vol. 29, No. 1. Louvain, 1964.

104 Derkinderen, Gaston. *Atlas du Congo Belge et du Ruanda-Urundi*. Brussels, 1955.

105 de Rouck, René. *Atlas géographique et historique du Congo Belge* . . . . 4th ed. Brussels, n.d.

106 De Ryck, F. *Les Lalia-Ngolu*. N.p., n.d.

107 de Schlippe, Pierre. "Sous-station d'essais de l'INÉAC à Kurukwata," *Bull. Agr. du Congo Belge*, June 1948.

108 ———. *Shifting Cultivation in Africa: The Zande System of Agriculture*. London, 1956.

109 ———. "Enquête préliminaire du système agricole des Barundi de la région Bututsi (Ruanda-Urundi)," *Bull. Agr. du Congo Belge*, Aug. 1957.

110 Devred, R., and R. Hardy. "Résultats et commentaires agronomiques d'une mission pédo-botanique au Kwango," *ibid.*, Dec. 1957.

111 Dewèvre, A. *Les Plants utiles du Congo.* Brussels, 1894.

112 de Wildeman, É. *Documents pour l'étude de l'alimentation végétale de l'indigène au Congo Belge*, Institut Royal Colonial Belge, Section des Sciences Naturelles et Médicales, Mémoires in 8°, Vol. 2, fasc. 4. Brussels, 1934.

113 Diagre, Father. "Plantes alimentaires du pays Banda," *Bulletin de la Société des Recherches Congolaises*, Vol. 8, 1927.

114 ———. "Les Bandas," *Anthropos*, Vol. 26, 1931–32.

115 Doke, Clement M. *The Lambas of Northern Rhodesia.* London, 1931.

116 Douglas, Mary. "The Lele of Kasai," in C. Daryll Forde, ed., *African Worlds: Studies in the Cosmological Ideas and Social Values of African Peoples.* London, 1954.

117 ———. "The Environment of the Lele," *Zaïre*, Oct. 1955.

118 ———. "Lele Economy Compared with the Bushong . . . ," in Paul Bohannan and G. Dalton, eds., *Markets in Africa*, Evanston, Ill., 1962.

119 ———.*The Lele of the Kasai.* Oxford, 1963.

120 Drachoussoff, V. "Essai sur l'agriculture indigène au Bas-Congo," *Bull. Agr. du Congo Belge*, Sept. 1947.

121 *Ibid.*, Dec. 1947.

122 Dumont, René. *Types of Rural Economy.* London, 1957.

123 Dupire, M., and J. L. Boutillier. *Le Pays Adioukrou et sa palmeraie*, L'Homme d'Outre-Mer, No. 4, France, Office de la Recherche Scientifique et Technique Outre-Mer. Paris, 1958.

124 Dupont, É. *Lettres sur le Congo.* Paris, 1889.

125 Eeckhout, L. E. "Monographie agricole de la région d'Ikoma (Kivu)," *Bull. Agr. du Congo Belge*, Sept.–Dec. 1949.

126 Elskens, O. E. "La Culture du manioc dans la région de Yangambi (District de Stanleyville)," *ibid.*, Sept. 1913.

127 ———. "La Production de l'huile palmiste dans la région de Yangambi (District de Stanleyville)," *ibid.*

128 Engles: Information provided by him in *12.*

129 Epoma, F. "Moeurs et habitudes de chez nous," *La Voix du Congolais*, Vol. 5, 1949.

130 État Indépendant du Congo. *Instructions pour le personnel du Service de Agriculture.* Brussels, 1903.

131 Evans-Pritchard, E. E. "A Contribution to the Study of Zande Culture," *Africa*, Oct. 1960.

132 Everaerts, E. "Monographie agricole du Ruanda-Urundi," *Bull. Agr. du Congo Belge*, Dec. 1939.

133 Fallers, M. C. "The Eastern Lacustrine Bantu," International African Institute, *Ethnographic Survey of Africa*, East Central Africa, Part 11. London, 1960.

134 Fallon, F. "La Multiplication de certaines cultures pour combattre la famine au Ruanda-Urundi," *Bull. Agr. du Congo Belge*, Sept. 1930.

135 Faulkner, O. T. "Experiments on Ridged Cultivation in Tanganyika and Nigeria," *Tropical Agriculture*, Vol. 21, No. 9, Sept. 1944.

136 Félix, H. Jacques "L'Agriculture noire au Cameroun. Une forme particulière d'écobuage," *L'Agronomie Tropicale*, France, Ministère Outre-Mer, Vol. 11, 1947.

137 Ferguson, H. "The Food Crops of the Sudan and Their Relation to Environment," in Philosophical Society of the Sudan, *Food and Society in the Sudan*. Khartoum, 1955.

138 Flame, J. *Dans la Belgique Africaine*. Brussels, 1908.

139 Flamingi, A. "Le Palmier à huile au Mayumbe," *Bull. Agr. du Congo Belge*, Dec. 1930.

140 ———. "Note sur l'élevage des bovidés du Dahomey au Mayumbe," *ibid.*, June 1939.

141 *Ibid.*, Sept. 1948.

142 Flatz, J. *Die Kulturen Ostafrikas*. Linz, 1936.

143 Food and Agriculture Organization of the United Nations (FAO). *Yearbook of Food and Agricultural Statistics*, Pt. 1: Production. Rome.

144 ———. *Report on the 1950 World Census of Agriculture*. Rome, 1955.

145 ———. "Shifting Cultivation," *Unasylva*, 11, No. 1, reprinted in *Tropical Agriculture*, Vol. 34, July 1957.

146 ———. *Agriculture in Ethiopia*. Rome, 1961.

147 Forde, C. Daryll, et al. "Peoples of the Niger-Benue Confluence," International African Institute, *Ethnographic Survey of Africa*, Western Africa, Pt. 10. London, 1955.

148 Fox Bourne, H. R. *Civilisation in Congoland*. London, 1903.

149 Gamble, D. P. "The Wolof of Senegambia," International African Institute, *Ethnographic Survey of Africa*, Western Africa, Pt. 14. London, 1957.

150 Gaud, Fernand. *Les Mandja*. Brussels, 1911.

151 Ghys, J. "Étude agricole de la région Batéké-Batende-Baboma," *Bull. Agr. du Congo Belge*, Mar. 1934.

152 Goffinet, J. "Aperçu sur l'agriculture de l'Uélé," *ibid.*, Sept. 1913.

153 Gomez, P. A., R. Halut, and A. Collin. "Productions de protéines animales au Congo," *ibid.*, Aug. 1961.

154 Gorju, M. *En zigzags à travers l'Urundi*. Antwerp, 1926.

155 Gossens, V. "*Allanblackia Floribunda Oliv.* (Bondjo) et l'*Ongokea Klaineana Pierre* (Boleko)," in Belgium, Ministère des Colonies, *Quelques plantes oléagineuses du Congo Belge*. Brussels, 1929.

156 ———. "La Multiplication de l'arbre à pain (*Artocarpus incisa*) pour le ravitaillement des indigènes," *Bull. Agr. du Congo Belge*, Sept. 1930.

157 Gouldsbury, G., and H. Sheane. *The Great Plateau of Northern Rhodesia*. London, 1911.

158 Gourou, Pierre. *The Tropical World*. Paris, 1947.

159 ———. "The Quality of Land Use of Tropical Cultivators," in W. L. Thomas, ed., *Man's Role in Changing the Face of the Earth*. Chicago, 1951.

160 Grant, C. H. B. "Uha in Tanganyika Territory," *Geographical Journal*, Vol. 66, 1925.

161 Gray, R. F. "Economic Exchange in a Sonjo Village," in P. Bohannan and G. Dalton, eds., *Markets in Africa*. Evanston, Ill., 1962.

162 Gray, R. *A History of the Southern Sudan 1839–1889*. Oxford, 1961.

163 Great Britain, Colonial Office. *Colonial Primary Products Committee, Second Report*. London, Jan. 1949.

164 Griffiths, J. E. S. "The Aba-Ha of the Tanganyika Territory . . . ," *Tanganyika Notes and Records*, Vol. 2, 1936.

165 Guiral, L. *Le Congo Français*. Paris, 1889.

166 Gunn, H. D. "The Peoples of the Plateau Area of Northern Nigeria," International African Institute, *Ethnographic Survey of Africa*, Western Africa, Pt. 7. London, 1953.

167 Gunn, H. D., and F. P. Conant. "Peoples of the Middle Niger Region, Northern Nigeria," International African Institute, *Ethnographic Survey of Africa*, Western Africa, Pt. 15. London, 1960.

168 Gustin. Information provided by him in *12*.

169 Guyaux, R. "Considérations sur l'élevage bovin dans les Chefferies Bashi (Province du Kivu)," *Bull. Agr. du Congo Belge*, Mar. 1950.

170 Halkin, Joseph. *Les Ababua*. Brussels, 1911.

171 Hargot, F. "Monographie agricole du Maniema," *Bull. Agr. du Congo Belge*, Feb. 1955.

172 Hathcock, J. S. *A Study of Agricultural Conditions in the Belgian Congo and Ruanda-Urundi*, Office of the U.S. Special Representative in Europe, Food and Agriculture Division, Paris, Sept. 1952.

173 Hauzer de Fooz, C. *Un demi-siècle avec l'économie du Congo Belge*. N.p., n.d.

174 Hecq, J. "Le Système de culture des Bashi (Kivu, territoire de Kabare) et ses possibilités," *Bull. Agr. du Congo Belge*, Aug. 1958.

175 Hecq, J., and A. Lefebvre. "Éléments de la production agricole au Bashi (Kivu — territoire de Kabare)," *ibid.*, Mar. 1959.

176 Hendrickx, F. L. "Plantes alimentaires et agriculture des régions d'altitude du Kivu," *Comptes rendus de la semaine agricole de Yangambi, Feb. 26–Mar. 5, 1947*. Brussels, n.d.

177 Herskovits, Melville J. "The Cattle Complex in East Africa," *American Anthropologist*, Vol. 28, 1926.

178 Hilberth, John. *Les Gbaya*. Uppsala, 1962.

179 Hilton-Simpson, Melville W. *Land and Peoples of the Kasai*. London, 1911.

180 Hopen, C. E. *The Pastoral Fulube Family in Gwandu*. London, 1958.

181 Hughes, Joseph E. *Eighteen Years on Lake Bangweulu*. London, 1933.

182 Huntingford, G. W. B. "The Southern Nilo-Hamites," International African Institute, *Ethnographic Survey of Africa*, East Central Africa, Pt. 8. London, 1953.

183 ———. "The Northern Nilo-Hamites," International African Institute, *Ethnographic Survey of Africa*, East Central Africa, Pt. 6. London, 1953.

184 Ignatieff, V., and H. J. Page. *Efficient Use of Fertilizers*, FAO Agricultural Studies, No. 43. Rome, 1958.

185 Institut National pour l'Étude Agronomique du Congo Belge (INÉAC). Information from the files.

186 Ishmael, G. C. "The Babinza," *Man*, Vol. 10, 1910.

187 Jamoulle, M. "Notre territoire à mandat — Le Ruanda-Urundi," *Congo*, Mar. 1927.

188 Janssens, P. "Aperçu sur les cultures indigènes au District du Kasai," *Bull. Agr. du Congo Belge*, Sept.–Dec. 1916.

189 Jaspar, H. "Le Ruanda-Urundi, pays à disettes périodiques," *Congo*, Vol. 2, 1929.

190 Johnston, Bruce F. *The Staple Food Economies of Western Tropical Africa*. Stanford, Calif., 1958.

191 Johnston, Sir Harry. Letter to the British Foreign Office, July 10, 1901.

192 ———. *The Uganda Protectorate*, 2 vols. London, 1902.

193 ———. *George Grenfell and the Congo*. 2 vols. London, 1908.

194 Jones, E. Data provided, Entebbe, Uganda, Apr. 1959.

195 Jones, William O. *Manioc in Africa*. Stanford, Calif., 1959.

196 Joset, P. E. *Les Babira de la plaine*. Antwerp, 1936. (Extract from *Le Trait d'Union*, n.d.)

197 ———. "Notes ethnographiques sur la sous-tribu des Walese-Abfunkotou," *Bulletin des Juridictions Indigènes* (Elisabethville), No. 1, 1949.

198 Junker, W. *Travels in Africa during the Years 1879–1883*. London, 1891.

199 Jurion, F. "Le Rôle de l'INÉAC dans le développement de l'agriculture congolaise," *Bulletin d'Information de l'INÉAC*, Belgium, INÉAC, June 1952.

200 Jussiant, M. "Le Bétail indigène au Kivu," *Bull. Agr. du Congo Belge*, June 1930.

201 Kaberry, Phyllis M. *Women of the Grassfields: A Study of the Economic Position of Women in Bamenda, British Cameroons*, Great Britain, Colonial Office, Col. Res. Pub. No. 14. London, 1952.

202 Kellersberger, J. L. *A Life for the Congo*. New York, 1947.

203 Kellog, C. E. "Shifting Cultivation," *Soil Science*, Vol. 95, No. 4, 1963.

204 Kevers, G. "Monographie du groupement politique de Chigoshole en territoire de Kabare," *Bull. Agr. du Congo Belge*, Oct. 1953.

205 ———. "Monographie de la région de Walungu en territoire de Kabare," *ibid.*, Oct. 1956.

206 Kluckhohn, Richard. "The Konso Economy of Southern Ethiopia," in P. Bohannan and G. Dalton, eds., *Markets in Africa*. Evanston, Ill., 1962.

207 Kopytoff, Igor. Data provided, May 1962.

208 Lacomblez, M. "L'Agriculture chez les Mangbetu de l'Ituri," *Bull. Agr. du Congo Belge*, Mar.–Dec. 1918.

209 ———. "Notice agricole sur les populations Walesse et Mamvu habitant le District de l'Ituri," *ibid.*, June 1924.

210 Lagae, C. R., and V. H. Vanden Plas. *La Langue des Azande*, Bibliotèque Congo, Vol. 2, No. 7. Gand, 1922.

211 Lagercrantz, S. *Contribution to the Ethnography of Africa*. Uppsala, 1950.

212 Lamal, F. *Basuku et Bayaka*, Annales du Musée Royal de l'Afrique Centrale, Tervuren, Série in 8°, Sciences Humaines, No. 56, 1965.

213 Laman, K. *The Kongo I*. Uppsala, 1953.

214 Landor, A. H. S. *Across Widest Africa*. 2 vols. London, 1907.

215 Lane-Poole, E. H. *Native Tribes of the Eastern Province of Northern Rhodesia*. Lusaka, 1949.

216 Laurent, J. F. "Rapport agricole," in Belgium, Ministère des Colonies, *Monographie des Groupements Mumosho-Mugabo*. Brussels, 1952.

217 Laurent, M. "Notes sur l'Elaeis au Congo Belge," *Bull. Agr. du Congo Belge*, Dec. 1912.

218 Leakey, E. A., and N. V. Rounce. "The Human Geography of the Kasulu District, Tanganyika . . . ," *Geography*, Vol. 18, 1919.

219 Lebrun, J. "Études botaniques dans le District de l'Ubangi," *Bull. Agr. du Congo Belge*, June 1932.

220 Lefevre, M. A. "La Vie dans la brousse du Haut-Katanga," *Bulletin de la Société Belge d'Études Géographiques*, Vol. 24, No. 2. Louvain, 1955.

221 Lelong, M. H. *Mes frères du Congo*. 2 vols. Brussels, 1946.

222 Lemaire, Lt. *Au Congo, comment les Noirs travaillent*. Brussels, 1895.

223 Lembezat, B. *Les Populations Païennes du Nord-Cameroun et de l'Adamaoua*. Paris, 1961.

224 Léontovitch, C. "L'Agriculture indigène dans l'Ubangi," *Bull. Agr. du Congo Belge*, Mar. 1933.

225 Leplae, Edmond. "L'Agriculture du Congo Belge: Rapport sur les années 1911 et 1912," *ibid.*, Mar. 1913.

226 ———. "La Situation de l'Agriculture au Congo-Belge," *Congo*, June and July 1920.

227 ———. "Les Cultures obligatoires dans les pays d'agriculture arriérée," *Bull. Agr. du Congo Belge*, Dec. 1929.

228 ———. *Méthode suivie pour le développement de l'agriculture au Congo Belge*. Louvain, 1930.

229 ———. *La Crise agricole coloniale et les phases du développement de l'agriculture dans le Congo central*, Institut Royal Colonial Belge, Section des Sciences Naturelles et Médicales, Mémoires in 8°, Vol. 1, fasc. 2. Brussels, 1932.

230 ———. "Histoire et développement des cultures obligatoires de coton et de riz au Congo Belge de 1917 à 1933," *Congo*, May 1933.

231 ———. *Les Plantations de café au Congo Belge*, Institut Royal Colonial Belge, Section des Sciences Naturelles et Médicales, Mémoires in 8°, Vol. 3, fasc. 5. Brussels, 1936.

232 ———. "Élevage de chèvres laitières au Congo," *Bull. Agr. du Congo Belge*, June 1937.

233 Leruth, A., and R. Chambon. "Monographie des Bena Muhona," *ibid.*, June 1954.

234 Leurquin, P. "Économie de subsistance et alimentation au Ruanda-Urundi: Quelques cas concrets," *Zaïre*, No. 1, 1958.

235 ———. *Le Niveau de vie des populations rurales du Ruanda-Urundi*,

Université Catholique de Louvain, Faculté des Sciences Économiques et Sociales, Collection de l'École des Sciences Économiques, No. 68. Louvain, 1960.

236 Liebrechts, Charles. *Congo; suite à mes souvenirs d'Afrique.* Brussels, 1920.

237 Loeckx, M. A. "Plan de cultures de la famille Jupaliri," *Bull. Agr. du Congo Belge*, Sept.–Dec. 1949.

238 Macalpine, G. W. *Abstract of the Report of the Commission of Enquiry into the Administration of the Congo Free State.* London, 1906.

239 McCulloch, Merran. "The Southern Lunda and Related Peoples," International African Institute, *Ethnographic Survey of Africa.* London, 1951.

240 McMaster, David N. Data provided, Kampala, Uganda, Apr. 1959.

241 Maes, Joseph. *Notes on the Populations of the Kasai, Lukenie, and Lake Leopold II Basins.* Human Relations Area Files, New Haven, Conn., 1960.

242 Maes, Joseph, and O. Boone, Musée du Congo Belge, *Les Peuplades du Congo Belge, Nom et situation géographique.* Brussels, 1935.

243 Manoukian, M. "The Akan and Ga-Adangme Peoples of the Gold Coast," International African Institute, *Ethnographic Survey of Africa*, Western Africa, Pt. 1. London, 1952.

244 Marc de Montipellier d'Annevoie, D. *Deux ans au Katanga.* Brussels, 1921.

245 Marchi, F. "L'Élevage du gros et du petit bétail au Ruanda-Urundi," *Bull. Agr. du Congo Belge*, Dec. 1939.

246 Marques, J. Montalvão. *Esboço para uma monografia agrícola do posto-sede dos Muchopes e de alguns regulados do Chibuto*, Memórias de Junta de Investigações do Ultramar, No. 22. Lisbon, 1960.

247 Martin, W. S. "Manures," in J. D. Tothill, ed., *Agriculture in Uganda.* London, 1940.

248 Masseyeff, R., M. L. Pierme, and B. B. Bergeret. *Enquêtes sur l'alimentation du Cameroun, II. Subdivision de Batouri*, Ministère de la France d'Outre-Mer, Institut de Recherches, Office de la Recherche Scientifique et Technique, Outre-Mer, Territoire du Cameroun (IRCAM), No. 4173. 1958.

249 Mathieu, P. "L'Élevage en Urundi," *Bull. Agr. du Congo Belge*, Aug. 1960.

250 Merlon, A. *Le Congo producteur.* Brussels, 1888.

251 Merriam, Alan P., et al. "The Concept of Cultural Clusters Applied to the Belgian Congo," *Southwestern Journal of Anthropology*, Vol. 15, No. 4, Winter 1959.

252 Mertens, J. *Les Ba Dzing de la Kamtsha*, Institut Royal Colonial Belge, Section des Sciences Morales et Politiques, Mémoires in 8°, Vol. 4. Brussels, 1935.

253 Mestdagh, E. "La Culture du riz au Kasai, methode indigène," *Bull. Agr. du Congo Belge*, Sept. 1912.

254 ———. "Note sur deux plantes textiles du Congo Belge," *ibid.*

255 ———. "Note sur la préparation du manioc amer (*Manihot utilissima* Pohl) dans la région de Katako-Kombe (District du Sankuru)," *ibid.*

256 ———. "La Culture du maïs par les indigènes de l'Ubangi (Congo Belge)," *ibid.*, Dec. 1913.

257 ———. "L'Exploitation des palmiers Elaeis à la station expérimentale de Gazi (Stanleyville)," *ibid.*, June 1921.

258 Meyer, Hans J. *The Barundi*, trans. Helmut Handzik, Human Relations Area Files. New Haven, Conn., 1960.

259 Middleton, John F. M. "Trade and Markets among the Lugbara of Uganda," in P. Bohannan and G. Dalton, eds., *Markets in Africa*. Evanston, Ill., 1962.

260 ———. *The Lugbara of Uganda*. New York, 1965.

261 Middleton, John F. M., and D. J. Greenland. "Land and Population in West Nile District Uganda," *Geographical Journal*, Vol. 120, 1954.

262 Miny, P. *Rapport d'un voyage au Mayumbe*, Belgium, Ministère des Colonies. Brussels, 1926.

263 Miracle, Marvin P. "Plateau Tonga Entrepreneurs in Historical Inter-Regional Trade," *Rhodes-Livingstone Journal* (Manchester, Eng.), Dec. 1959.

264 ———. *Maize in Tropical Africa*. Madison, Wis., 1966.

265 Molin, S. "Notes sur les Boyela," *Congo*, Mar. 1933.

266 Moller, A. *Les Grandes Lignes migrations des Bantous de la Province Orientale du Congo Belge*, Institut Royal Colonial Belge, Mem. VI. Brussels, 1936.

267 Monteiro, Joachim J. *Angola and the River Congo*. 2 vols. London, 1876.

268 Morel, Edmond D. *King Leopold's Rule in Africa*. London, 1904.

269 ———. *Red Rubber*. London, 1906.

270 Mortehan, M. "L'Agriculture au Ruanda-Urundi," *Bull. Agr. du Congo Belge*, Sept. 1921.

271 Mountmorres, W. G. B. *The Congo Independent State. A Report on a Voyage of Enquiry*. London, 1906.

272 Murdock, George P. *Africa, Its Peoples and Their Culture History*. McGraw-Hill: New York, 1959.

273 Nannan, M. "Le Busoni région naturelle de Muhinga (Ruanda-Urundi)," *Bull. Agr. du Congo Belge*, Apr. 1960.

274 Ngondo, Claude Bernard, of the University of Lovanium. Data provided, Apr. 1962.

275 Nicolaï, H. *Luozi, Géographie régionale d'un pays du Bas-Congo*, Académie Royale des Sciences d'Outre-Mer, Mémoires in. 8°, N.S., Vol. 12, fasc. 5. Brussels, 1961.

276 ———. *Le Kwilu*. Brussels, 1963.

277 Noss, Philip A. Data provided, Nov. 1964.

278 Nye, P. H., and D. J. Greenland. *The Soil under Shifting Cultivation*, Commonwealth Agricultural Bureau, Technical Communication, No. 51. London, 1960.

279 Nys, F. *Chez les Abarambos*. Antwerp, 1896.

280 Orchardson, I. Q. *The Kipsigis*. Nairobi, 1961.
281 Pagès, R. P. "Flore domestique du Ruanda," *Bull. Agr. du Congo Belge*, Mar. 1928.
282 *Ibid.* June 1928.
283 Papy, Louis. "Les Populations Batéké," *Les Cahiers d'Outre-Mer*, No. 6-2, Apr.–June 1949.
284 Pauquet, Edgar. "La Culture du riz en région Itimbiri," *Bull. Agr. du Congo Belge*, Oct. 1955.
285 Pauwels, Frans M. *Landuishoudkundig Onderzoek bij de Jupaliri*. Ghent, 1960.
286 Pedler, F. J. *Economic Geography of West Africa*. London, 1954.
287 Pendleton, R. L. "Agriculture and Forestry Potentialities of the Tropics," *Agronomy Journal*, Vol. 42, No. 3, 1950.
288 Peristiany, J. G. *The Social Institutions of the Kipsigis*. London, 1939.
289 Peters, D. U. *Land Usage in Serenje District*, Rhodes-Livingstone Papers, No. 19. Oxford, 1950.
290 Pieraerts, J. "Le Grand Soleil du Tournesol," in Belgium, Ministère des Colonies, *Quelques plantes oléagineuses du Congo Belge*. Brussels, 1929.
291 ———. "Les Irvingia olérifères," *ibid.*
292 Pike, A. G. "Kilimanjaro and the Furrow System," *Tanganyika Notes and Records*, No. 64, Mar. 1965.
293 Pim, Sir Alan W., and S. Milligan. *Report of the Commission Appointed to Enquire into the Financial and Economic Position of Northern Rhodesia*, Great Britain, Colonial Office, Colonial 145. London, 1938.
294 Plancquaert, M. *Les Jaga et les Bayaka du Kwango*, Institut Royal Colonial Belge, Section des Sciences Morales et Politiques, Mémoires in 8°, Vol. 3, fasc. 1. Brussels, 1932.
295 Poupon, A. "Étude ethnographique des Baya de la circonscription du M'Bimou," *L'Anthropologie*, Vol. 26. Paris, 1915.
296 Poutrin. "Notes ethnographiques sur les populations M'baka du Congo Français," *L'Anthropologie*, Vol. 21, 1910.
297 Prevost, Roger. *Étude socio-économique du Plateau Koukouya (1956–1957)*. Djambala, French Equatorial Africa, 1957.
298 Prins, A. H. J. "The Coastal Tribes of the North-eastern Bantu," International African Institute, *Ethnographic Survey of Africa*, East Central Africa, Pt. 3. London, 1952.
299 Pynaert, L. "Le Sorgho," *Bull. Agr. du Congo Belge*, Sept. 1931.
300 Rassel, A. "Le Mil à chandelles (*Pennisetum typhoides* Burm.) et sa culture au Kwango," *ibid.*, Feb. 1958.
301 ———. "Le Voandzou *Voandzeia subterranea* Thouars et sa culture au Kwango," *ibid.*, Feb. 1960.
302 Regnault, M. "Les Babinga (Négrilles de la Sanga)," *L'Anthropologie*, Vol. 22, 1911.
303 Reining, Conrad C. "Zande Markets and Commerce," in P. Bohannan and G. Dalton, eds., *Markets in Africa*. Evanston, Ill., 1962.

304 Renier, M. "Le Système de culture des Bantous en évolution au Moyen Congo," *Congo*, Dec. 1921.

305 Richards, Audrey I. *Land, Labour and Diet in Northern Rhodesia: An Economic Study of the Bemba Tribe*. London, 1939.

306 Robert, J. L. "Monographie agricole du District du Lac Léopold II," *Bull. Agr. du Congo Belge*, Sept. 1952.

307 Roelens, Victor. "Élevage du petit bétail dans les missions des Pères Blancs d'Afrique," *Bull. Agr. du Congo Belge*, June 1911.

308 ———. *Notre vieux Congo (1891–1917)*. Éditions Grands-Lacs. N.p., 1948.

309 Rounce, N. V., and D. Thornton. *Ukara Island and the Agricultural Practices of the Wakara*. Nairobi, n.d. Published in earlier form in *Tanganyika Notes and Records*, Mar. 1936.

310 Roy, R. "Notes sur les Banybungu, *Congo*, Oct. 1924.

311 Russell, E. R. "Primitive Farming in Nigeria; the Mumuye Tribe," *Empire Journal of Experimental Agriculture*, Vol. 8, 1940.

312 Sautter, Gilles. "Une économie indigène progressive: les Bacongo du District de Boko (Moyen-Congo)," *Bull. Assoc. des Géogr. Franç.*, 1951.

313 ———. "Notes sur l'agriculture des Bakamba de la Vallée du Niari," *Bulletin de l'Institut d'Études Centrafricaines*, No. 9. Brazzaville-Paris 1955.

314 ———. "Le Plateau Congolais de Mbé," *Cahiers d'Études Africaines*, Vol. 1, Nos. 2, 3, and 4. May 1960.

315 Scherer, J. H. "The Ha of Tanganyika," *Anthropos*, Vol. 54, 1959.

316 ———. "Le Buha," in M. d'Hertefelt, A. A. Throuwborst, and J. H. Scherer, *Les Anciens Royaumes de la zone interlacustre méridionale Rwanda, Burundi, Buha*, Musée Royal de l'Afrique Centrale, Monographies Ethnographiques, No. 6. Brussels, 1962.

317 Schmitz, Robert. *Les Baholoholo*. Brussels, 1912.

318 Schuebesta, P. *Vollblutneger und Halbzwerge. Forschungen unter Waldnegern und Halbpygmaen am Ituri in Belgisch-Kongo*. Leipzig, 1934.

319 ———. *Les Pygmées du Congo*, Institut Royal Colonial Belge, Section des Sciences Morales et Politiques, Mémoires in 8°, Vol. 26, fasc. 2. Brussels, 1952.

320 Schultz, Theodore W. *Transforming Traditional Agriculture*. Yale University Press: New Haven, Conn., 1964.

321 ———. "Transforming Traditional Agriculture: Reply," *Journal of Farm Economics*, Vol. 48, No. 4, Pt. 1, Nov. 1966.

322 Schumacher, M. A. "Contribution au calendrier agricole indigène du Ruanda," *Bull. Agr. du Congo Belge*, Dec. 1942.

323 Schweinfurth, Georg. *The Heart of Africa*. 2nd ed. 2 vols. London, 1874.

324 Servais, Lt. Col. "La Culture de l'arbre à pain dans les camps de la Force Publique au Congo-Kasai," *Bull. Agr. du Congo Belge*, Sept. 1930.

325 Service de l'Agriculture Congolaise. *L'Institut National pour l'Étude Agronomique du Congo Belge* . . . . Brussels, Oct. 1957.

326 Shantz, H. L. "Urundi, Territory and People," *Geographical Review*, July 1922.

327 Shekleton, C. "The Inhabitants of the 'Utwa' or Great Lukanga Swamp." Unpublished MS, Central African Archives, Salisbury, Rhodesia.

328 Sibree, James. *A Naturalist in Madagascar*. London, 1915.

329 Simoons, Frederick J. *Northwest Ethiopia*. Madison, Wis., 1960.

330 ————. *Eat Not This Flesh*. Madison, Wis., 1961.

331 Soret, Marcel. *Les Kongo Nord Occidentaux*. Paris, 1959.

332 Speke, John H. *Journal of the Discovery of the Source of the Nile*. London, 1864.

333 Stanley, Sir Henry M. *Through the Dark Continent*. New York, 1879.

334 Stenhouse, A. S. "Agriculture in the Matengo Highlands," *East African Agricultural Journal*, July 1944.

335 Stuhlmann, Franz. *Mit Emin Pascha ins Herz von Afrika*. Berlin, 1894.

336 Swan, A. J. *Fighting the Slave-Hunters in Central Africa*. London, 1910.

337 T, J. E. "Termite Mounds Used for Manure," *Farm and Forest* (Nigeria), Mar., 1942.

338 Tharin, M. "Note sur les peuplements de Raphia dans la région de Yanonghe (Province Orientale)," *Bull. Agr. du Congo Belge*, Mar.–June 1915.

339 ————. "L'Agriculture indigène dans la Province Orientale du Congo Belge," *ibid.*, Sept.–Dec. 1915.

340 Theuwissen, L. Information provided from Tanganyika District archives, April 21, 1933.

341 Thomas, J. M. C. "Sur quelques plantes cultivées chez les Ngbaka de la Lobaye (République Centrafricaine)," *Bulletin de l'Institut d'Etudes Centrafricaines*, Nos. 19–20, 1960.

342 Thompson, Virginia, and Richard Adloff. *The Emerging States of French Equatorial Africa*. Stanford, Calif., 1960.

343 Tihon, L. "Contribution à l'étude des produits végétaux de la colonie," *Congo*, July 1923.

344 ————. "Le Palmier à huile au Sankuru," *Bull. Agr. du Congo Belge*, June 1924.

345 ————. "Le Palmier à huile au Kasai," *ibid.*, Sept. 1924.

346 Tisserant, C. "L'Agriculture dans les savanes de l'Oubangui," *Bulletin de l'Institut d'Études Centrafricaines*, N.S., No. 6, 1953.

347 Tobback, L. "Introduction du bétail au Bas-Congo," *Bull. Agr. du Congo Belge*, June 1930.

348 ————. "L'Élevage des chevaux, ânes et mulets au Congo Belge," *ibid.*

349 ————. "L'Élevage du mouton et de la chèvre au Congo Belge," *ibid.*

350 Tompson, Betty P. *Two Studies in African Nutrition*, Rhodes-Livingstone Papers, No. 24. Manchester, Eng., 1954.

351 Torday, Emil. *Camp and Tramp in African Wilds*. London, 1913.

352 ————. "The Northern Babunda," *Man*, Vol. 19, 1919.

353 ————. *On the Trail of the Bushongo*. London, 1925.

354 Torday, Emil, and T. A. Joyce. "Notes on the Ethnography of the Ba-Mbala," *Journal of the Royal Anthropological Institute*, Vol. 35, 1905.

355 ———. "Notes on the Ethnography of the Ba-Huana," *ibid.*, Vol. 36, 1906.

356 ———. "Notes on the Ethnography of the Ba-Yaka," *ibid.*

357 ———. "On the Ethnology of the South-western Congo Free State," *ibid.*, Vol. 37, 1907.

358 ———. *Notes ethnographiques sur les peuples communément appelés Bakuba, ainsi que sur les peuplades apparentées. — Les Bushongo*, Belgium, Ministère des Colonies, Annales du Musée du Congo Belge. Ethn., Anth.-Sér. III: Doc. ethn. concernant les populations du Congo Belge, Vol. 2, fasc. 1, Feb. 1911.

359 Tothill, J. D., ed. *Agriculture in the Sudan*. London, 1948.

360 Trapnell, C. G. *The Soils, Vegetation and Agriculture of North-eastern Rhodesia*, Northern Rhodesia, Report of the Ecological Survey. Lusaka, 1953.

361 Trapnell, C. G., and J. N. Clothier. *The Soils, Vegetation and Agricultural Systems of North-western Rhodesia*, Northern Rhodesia, Report of the Ecological Survey. Lusaka, 1957.

362 Turco, M. "Les Fermes d'élevage de la Société des Mines d'Or de Kilo-Moto," *Bull. Agr. du Congo Belge*, Dec. 1934.

363 Turner, E. L. B., and V. W. Turner. "Money Economy among the Mwinilunga Ndembu: A Study of Some Individual Cash Budgets," *Rhodes-Livingstone Journal*, No. 18, 1955.

364 United Nations. *Demographic Yearbook, 1961*. New York, 1961.

365 Van Daele, E. "L'Agriculture indigène dans la région de Beni-Lubero," *Bull. Agr. du Congo Belge*, Apr. 1955.

366 Van den Abeele, M. *Le Rôle des services officiels dans le développement de l'agriculture congolaise*. N.p., 1942.

367 Van den Eynde, P. "Notes sur les Walendu ou Bale," *Congo*, Nov. 1923.

368 Van der Kerken, G. *L'Ethnie Mongo*, Institut Royal Colonial Belge, Section des Sciences Morales et Politiques, Mémoires in 8°, Vol. 13, fasc. 1–3. Brussels, 1944.

369 Vandersmissen, J. H. "Essais d'introduction de matériel de culture à traction animale dans la région de Sandoa," *Bull. Agr. du Congo Belge*, Dec. 1944.

370 Van der Straeten, E. "Quelques aspects de l'agriculture, de l'élevage, et de l'industrie frigorifique dans le Bas-Congo," *Congo*, June 1931.

371 Vanderyst, H. "Contributions a l'étude du palmier à huile au Congo Belge: Le Vin de palme ou malafu," *Bull. Agr. du Congo Belge*, Sept.–Dec. 1920.

372 ———. "Le Systèm de culture des Bantous et la destruction des formations forestières dans le Moyen Congo," *Congo*, Apr. 1921.

373 ———. "Contributions a l'étude du palmier à huile au Congo Belge: La Récolte des régimes de l'*Elaeis*," *Bull. Agr. du Congo Belge*, June 1921.

374 ———. "Système de culture des Bantu," *Congo*, July 1922.

375 ———. "Les Palmeraies dans leurs rapports avec l'ethnologie," *ibid.*, June 1923.

376 ———. "Études géo-agronomiques congolaises: Le sous-district géo-agronomique schisto-gréseux de la Province du Congo-Kasai," *Bull. Agr. du Congo Belge*, June 1931.

377 Van de Walle, B. *Essai d'une planification de l'économie agricole congolaise*, Belgium, INÉAC, Série Technique, No. 61. Brussels, 1960.

378 Van Geluwe, H. "Les Bira et les peuplades limitrophes," International African Institute, *Ethnographic Survey of Africa*, Belgian Congo, Pt. 2. London, 1957.

379 ———. "Les Mamvu-Mangutu et Balese-Mvuba," International African Institute, *Ethnographic Survey of Africa*. Belgian Congo, Pt. 3. London, 1957.

380 ———. "Les Bali et les peuplades apparentées . . . ," International African Institute, *Ethnographic Survey of Africa*, Belgian Congo, Pt. 5. London, 1960.

381 Van Gheluwe, A. J. "Rapport vétérinaire," in Belgium, Ministère des Colonies, *Monographie des groupements Mumosho-Mugabo*. Brussels, 1952.

382 Van Lancker, J. "La Destruction des palmeraies naturelles," *Agriculture et Élevage au Congo Belge*, neuvième année, No. 10, Oct. 1935.

383 Van Moesieke, D. "Monographie agricole du district de la Lulonga (Équateur)," *Bull. Agr. du Congo Belge*, Sept. 1929.

384 *Ibid.*, Dec. 1929.

385 Van Overbergh, Cyr. *Les Bangala*. Brussels, 1907.

386 ———. *Les Mayombe*. Brussels, 1907.

387 ———. *Les Basonge*. Brussels, 1908.

388 ———. *Les Mangbetu*. Brussels, 1909.

389 Van Parijs, A. "Rotations des plantes vivrières dans la région de Nioka (Haut-Ituri)," *Bull. Agr. du Congo Belge*, Dec. 1957.

390 Vansina, Jan. *Les Tribus Ba-Kuba et les peuplades apparentées*, Annales du Musée Royal du Congo Belge, Série in 8°. Tervuren, 1954.

391 ———. "Les Tribus Ba-Kuba et les peuplades apparentées," International African Institute, *Ethnographic Survey of Africa*, Belgian Congo, Pt. 1. London, 1954.

392 ———. "Trade and Markets among the Kuba," in P. Bohannan and G. Dalton, eds., *Markets in Africa*. Evanston, Ill., 1962.

393 ———. Data from field notes, 1953–56.

394 ———. Data from field notes, 1963 and 1964.

395 Vennetier, P. "Banlieue noire de Brazzaville," *Les Cahiers d'Outre-Mer*, Apr.–June 1957.

396 Verdict, E. *Les Premiers Jours au Katanga (1890–1903)*. Brussels, 1952.

397 Vergait, A. M. *Moeurs et coutumes des Manjas*. Paris, 1937.

398 Verheyen, W. N. "De Honigdas en de Honigaanwizer," *Congo-Tervuren*, Vol. 6, No. 1, 1960.

399 Verhulpen, Edmond. *Baluba et Balubaisés du Katanga*. Antwerp, 1936.

400 Vermeesch, M. "Monographie agricole du District du Lomami (Katanga)," *Bull. Agr. du Congo Belge*, Mar. 1924.

401 Von Wissmann, Hermann. *My Second Journey through Equatorial Africa*. London, 1891.

402 ———. *In Inner Afrikas*. N.p., n.d.

403 Wack, Henry W. *The Story of the Congo Free State*. London, 1905.

404 Wallace, J. W. "Agriculture in Abakaliki and Afikpo," *Farm and Forest* (Nigeria), Oct. 1941.

405 Waller, Horace, ed. *The Last Journals of David Livingstone*. 2 vols. Hartford, Conn., 1875.

406 Wattenye, R. P. "Le Café du Kivu," *Bull. Agr. du Congo Belge*, Sept. 1930.

407 ———. "La Culture de la vanille dans les missions des Pères blancs du Lac Tanganyika," *ibid.*, Dec. 1930.

408 Watters, R. F. "The Nature of Shifting Cultivation," *Pacific Viewpoint*, Vol. 1.

409 Wauters, Alphonse J. *Le Congo au point de vue économique*. Brussels, 1885.

410 Weeks, John K. "Anthropological Notes on the Bangala of the Upper Congo River," *Journal of the Royal Anthropological Institute*, Vol. 39, 1909.

411 ———. *Among Congo Cannibals*. London, 1913.

412 ———. *Among the Primitive Bakongo*. London, 1914.

413 Weis, G. *Le Pays d'Uvira*, Académie Royale des Sciences Coloniales, Classe des Sciences Naturelles et Médicales, Mémoires, in 8°, N.S., Vol. 8, fasc. 5. Brussels, 1959.

414 Welsch, Delane E. "Response to Economic Incentive by Abakaliki Rice Farmers in Eastern Nigeria," *Journal of Farm Economics*, Vol. 47, No. 4, Nov. 1965.

415 White, Charles M. N. *The Material Culture of the Lunda-Lovale Peoples*, Occasional Papers of the Rhodes-Livingstone Museum, No. 3. Livingstone, Northern Rhodesia, 1948.

416 ———. "The Balovale Peoples and Their Historical Background," *Rhodes-Livingstone Journal*, No. 8, 1949.

417 ———. *A Preliminary Survey of Luvale Rural Economy*, Rhodes-Livingstone Papers, No. 29. Manchester, Eng., 1959.

418 ———. Data provided, June 1962.

419 White, Stanhope. "Agricultural Economy of the Hill Pagans of Dikwa Emirate, Cameroons (British Mandate)," *Farm and Forest* (Nigeria), Sept. 1944.

420 Whiteley, Wilfred, et al. "Bemba and Related Peoples . . . ," International African Institute, *Ethnographic Survey of Africa*. London, 1951.

421 Whittlesey, Derwent. "Fixation of Shifting Cultivation," *Economic Geography*, Vol. 13, 1947.

422 Willaert, M. "L'Élevage et les races d'animaux domestiques dans l'Uélé (Congo Belge)," *Bull. Agr. du Congo Belge*, Mar. 1922.

423 Williamson, Jesse. *The Useful Plants of Nyasaland.* Zomba, Nyasaland, 1955.

424 Willis, R. G. "The Fipa and Related Peoples of South-west Tanzania and North-east Zambia," International African Institute, *Ethnographic Survey of Africa*, East Central Africa, Pt. 15. London, 1966.

425 Wilmet, J. "Essai d'une écologie humaine au territoire de Luiza, Kasai, Congo Belge," *Bulletin de la Société Belge d'Études Géographiques*, Vol. 27, No. 2. Louvain, 1958.

426 ———. *Systèmes agraires et techniques agricoles au Katanga*, Académie Royale des Sciences d'Outre-Mer, Classe des Sciences Naturelles et Médicales, N.S., Vol. 14, fasc. 5. Brussels, 1963.

427 Wilson, S. G. "Agricultural Practices among the Angoni-Tumbuka Tribes of Mzimba (Nyasaland)," *East African Agricultural Journal*, Oct. 1941.

428 Winterbottom, J. M. "The Ecology of Man and Plants in Northern Rhodesia," *Rhodes-Livingstone Journal*, June 1945.

429 Yudelman, Montague. *Africans on the Land.* Cambridge, Mass., 1964.

Index

Abarambos tribe, 22

Abercorn, Zambia, 123, 308

Abiranga peanut variety, 259, 261

Abubua tribe, 261

Acacia macrothyrsa: as indicator of soil fertility, 158

Adio tribe, 61

Administration, administrators. *See* Belgian administration; French administration; European rule

Aframomum Saguineum: as indicator of soil fertility

Agidi, term for a maize product, 223

Agobu variety of peanuts, 261

Agricultural development: by Belgian, British, French, 242; programs for, 288–89

Agricultural systems. *See* Systems, agricultural

Agricultural year: for the Alur, 103; for the Congo Azande, 259; for the Kuku, 313 n *11*

Agriculture: permanent field, 33; traditional, 245, 287; complexity of, 283; labor required of men in, 284; diversity, importance and organization of, in Africa, 288

Alcohol: distillation techniques introduced by Arabs, 262; made from maize, 264. *See also* Beer; Beverages, alcoholic; Wine

Allanblackia floribunda: extraction of oil from, 219

Alur tribe, 87, 102, 183, 234–35, 263–64, 311

Amadamu variety of peanuts, 261

Amaranth, 44, 49, 66, 103, 152, 164

Amaranthus caudatus, 106

Amase, term for ashes from burned plants: use as fertilizer, 150

Amazon River, 3

Amboumu tribe, 261–62

Amiangba tribe, 262

Angola: Holo territory in, 70, 202; Luvale territory in, 72, 80; Portuguese in, 198; mentioned, 222, 236, 271, 273, 293

Angole peas. *See* Pigeon peas

Animal husbandry, 19–20, 176–191

Animals, wild: protection from, 114; problem of, 164

Anisophyneo fruit: used in making porridge, 303 n *5*

Ankole cattle: introduction of, 276

Annona reticulata. See Bullock's heart

Anthills: cultivation on, 68, 73, 115, 133. *See also* Termite mounds

Apples, thorn, 66

Arabs: as settlers, 232; as traders, 232; culture of, 232; influence of, 232; marriage of, to African women, 232; raids by, 266; wars of, 236, 312 n *4;*